Eye Movement

Desensitization and

Reprocessing (EMDR)

Scripted Protocols

About the Editor

Marilyn Luber, PhD, is a licensed clinical psychologist in general private practice in Center City, Philadelphia, Pennsylvania. She was trained in Eye Movement Desensitization and Reprocessing (EMDR) in 1992. She has coordinated trainings in EMDR-related fields in the greater Philadelphia area since 1997. She teaches Facilitator and Supervisory trainings and other EMDR-related subjects both nationally and internationally and was on the EMDR Task Force for Dissociative Disorders. She was on the Founding Board of Directors of the EMDR International Association (EMDRIA) and served as the Chairman of the International Committee until June 1999. In 1997, Dr. Luber was given a Humanitarian Services Award by the EMDR Humanitarian Association, and later, in 2003, she was presented with the EMDR International Association's award "For Outstanding Contribution and Service to EMDRIA." In 2005, she was awarded "The Francine Shapiro Award for Outstanding Contribution and Service to EMDR." In 2001, through EMDR HAP (Humanitarian Assistance Programs), she published *Handbook for EMDR Clients*, which has been translated into eight languages. She has written the "Around the World" and "In the Spotlight" articles for the EMDRIA Newsletter, four times a year since 1997. She has worked as a Primary Consultant for the FBI field division in Philadelphia. Dr. Luber has a general psychology practice, working with adolescents, adults, and couples, especially with Complex Posttraumatic Stress Disorder (C-PTSD), trauma and related issues, and dissociative disorders. She runs Consultation Groups for EMDR practitioners.

Eye Movement Desensitization and Reprocessing (EMDR) Scripted Protocols: Basics and Special Situations

EDITOR Marilyn Luber, PhD

SPRINGER PUBLISHING COMPANY

New York

Springer Publishing Company, LLC
11 West 42nd Street
New York, NY 10036
www.springerpub.com

Acquisitions Editor: Sheri W. Sussman
Project Manager: Julia Rosen
Cover design: Steve Pisano
Composition: Apex CoVantage, LLC

Ebook ISBN: 978-0-8261-2238-4

12 13 14 / 9 8 7 6

Library of Congress Cataloging-in-Publication Data

Eye movement desensitization and reprocessing (EMDR) scripted protocols : basics and special situations / Marilyn Luber, editor.
       p. cm.
   Includes bibliographical references.
   ISBN 978-0-8261-2237-7 (alk. paper)
   1. Eye movement desensitization and reprocessing.   2. Medical protocols.
I. Luber, Marilyn.
      [DNLM: 1. Desensitization, Psychologic—methods.   2. Eye Movements—physiology.
3. Mental Disorders—therapy.   4. Psychotherapy—methods.   WM 425.5.D4 E97 2009]
   RC489.E98E94   2009
   617.7—dc22   2009006157

Printed in the United States of America by Gasch Printing

Dedication

To my colleagues who bring their hearts and souls to their work

To our clients who allow us to participate in their healing journeys

Epigraph

We shall not cease from exploration
And, the end of all our exploring
Will be to arrive where we started
And know the place for the first time.

T. S. Eliot
"Little Gidding"

Contents

PART I

Client History

PART II

EMDR, Trauma, and Adaptive Information Processing (AIP) Model Explanations

P A R T   V I

EMDR and Early Intervention Procedures for Man-Made and Natural Catastrophes

P A R T   V I I

EMDR and Early Interventions for Groups

EMDR and Performance Enhancement

EMDR and Clinician Self-Care

Contributors

Nicté Alcalá, MA, has been working with survivors of traumatic events during her professional life. The clients, with whom she has been working the most, are those who have suffered from complex interpersonal trauma, rape, assault, robbery, kidnapping, and natural or human provoked disasters. She has been involved in humanitarian projects in Latin America since 1998. Her private practice is in Mexico City.

Lucina Artigas, MA, MT, is a Trainer of Trainers, and EMDRIA and EMDR-Ibero-America Approved Consultant. She is cofounder and Executive Director of EMDR-Mexico, AMAMECRISIS, and International Center of Psychotraumatology. In 2000, she received the EMDRIA Creative Innovation Award for the Butterfly Hug, and, in 2007, she received the EMDR-Ibero-America Francine Shapiro Award. She is a trainer for the International Critical Incident Stress Foundation and Green Cross Academy of Traumatology. She is coauthor of the EMD-Integrative Group Treatment Protocol that has been applied successfully with disaster survivors worldwide. She has presented workshops and has published articles on EMDR, Crisis Intervention and Compassion Fatigue. Since 1997, she has been involved in humanitarian projects in Latin America and Europe.

Esti Bar-Sade, MA, is a child psychologist specializing in trauma work with children and adolescents over the past 27 years. She serves as the Director of Psychological Services in Nazareth Ilit. She is an EMDR-Europe Accredited Consultant and Certified Child Trainer and provides training for EMDR practitioners who work with children internationally. She is a consultant in educational settings as well as working in a clinical private practice. She is a member of the Children and Youth at Risk, a faculty member at Oranim College, and is a consultant on the JDC educational programs. She has served as an advisor on the Afula Project during the Eintifada terror attacks and has conducted many supervision groups on trauma-focused therapy with children. Esti has lectured at the European EMDR Conferences in Rome (2003), Stockholm (2005), and gave a keynote presentation on Acute Stress Intervention and EMDR with Children in London (2008). She and Brurit Laub developed the Imma EMDR Group Protocol, and she has used it with many groups of children during the Second Lebanese War.

Sheila Sidney Bender, PhD, is a New Jersey licensed psychologist and retired faculty from the University of Medicine and Dentistry of New Jersey. She is certified as an EMDRIA-Approved Consultant and Approved Provider of Basic Training. She has published or lectured on EMDR in relation to hypnosis, transference and family systems and held two small grants for EMDR, one involving treating PTSD in an MRI scanner. She is coauthor of *Evolving Thought Field Therapy: The Clinician's Handbook* (2004) and *The Energy of Belief: Psychology's Power Tools to Focus Intention and Release Blocking Belief* (2007). She maintains a private practice in Florham Park, New Jersey.

Aiton Birnbaum, PsyD, is a clinical psychologist, college lecturer, Facilitator, and EMDR-Europe Approved Consultant in EMDR. He has gone on EMDR HAP missions to Turkey, Thailand, Sri Lanka, and the Palestinian Authority. He publishes and lectures on psychology, trauma, and the Bible, and maintains a private psychotherapy practice in Kfar Yona, Israel.

David Blore, BSc (Hons), DipBPsych, SRN, RMN, ENBHA, is an EMDR-Europe accredited EMDR Consultant and Facilitator and an accredited cognitive-behavioral therapy (CBT) therapist in York, England. He has been working with victims of psychological trauma for 20 years and using EMDR for 15 years mainly in Occupational Mental Health. He is a Consultant to the United Kingdom railway industry, police forces, the petrochemical industry, and various other organizational groupings. David is cofounder of the Jane Tomlinson special interest group on Post Traumatic Growth at the Centre for Applied Positive Psychology (CAPP). He is the author of 20 peer-reviewed papers and conference presentations, mainly on EMDR, and is currently a PhD student at the University of Birmingham researching the lived experience of Post Traumatic Growth, post-road traffic accident, and post-EMDR.

Teresa López Cano, MA, has worked with survivors of traumatic events throughout her professional career. She treats clients who have suffered from complex interpersonal trauma, rape, assault, robbery, kidnapping, and natural or human provoked disasters. Since 1998, she is actively involved in humanitarian projects in Latin America. Her private practice is in Mexico City.

Esly Regina Carvalho, MS, LPC, is a Licensed Clinical Psychologist in Brazil and is working on her PhD in Psychology. She has been involved in clinical practice for over 25 years in four countries and in three languages. She returned to Brazil 2 years ago and is involved in the start-up of the EMDR movement in Brazil and Ibero-America. She is currently serving as the first President of EMDR-Ibero-America. She is a Facilitator and EMDRIA Approved Consultant and a Trainer of Trainers for practitioners in Spanish- and Portuguese-speaking countries. She has trained psychotherapy professionals to do EMDR in Brazil, Ecuador, and Portugal and, in 1997, trained lay people and mental health professionals about grief and recovery in the aftermath of Hurricane Mitch in Honduras. She is a Fellow of the American Society for Group Psychotherapy and Psychodrama, a Trainer, and Educator Practitioner of Psychodrama by the American Board of Examiners in Psychodrama, Sociometry and Group Psychotherapy. She is the author of many books in Spanish and Portuguese that focus on healing and recovery. Recently, she published an article on EMDR applied to domestic violence.

Neal Daniels, PhD, received his MA in Social Psychology from the New School for Social Research and his PhD from Kansas University and Menninger Clinic. In 1981, he left his long service as a Family Therapist with the Philadelphia Child Guidance Clinic to become Director of the newly formed program for PTSD at the Philadelphia VA Hospital where EMDR became an integral part of the treatment program. An article, "Post Traumatic Stress Disorder and Competence to Stand Trial," was published in the *Journal of Psychiatry and Law,* Spring 1984. His research on the EMDR treatment of triggers remains unfinished due to his retirement and final illness.

Mark Dworkin, LCSW, has practiced EMDR since 1991. His experience in treating traumatized populations started in 1975 when he began working for the Bronx VA Medical Center, just as the war in Viet Nam was ending. He is a Facilitator; an Approved Consultant and Approved Trainer for the EMDR International Association, and served on its Board of Directors. He is a graduate of The Manhattan Institute for Psychoanalysis, and studied Gestalt Therapy with Laura Perls, PhD. He is published in the *Journal of Psychotherapy Integration* and he taught Consultation Psychiatry on the Faculty of the Mount Sinai School of Medicine. He is currently in full-time private practice in East Meadow, New York, and consults to different professional organizations. He is the author of *EMDR and the Relational Imperative: The Therapeutic Relationship in EMDR Treatment* (2005).

Sandra Foster, PhD, is a performance enhancement psychologist formerly based in San Francisco, California, where she worked both as a peak performance coach and EMDR psychotherapist. Currently, she is a Principal in Korn/Ferry's London-based Leadership and Talent Consulting practice. She served as Acting Assistant Professor and Consulting Associate Professor at Stanford University where she received her doctorate. She attended the first public EMDR training (March 1990) in the United States and was one of three initial facilitators. Dr. Foster founded the Peak Performance SIG, was Founding Chair of the EMDRIA Public Relations Committee, and received the 2000 Francine Shapiro Award for Innovations in EMDR.

Tanos Freiha, DPhil, Dipl Psych, is a psychologist and psychotherapist who holds a German Diploma in Psychology from the University of Tübingen. He is an EMDR therapist, Approved Consultant and a Facilitator for the EMDR-Institut-Deutschland. Since 1994, he has been a practicing psychologist in the Social Pediatrics Unit at the University Children's Hospital in Cologne, Germany. In 1997, he was awarded his PhD in Psychology. Since 1998, his major interest is in working with EMDR-traumatized children; in 2006, he began a project extending his work in EMDR to treating children diagnosed with Diabetes Mellitus Type I concerning their trauma and fears.

Judith S. B. Guedalia, PhD, is Senior Medical Psychologist and a member of the ER (Emergency Room) Trauma Staff in times of Mass Community Events (MCE, or ARAN the Hebrew acronym). She is Director of Shaare Zedek Medical Center's Neuropsychology Unit and among the many symptoms the Neuropsychology Unit has treated are emotional trauma, anxiety, depression, parenting and family issues, stress, children of divorce, self-esteem, patient adjustment to neurological or cognitive problems, adjustment to chronic illness, family adjustment to and coping with a member's illness, and adjustment to developmental disabilities. Dr. Guedalia is an EMDR Therapist and is in the process of completing the requirements to be a supervisor of other EMDR therapists. Dr. Guedalia is the founder and cochair of Nefesh Israel, the Israeli branch of the NEFESH International Organization the Networking Association for Orthodox Mental Health Professionals. She has published in peer review journals in both Neuropsychology and the Judaism and Mental Health. She is also a regular columnist for *The Jewish Press,* the American's largest independent Jewish weekly. She was born in New York City, has studied and worked in New York, New York; London, England; Holyoke, Massachusetts; Los Angeles, California; and Jerusalem, Israel (since 1980).

John Hartung, PhD, is coordinator of the EMDR-Ibero-American Association, an organization that provides humanitarian and for-profit services to Spanish- and Portuguese-speaking countries. As professor with the University of the Rockies, executive coach with the Center for Creative Leadership, and codirector of the Body-Mind Integration Institute of Singapore, he has taught coaching, leadership, EMDR, and energy medicine in 25 countries. He received his doctorate in psychology from the University of Denver. He and his wife, Nikki, live in Colorado Springs near their grandchildren.

Arne Hofmann, MD, is a specialist in Psychosomatic and Internal Medicine. He is a Senior Trainer and is a Trainers' Trainer in Europe. He introduced EMDR into the German-speaking countries of Europe after a 1991 residency at the Mental Research Institute in Palo Alto, California where he learned about EMDR and went on to head the German EMDR Institute. In 1994, he started the first inpatient trauma program in a Psychiatric Hospital near Frankfurt, Germany, where he assisted in developing Aftercare programs subsequent to mass disaster events like the 1998 train catastrophe in Eschede, the 2002 school shooting in Erfurt, and the 2004 Tsunami in Southeast Asia. He is a Founding Board Member of the German-speaking Society of Traumatic Stress Studies (DeGPT) and EMDR-Europe where he currently serves as vice president. He also is a member of a German National Guideline Commission on the treatment of PTSD and Acute Stress Disorder. He has published a number of articles (mostly in German), a book on EMDR, and coedited three other books on trauma and EMDR. He has been teaching at the Universities of Cologne, Witten-Herdecke, and Peking. He lectures internationally and received the Ron Martinez Award from the EMDR International Association in 2005.

Manda Holmshaw, PhD, is a Consultant, Clinical Psychologist, and Clinical Director of Moving Minds, a national rehabilitation organization in the United Kingdom, which treats adults and children after traumatic experiences, especially road traffic accidents, assaults, and accidents at work. She is an EMDR-Europe accredited Trainer and Consultant and divides her time between supervision, clinical work, research, and EMDR training and is based in London.

Ignacio Jarero, PhD, EdD, MT, is a Trainer of Trainers, EMDRIA and EMDR-Ibero-America cofounder and Approved Consultant. He is cofounder and President of EMDR-Mexico, AMAMECRISIS, and International Center of Psychotraumatology. In 2007, he received the EMDR-Ibero-America Francine Shapiro Award and, in 2008, the Argentinian Society of Psychotrauma (ISTSS Affiliate) awarded him the Psychotrauma Trajectory Award. He is a Trainer for the International Critical Incident Stress Foundation and Green Cross Academy of Traumatology. He is coauthor of the EMDR Integrative Group Treatment Protocol that has been applied successfully with disaster survivors worldwide. He has presented workshops and has published articles on EMDR, Crisis Intervention, and Compassion Fatigue. Since 1997, he has been involved in humanitarian projects in Latin America and Europe.

Roy Kiessling, LISW, ACSW, has been an active participant in the EMDR community since he was trained; first as an EMDR Facilitator, and then as a Trainer. He is an EMDRIA Approved Provider and Consultant. In 2000, he became the second worldwide Internet discussion list moderator on EMDR. Since 1998, he has presented annually at the EMDRIA International Conference. In 2001, he began volunteering as a Trainer for EMDR HAP and has helped teach clinicians around the world as well as within the continental United States. In 2007, he received the Liz Snyker Humanitarian Award for his volunteer work with EMDR HAP. He maintains a general private practice for adults, couples, families, and children specializing in brief treatment and EMDR consultation for clinicians seeking to become certified in EMDR in Cincinnati, Ohio.

Brurit Laub, PhD, is a senior Clinical Psychologist, with over 30 years of experience working in community mental health in Israel. She is also a teacher and supervisor at the Machon Magid School of Psychotherapy at Hebrew University in Jerusalem and at different marriage and family counseling centers. She is an accredited hypnotherapist, and a supervisor in psychotherapy and family therapy. She presents workshops concerning models developed independently and together with colleagues on narrative therapy, script changing therapy, coping with monsters, dialectical cotherapy, trans-generational tools, recent trauma, resource development and work with subpersonalities nationally and internationally. She has published 15 articles on the above topics in International and Israeli journals. In 1998, she became an EMDR Facilitator and she is an EMDR-Europe Accredited Consultant. She has been involved with HAP trainings in Turkey and Sri-Lanka. She developed a Resource Connection Envelope (RCE) for the Standard EMDR Protocol and presented it in workshops and for EMDR conferences in Tel-Aviv, London, Vancouver, Denver, Istanbul, and Norway. With Esti Bar-Sade, she developed the Imma EMDR Group Protocol, which is an adaptation of Artigas, Jarero, Alcalá, and López's IGTP. Together with Elan Shapiro, she presented their Recent Traumatic Episode Protocol (R-TEP) at a workshop for the EMDR-Europe Consultants day at the 2008 EMDR-Europe Annual Conference in London, following the publication of their article in the *Journal of EMDR Practice & Research*. In 1994, she coauthored, with S. Hoffman and S. Gafni, "Co-therapy With Individuals, Families." In 2006, she collaborated again with S. Hoffman on "Innovative Interventions in Psychotherapy." She lives in Rehovot and is in private practice.

Jennifer Lendl, PhD, is a licensed psychologist with a clinical private practice in Silicon Valley, California. She specializes in trauma, performance for sports, business, health, and the arts. She coauthored *EMDR Performance Enhancement for the Workplace: A Practitioners' Manual* (1997). Dr. Lendl was the trauma and performance specialist at the Amen Clinic for 6 years and continues to consult with them. She is the Sports Psychologist with an interdisciplinary training group called Women Involved with Sports Evolution in Ventura, California. She presents at conferences nationally and internationally on EMDR, Performance and Sports Psychology. In 2006, Dr. Lendl was awarded the Francine Shapiro Award by the EMDR International Association for her outstanding contribution to EMDR.

Tessa Prattos, MA, MAAT, is a Certified Traumatologist, Facilitator, EMDR-Europe Consultant, and the Director of the International Trauma Center in Athens, Greece. She has been a professional psychologist for the past 23 years working in prominent psychotherapy centers in Athens and has an ongoing private practice in Athens. Her areas of expertise are in EMDR, systemic psychotherapy, developmental psychology, and art therapy. Founder and director of the International Trauma Center, fully trained and accredited in EMDR, and the organizer of EMDR Hellas Association, her focus is on trauma victims from man-made and natural disasters, PTSD, anxiety disorders, dissociation, grief, and works with groups, individuals, children, and families. She has experience as a trainer to mental health professionals in systemic psychotherapy and art therapy. She has presented at numerous conferences on EMDR and Dissociation topics. She and Frances R. Yoeli have coauthored the published chapter "Terrorism is the Ritual Abuse of the Twenty-first Century" and, currently, they are working on the further development of the Multi-Tiered Trans-Generational Genogram. She has participated in EMDR HAP fieldwork in Asia.

Gary Quinn, MD, is Director of the Jerusalem Stress and Trauma Institute and Clinical Assistant Professor of Psychiatry at Ohio State University. He specializes in Crisis Intervention, the treatment of Anxiety Disorders, and the treatment of Post-Traumatic Stress Disorder following military trauma, terrorist attacks, and motor vehicle accidents. He is the cofounder and cochairman of EMDR-Israel.

Luise Reddemann, MD, is one of the pioneers of trauma therapy in Germany. After 20 years as the Director of a Clinic for Psychosomatic Disorder, she is now a Professor of Psychotraumatology at the University of Klagenfurt, Austria, and is teaching her own seminars in Trauma Therapy throughout the German-speaking world.

Gene Schwartz, LCSW-C, is a Licensed Clinical Social Worker, practicing in Baltimore, Maryland, since 1971. He spent 30 years working at the Veterans Administration Hospital in Baltimore. Since his retirement, in December 2000, he is in private practice in Towson, Maryland.

Elan Shapiro, MA, is a Psychologist in private practice in Israel with over 30 years of experience. He works as a Senior Consulting Psychologist in a Community Psychological Service in Upper Nazareth. Originally specializing in Adlerian psychology, he came to EMDR in 1989 after attending one of the first trainings ever given. After additional training in the United States and Europe, in 1994, he became an EMDR Facilitator. He was among the founding members of EMDR-Europe, EMDR-Israel, and a charter member of EMDRIA. He is an EMDR-Europe Accredited Consultant and was recently re-elected for a second term as Secretary of EMDR-Europe. He has been involved with HAP trainings in Turkey, Sri-Lanka, and Thailand. With Brurit Laub, they presented their Recent Traumatic Episode Protocol (R-TEP) at a workshop for the EMDR-Europe Consultants day at the 2008 EMDR-Europe Annual Conference in London, following the publication of their article on the same topic in the *Journal of EMDR Practice & Research.*

Frances R. Yoeli, MSc, MFT, CAC, LISW, is a Certified Traumatologist, EMDR HAP Facilitator, and Consultant for the Life Energy Center in Israel. Her clinical experience has spanned three continents and 4 decades. She works with PTSD from abuse, wars, mass disasters, terrorism, critical incidents, and traumatic events. Other specialties include anxiety, eating disorders, addictions, new religious movement issues, cults, ritual abuse with trauma victims, couples, families, and clients presenting with depressions, loss, grief, and the full range of psychosomatic and dissociative disorders. She headed the Emergency Mental Health Team in the Emek Bet-Shean Valley for many years. As a HAP Facilitator and Consultant, she faced several Asian challenges in Humanitarian field work, and facilitated EMDR trainings in the region. For 6 years, she worked as coordinator for HAP events in Israel. She has given numerous presentations in professional conferences on EMDR, dissociation, cult and ritual abuse, and terrorism. With her colleague Tessa Prattos, they completed the book chapter "Terrorism Is the Ritual Abuse of the Twenty-First Century" and they are refining their Multi-Tiered Trans-Generational Genogram, cooperating with the International Trauma Center in Athens, Greece, and with other international treatment centers on its clinical application.

Preface

Marilyn Luber

As the practice of Eye Movement Desensitization and Reprocessing (EMDR) approaches its third decade, it is helpful to reflect on the astonishing development of this psychological treatment model. Over these 20 years, EMDR has grown into an approach to psychotherapy that has been extensively researched and proven effective for the treatment of trauma. This is, in part, due to the number of institutions and researchers that are validating the efficacy of EMDR. In the United States, these include the American Psychological Association (APA, 2004; Chambless et al., 1998), the International Society for Traumatic Stress Studies (Chemtob, Tolin, van der Kolk, & Pitman, 2000; Foa, Keane, & Friedman, 2000), the National Institute of Mental Health Web site (Shapiro, 2004–2007), and the Department of Veterans Affairs and Department of Defense (2004). In Europe, EMDR is considered one of the treatments of choice for trauma victims by the Dutch National Steering Committee for Guidelines Mental Health Care (2003); the French National Institute of Health and Medical Research (INSERM, 2004); The Clinical Resource Efficiency Support Team of the Northern Ireland Department of Health, Social Services and Public Safety (CREST, 2003); the National Institute for Clinical Excellence in England (NICE, 2005); and the United Kingdom Department of Health (2001). In the Middle East, the Israeli National Council for Mental Health (Bleich, Kotler, Kutz, & Shalev, 2002); has named EMDR as one of the methods recommended for the treatment of terror victims. EMDR is an important therapy for the treatment of trauma and is taught in many universities. It has also gained a great deal of respect in the therapeutic world for being a modality that is effective.

As a therapeutic approach, EMDR is on the same par as cognitive behavior therapy and psychodynamic therapy. It is composed of a complex methodology applicable to a wide range of disorders. As such, new procedures and protocols have been introduced to address a variety of issues. Whereas the EMDR procedures and original protocol for trauma (Shapiro, 1995, 2001, 2006) have been extensively researched, many of the protocols in this book are not yet validated by research. Information concerning research will be mentioned in the body of the chapter as appropriate. The protocols are included because they have been reported in books and articles and at EMDR conferences worldwide to be of value to practicing clinicians as they work with their clients, and because they can serve as a stimulus and inspiration to other clinicians for research in the future.

Research in other areas of treatment are referenced below and represent a small sample of the ongoing investigations into the applications of this treatment modality, such as addictions (Amundsen & Kårstad, 2006; Besson et al., 2006; Cox & Howard, 2007; Henry, 1996; Popky, 2005; Shapiro & Forrest, 1997; Shapiro, Vogelmann-Sine, & Sine, 1994; Vogelmann-Sine, Sine, Smyth, & Popky, 1998; Zweben & Yeary, 2006), anxiety (Doctor, 1994; Feske & Goldstein, 1997; Goldstein & Feske, 1994; Maxwell, 2003; Nadler, 1996; Shapiro, 1991, 1994, 1999; Shapiro & Forrest, 1997), body dysmorphia (Brown, McGoldrick, & Buchanan, 1997), children and adolescents (Greenwald, 1994, 1998, 1999, 2000, 2002; Hensel, 2006; Maxfield, 2007; Russell & O'Connor, 2002; Tinker & Wilson, 1999), dissociative disorders (Fine, 1994; Fine

& Berkowitz, 2001; Gelinas, 2003; Lazrove, 1994; Lazrove & Fine, 1996; Marquis & Puk, 1994; Paulsen, 1995; Rouanzoin, 1994; Twombly, 2000, 2005; Young, 1994), family, marital, and sexual dysfunction (Capps, 2006; Errebo & Sommers-Flanagan, 2007; Kaslow, Nurse, & Thompson, 2002; Madrid, Skolek, & Shapiro, 2006; Shapiro, Kaslow, & Maxfield, 2007; Talan, 2007; Wernik, 1993), multiply traumatized combat vets (Carlson, Chemtob, Rusnak, Hudlund, & Muraoka, 1998; Errebo & Sommers-Flanagan, 2007; Lipke, 2000; Russell, 2006, 2008; Russell & Silver, 2007; Russell, Silver, Rogers, & Darnell, 2007; Shapiro, 1995; Silver, Brooks, & Obenchain, 1995; Silver & Rogers, 2002), pain (Grant & Threlfo, 2002; Ray & Zbik, 2001), performance enhancement (Crabbe, 1996; Foster & Lendl, 1995, 1996; Graham, 2004), phantom limb pain (Russell, 2008; Schneider, Hofmann, Rost, & Shapiro, 2007; Tinker & Wilson, 2006; Wilensky, 2006; Wilson, Tinker, Becker, Hofmann, & Cole, 2000), previously abused child molesters (Ricci, 2006; Ricci, Clayton, & Shapiro, 2006), stress management (Wilson, Becker, Tinker & Logan, 2001), victims of natural and man-made disasters (Jarero, Artigas, Mauer, López Cano, & Alcalá, 1999; Knipe et al., 2003; Konuk et al., 2006), and so forth, is ongoing (for more information go to the EMDR International Association Web site: http://www.emdria.org or the EMDR Institute Web site: http://www.emdr.com).

EMDR is based on the Adaptive Information Processing Model (AIP; for comprehensive descriptions, see Shapiro, 1995, 2001, 2006; Shapiro et al., 2007). The premise of Adaptive Information Processing is that every person has both an innate tendency to move toward health and wholeness, and the inner capacity to achieve it. When this movement to health is blocked—and not related to organic difficulties or lack of information—it is likely that the experiences related to the block have been stored in a way that does not allow them to connect with any other adaptive information and maladaptive perceptual distortions, images, feelings, and sensations can ensue. When these dysfunctionally stored memories are triggered, this unprocessed material/experience often results in pathological or maladaptive responses to what might be an ordinary event and/or an event that does not warrant the type of response triggered. These dysfunctionally stored memories seem to be frozen in time and they are unable to connect with other memory networks that hold adaptive information. The goal of trauma treatment is to unfreeze these dysfunctionally stored memories so that they can connect with the adaptive information held in other neural networks and resume the normal functioning of memory processing. Over time, this type of maladaptive information processing—when unresolved—can result in a continuum of difficulties leading from maladaptive thoughts and behaviors, to psychological symptoms that can escalate into psychological disorders.

The EMDR approach integrates elements from both psychological theories (e.g., affect, attachment, behavioral, bio-information processing, cognitive, family systems, humanistic, psychodynamic, and somatic) and psychotherapies (e.g., body-based, cognitive-behavioral, interpersonal, personality-centered, and psychodynamic) into a standardized set of procedures and clinical protocols. Research on how the brain processes information and generates consciousness also informs the evolution of EMDR theory and procedure (see EMDR International Association Web site: http://www.emdria.org or the EMDR Institute Web site: http://www.emdr.com). *EMDR is an approach to psychotherapy that is comprised of principles, procedures, and protocols. It is not—as often depicted—a simple technique characterized primarily by the use of eye movements.*

Learning EMDR, at first, was considered easy, however, after many years of training over 100,000 mental health practitioners, it has become clear to the trainers, facilitators, and consultants that learning EMDR is not as simple as "a walk in the park" (Shapiro, 1995, 2001). In fact, solid instruction, training, and consultation are essential components in the learning curve of mastering this complex psychotherapy. Shapiro's text, *Eye Movement Desensitization and Reprocessing: Basic*

Principles, Protocols and Procedures (2001) is required reading for a comprehensive understanding of EMDR as a clinical approach.

Eye Movement Desensitization and Reprocessing (EMDR) Scripted Protocols: Basics and Special Situations grew out of a perceived need that mental health practitioners could be served by a place to access both traditional and newly developed protocols in a way that adheres to best clinical practices incorporating the *Standard EMDR Protocol* that includes working on the past, present, and future issues (the 3-Pronged Protocol) related to the problem and the *11-Step Standard Procedure* that includes attention to the following steps: image, negative cognition (NC), positive cognition (PC), validity of cognition (VoC), emotion, subjective units of disturbance (SUD), and location of body sensation, desensitization, installation, body scan, and closure. Often, EMDR texts embed the protocols in a great deal of explanatory material that is essential in the process of learning EMDR. However, sometimes, as a result, practitioners move away from the basic importance of maintaining the integrity of the Standard EMDR Protocol and keeping adaptive information processing in mind when conceptualizing the course of treatment for a patient. It is in this way that the efficacy of this powerful methodology is lost.

"Scripting" becomes a way not only to inform and remind the EMDR practitioner of the component parts, sequence, and language used to create an effective outcome, but it also creates a template for practitioners and researchers to use for reliability and/or a common denominator so that the form of working with EMDR is consistent. The concept that has motivated this work was conceived within the context of assisting EMDR clinicians in accessing the scripts of the full protocols in one place and to profit from the creativity of other EMDR clinicians who have kept the spirit of EMDR but have also taken into consideration the needs of the population with whom they work or the situations that they encounter. *Reading a script is by no means a substitute for adequate training, competence, clinical acumen, and integrity; if you are not a trained EMDR therapist and/or you are not knowledgeable in the field for which you wish to use the script, these scripts are not for you.*

As EMDR is a fairly complicated process, and indeed, has intimidated some from integrating it into their daily approach to therapy, this book provides step-by-step *scripts* that will enable beginning practitioners to enhance their expertise more quickly. It will also appeal to seasoned EMDR clinicians, trainers, and consultants because it brings together the many facets of the eight phases of EMDR and how clinicians are using this framework to work with a variety of therapeutic difficulties and modalities, while maintaining the integrity of the AIP model. Although there are a large number of resources, procedures, and protocols in this book, they do not constitute the universe of protocols that are potentially useful and worthy of further study and use.

These scripted protocols are intended for clinicians who have read Shapiro's text (2001) and received EMDR training from an EMDR-accredited trainer. An EMDR trainer is a licensed mental health practitioner who has been approved by the association active in the clinician's country of practice. The following associations are upholding the standard of EMDR worldwide: EMDRIA in the United States (http://www.emdria.org), EMDR-Canada (http://www.emdrcanada.org), EMDR-Europe (http://www.emdr-europe.org), Ibero-America for Central and South America and Spain (http://www.EMDRiberoamerica.org), EMDR Association of Australia (http://www.emdraa.org), EMDR-Asia is in formation, and EMDR in Africa is evolving. For more in-depth information concerning standards and EMDR practice, it would be judicious to contact these organizations. The names and contact information of EMDR organizations and/or associations are available in Appendix C, the EMDR resources section of this book.

These scripts are not *intended for use by unlicensed practitioners or clinicians who do not understand the complexity of EMDR or the type of problem with which they are working with their client. It is essential that clinicians know their own strengths and limitations and seek supervision and/or consultation when needed. Again, access to information concerning clinicians accredited to do supervision and/ or consultation is available through the associations.*

This book is separated into sections that loosely follow the structure of Francine Shapiro's original texts (1995, 2001): client history, adaptive information processing, preparation, desensitization, and procedures for special situations. Work with special populations is included in a second volume, *Eye Movement Desensitization and Reprocessing (EMDR) Scripted Protocols: Special Populations* (Luber, in press). Both books include chapters that focus on supporting clinicians through clinician self-care as they work with the difficulties of their clients and, in this way, under-lining the importance of this subject.

In order to uphold the American Psychological Association's standard of nonbias concerning gender, this editor has chosen to have authors use the personal pronouns opposite to their own gender while referring to a client and the personal pronouns of their own gender while referring to themselves as a way to avoid the awkwardness of using both pronouns together such as *he/she or (s)he,* and so forth.

The Client History section represents the first of the eight phases of EMDR treatment. The ability to gather, formulate, and then use the material in the intake part of treatment is crucial to an optimal outcome in any therapist's work. In Part I, material was chosen to support ways to conceptualize history taking according to the adaptive information processing way of thinking to inform EMDR treatment planning. It also includes several ways to summarize history-taking material after a thorough history has been taken.

Part II includes an important element of the Preparation Phase that addresses ways to introduce and explain EMDR, trauma, and the adaptive information pro-cessing (AIP) model. This material by Sheila Bender and Gene Schwartz can also be used during Phase One to explain to clients how their current and past predica-ments and distress about the future arose and can be connected.

The importance of teaching clients how to create personal resources is the topic of Part III. Here, an essential element of the Preparation/Second Phase of EMDR work is addressed to ensure clients' abilities to contain their affect and re-main stable as they move through the EMDR process. These contributions from Francine Shapiro, Luise Reddemann, Roy Kiessling, Brurit Laub, and Elan Shapiro are a representative sample of the many different ways to create resources during the Preparation Phase. Resources for children and adolescents, and clients who are dealing with difficulties that are in the Dissociative Spectrum are described in *Eye Movement Desensitization and Reprocessing (EMDR) Scripted Protocols: Special Populations* (Luber, in press), as they represent their own unique issues.

Part IV is a section on how to work with clients concerning the targeting of their presenting problems when the usual ways do not work. Esly Carvalho uses draw-ings as a way to concretize her clients' conceptualization of their issues for targeting while Tanos Freiha gives an alternative, initial targeting method that allows clients more control when issues are overwhelming. Sheila Bender in Part II also addresses this issue with strategies to work in her chapter, "When Words and Pictures Fail."

Although Part V could have been included in other sections, the choice to separate the original protocols that Francine Shapiro introduced in her original texts seemed appropriate as a way to underline the roots from which the rest of the chap-ters in this book grew and the comprehensiveness of her thinking from the begin-ning years of EMDR. This section includes protocols that have been scripted based on the material that appears in Francine Shapiro's EMDR textbook (2001) and later written work (2006). The work in these volumes forms the basis of EMDR, includ-ing the 11-Step Standard Procedure and the component aspects of the 3-Prong ap-proach of past, present, and future, essential to the effective use of EMDR.

Parts VI and VII address EMDR and Early Intervention Procedures for Man-made and Natural Catastrophes for Individuals and Groups. The core of this work began as a basic intent by Francine Shapiro to help address and transform the pain and suffering in the world to adaptive functioning and health and enable survivors to move on with their day-to-day lives. The result of this healing was to end the transmission of shame, hate, and retribution that historically has fostered the passing of this legacy into future generations. Although this vision began with individual work and the training of therapists to help the victims of rape, abuse, war, and other issues rampant in mental health centers, the tragedy of Oklahoma City with the bombing of the Alfred P. Murrah Federal Building on April 19, 1995, was the incentive to work with survivors of man-made catastrophes. In response to this tragedy came an outpouring of EMDR-trained clinicians who went to the aid of the victims and their families. Through the dedication and organizational skills of Sandra Wilson, mental health practitioners traveled to train our Oklahoma colleagues to work with EMDR and we assisted them in treating the survivors over a 6-month period. This effort grew into the EMDR Humanitarian Assistance Program (EMDR HAP), a nonprofit organization founded by Francine Shapiro; the first Executive Director was Barbara Korzun followed by Robert Gelbach. The mission of EMDR HAP states that, "We promote recovery from traumatic stress, through direct service and community-based training in EMDR for mental health workers all over the world." Colleagues with expertise in working in disaster situations such as Roger Solomon, Steve Silver, Susan Rogers, Elaine Alvarez, Gerry Puk, Kay Werk, Robert Tinker, and Barbara Parrett were the creators of the foundation from which EMDR HAP spread the importance of working with the psychological aspects of trauma. The work of EMDR HAP has fostered sister organizations in countries and continents around the world.

These were the seeds that grew into the protocols in Parts VI and VII. Elan Shapiro and Brurit Laub's idea on how to think about trauma over its developmental course in their "Recent-Traumatic Episode Protocol" is an important breakthrough and hypothesizes a way to integrate the fragmentation of memory and then how to address it within the EMDR framework to treat clients at different stages of their traumatic experiences. Judi Guedalia's work after seeing hundreds of victims of terrorist attacks in Jerusalem was enhanced by her collaboration with her colleague and EMDR-trained clinician, Frances Yoeli. The work of Lucina Artigas, who created the Butterfly Hug, a form of bilateral stimulation, is possibly one of the most creative and significant contributions of our EMDR community. With her colleagues Ignacio Jarero, Nicté Alcalá, and Teresa López Cano they created the EMDR Integrative Group Treatment (EMDR-IGTP); a treatment that has been used with children and adults around the world after massive man-made and natural disasters and inspired others such as Brurit Laub and Esti Bar-Sade and others to adapt this protocol to their own populations. Gary Quinn works with an Emergency Response Procedure and David Blore adapted the EMDR Standard Protocol to work with the particular issues concerning underground trauma while Aiton Birnbaum's innovative contribution of using EMDR in a workbook format for individuals and groups offers a novel way to approach EMDR for clients whose styles foster a more visual—with the option of a more private—way of working with their traumatic material; this protocol is more comprehensive as it includes the actual workbook that clients can use, as well as the script for therapists.

EMDR and Performance Enhancement featured in Part VIII showcases the work of Jennifer Lendl, Sandra Foster, and John Hartung. Their chapters demonstrate some of the fascinating possibilities when working in this field. Many of their suggestions can be adapted to work with traumatized individuals in the form of resources and addressing issues in the future. Both of these protocols are comprehensive tools as they are more manuals than single protocols.

The idea of clinician self-care is crucial to the welfare of mental health practitioners and their clients. The ability of therapists to tend to themselves and recognize their own triggers, vulnerabilities, and sink holes is an important aspect of training.

In Part IX, Neal Daniels addresses how clinicians can routinely work with their own distress to inoculate themselves against burn out and/or secondary PTSD and Mark Dworkin's work suggests ways to address countertransference issues as they arise.

Appendix A is a pull-out section that includes scripts for the protocols for past, present triggers, and future templates. In fact, the purpose of this book, in general, is to provide the practitioner with a script and/or scripts that can be copied and put in the client's chart to use with his particular issue so that all aspects of the eight phases are incorporated and accessible as a reminder of all of the elements needed for the work to be complete and/or a script to be used and followed specifically. Often, scripts repeat the elements of EMDR to support clarity and ease of using the scripts.

Appendix B addresses an interesting expansion of the 11-Step Standard Procedure by Gene Schwartz. Although this has not been tested, it brings up an interesting question concerning how to address possible changes or expansions in the protocol. The Standard EMDR Protocol is a protocol that has evolved since its inception in 1989 under the auspices of the EMDR Institute and the talented clinicians, facilitators, and trainers that were the foundation of EMDR and represented every psychotherapy tradition. As of 1995, when Francine Shapiro wrote the first comprehensive text on EMDR, *Eye Movement Desensitization and Reprocessing: Basic Principles, Protocols, and Procedures,* the standard of how to do EMDR was clearly stated. In 2001, she published the second edition of her original text and updated the standard. The chapters in this book follow the standard that is in this second edition of *Eye Movement Desensitization and Reprocessing: Basic Principles, Protocols, and Procedures.*

In Appendix C, worldwide EMDR associations and resources are listed. There are numerous EMDR associations throughout the world as EMDR trained practitioners have come together to share their knowledge, training, and uphold the standard of optimal EMDR practice. Through the interaction of these different groups, much has been learned and shared as clinicians encounter problems that cross cultures and also those that are distinctive and particular to the population and issue being addressed. Included in Appendix C are a number of the known Humanitarian Assistance Programs that have developed as EMDR practitioners have reached out to their peers in other countries in the face of man-made catastrophes and natural disasters. This is followed by resources that catalog information; the most recent is the Francine Shapiro Library, an online repository of all that is written about EMDR. Also included are the *EMDR Journal* and E-Journals and where to find trauma-related information.

In addition, references that are relevant to EMDR and the work of the contributors are included as a compendium of the wealth of information available about EMDR and a way to tap the expertise of those included in this book so that practitioners are able to deepen their own areas of learning. Additional references introduce other resources suggested by the authors or about the authors themselves. Some of these ideas are in the process of being researched while others are presented now for their helpfulness and may serve as the subject of a study in the future. This is a book that is rich in the accumulated knowledge of the clinicians trained in and using EMDR on a regular basis and formatted to support the learning and practice of the reader.

REFERENCES

American Psychiatric Association (APA). (2004). *Practice guideline for the treatment of patients with acute stress disorder and posttraumatic stress disorder.* Arlington, VA: American Psychiatric Association Practice Guidelines.

Amundsen, J. E., & Kårstad, K. (2006). Om bare Jeppe visste—EMDR og rusbehandling [Integrating EMDR and the treatment of substance abuse]. *Tidsskrift for Norsk Psykologforening, 43*(5), 469.

Besson, J., Eap, C., Rougemont-Buecking, A., Simon, O., Nikolov, C., & Bonsack, C. (2006). *Addictions. Revue Médicale Suisse, 47*(2), 9–13.

Bleich, A., Kotler, M., Kutz, I., & Shalev, A. (2002). *Guidelines for the assessment and professional intervention with terror victims in the hospital and in the community.* A position paper of the (Israeli) National Council for Mental Health, Jerusalem, Israel.

Brown, K. W., McGoldrick, T., & Buchanan, R. (1997). Body dysmorphic disorder: Seven cases treated with eye movement desensitization and reprocessing. *Behavioural and Cognitive Psychotherapy, 25*, 203–207.

Capps, F. (2006). Combining eye movement desensitization and reprocessing with gestalt techniques in couples counseling. *Family Journal: Counseling and Therapy for Couples and Families, 14*(1), 49.

Carlson, J. G., Chemtob, C. M., Rusnak, K., Hedlund, N. L., & Muraoka, M. Y. (1998). Eye movement desensitization and reprocessing treatment for combat related posttraumatic stress disorder. *Journal of Traumatic Stress, 11*(1), 3–24.

Chambless, D. L., Baker, M. J., Baucom, D. H., Beutler, L. E., Calhoun, K. S., Cris-Christoph, P., et al. (1998). Update on empirically validated therapies, II. *The Clinical Psychologist, 51*, 3–16.

Chemtob, C. M., Tolin, D. F., van der Kolk, B. A., & Pitman, R. K. (2000). Eye movement desensitization and reprocessing. In E. A. Foa, T. M. Keane, & M. J. Friedman (Eds.), *Effective treatments for PTSD: Practice guidelines from the International Society for Traumatic Stress Studies.* New York: Guilford Press.

Cox, R. P., & Howard, M. D. (2007). Utilization of EMDR in the treatment of sexual addiction: A case study. *Sexual Addiction & Compulsivity, 14*(1), 1.

Crabbe, B. (1996, November). Can eye-movement therapy improve your riding? *Dressage Today,* 28–33.

CREST. (2003). *The management of post traumatic stress disorder in adults.* A publication of the Clinical Resource Efficiency Support Team of the Northern Ireland Department of Health, Social Services and Public Safety, Belfast.

Department of Veterans Affairs and Department of Defense. (2004). *VA/DoD clinical practice guideline for the management of post-traumatic stress.* Washington, DC: Veterans Health Administration, Department of Veterans Affairs and Health Affairs, Department of Defense. Office of Quality and Performance publication 10Q-CPG/PTSD-04.

Doctor, R. (1994, March). *Eye movement desensitization and reprocessing: A clinical and research examination with anxiety disorders.* Paper presented at the 14th annual meeting of the Anxiety Disorders Association of America, Santa Monica, CA.

Dutch National Steering Committee for Guidelines Mental Health Care. (2003). *Multidisciplinary guideline anxiety disorders.* Quality Institute Heath Care CBO/Trimbos Institute. Utrecht, Netherlands.

Errebo, N., & Sommers-Flanagan, R. (2007). EMDR and emotionally focused couple therapy for war veteran couples. In F. Shapiro, F. Kaslow, & L. Maxfield (Eds.), *Handbook of EMDR and family therapy processes.* New York: Wiley.

Feske, U., & Goldstein, A. (1997). *Eye movement desensitization and reprocessing treatment for panic disorder:* A controlled outcome and partial dismantling study. *Journal of Consulting and Clinical Psychology, 36*, 1026–1035.

Fine, C. (1994, June). *Eye movement desensitization and reprocessing (EMDR) for dissociative disorders.* Presentation at the Eastern Regional Conference on Abuse and Multiple Personality. Alexandria, VA.

Fine, C., & Berkowitz, A. (2001). The wreathing protocol: The imbrication of hypnosis and EMDR in the treatment of dissociative identity disorder and other dissociative responses. *American Journal of Clinical Hypnosis, 43*, 275–290.

Foa, E. B., Keane, T. M., & Friedman, M. J. (2000). *Effective treatments for PTSD: Practice guidelines of the International Society for Traumatic Stress Studies.* New York: Guilford Press.

Foster, S., & Lendl, J. (1995). Eye movement desensitization and reprocessing: Initial applications for enhancing performance in athletes. *Journal of Applied Sport Psychology, 7*(Suppl.), 63.

Foster, S., & Lendl, J. (1996). Eye movement desensitization and reprocessing: Four case studies of a new tool for executive coaching and restoring employee performance after setbacks. *Consulting Psychology Journal, 48*, 155–161.

Gelinas, D. J. (2003). Integrating EMDR into phase-oriented treatment for trauma. *Journal of Trauma and Dissociation, 4*, 91–135.

Goldstein, A., & Feske, U. (1994). Eye movement desensitization and reprocessing for panic disorder: A case series. *Journal of Anxiety Disorders, 8*, 351–362.

Graham, L. (2004). Traumatic swimming events reprocessed with EMDR. *The Sport Journal, 7*(1), 1–5.

Grant, M., & Threlfo, C. (2002). EMDR in the treatment of chronic pain. *Journal of Clinical Psychology, 58*, 1505–1520.

Greenwald, R. (1994). Applying eye movement desensitization and reprocessing to the treatment of traumatized children: Five case studies. *Anxiety Disorders Practice Journal, 1*, 83–97.

Greenwald, R. (1998). Eye movement desensitization and reprocessing (EMDR): New hope for children suffering from trauma and loss. *Clinical Child Psychology and Psychiatry, 3*, 279–287.

Greenwald, R. (1999). *Eye movement desensitization and reprocessing (EMDR) in child and adolescent psychotherapy.* Northvale, NJ: Jason Aronson Press.

Greenwald, R. (2000). A trauma-focused individual therapy approach for adolescents with conduct disorder. *International Journal of Offender Therapy and Comparative Criminology, 44*, 146–163.

Greenwald, R. (2002). Motivation-adaptive skills-trauma resolution (MASTR) therapy for adolescents with conduct problems: An open trial. *Journal of Aggression, Maltreatment, and Trauma, 6*, 237–261.

Henry, S. (1996). Pathological gambling: Etiological considerations and treatment efficacy of eye movement desensitization/reprocessing. *Journal of Gambling Studies, 12*, 395–405.

Hensel, T. (2006). Effektivität von EMDR bei psychisch traumatisierten Kindern und Jugendlichen [Effectiveness of EMDR with psychologically traumatized children and adolescents]. *Kindheit und Entwicklung, 15*(2), 107.

INSERM. (2004). *Psychotherapy: An evaluation of three approaches.* Paris, France: French National Institute of Health and Medical Research.

Jarero, I., Artigas, L., Mauer, M., López Cano, T., & Alcalá, N. (1999, November). *Children's post traumatic stress after natural disasters: Integrative treatment protocols.* Poster presented at the annual meeting of the International Society for Traumatic Stress Studies, Miami, FL.

Kaslow, F. W., Nurse, A. R., & Thompson, P. (2002). EMDR in conjunction with family systems therapy. In F. Shapiro (Ed.), *EMDR as an integrative psychotherapy approach: Experts of diverse orientations explore the paradigm prism* (pp. 289–318). Washington, DC: American Psychological Association.

Knipe, J., Hartung, J., Konuk, E., Colleli, G., Keller, M., & Rogers, S. (2003, September). *EMDR Humanitarian Assistance Programs: Outcome research, models of training, and service delivery in New York, Latin America, Turkey, and Indonesia.* Symposium presented at the annual meeting of the EMDR International Association, Denver, CO.

Konuk, E., Knipe, J., Eke, I., Yuksek, H., Yurtsever, A., & Ostep, S. (2006). The effects of eye movement desensitization and reprocessing (EMDR) therapy on posttraumatic stress disorder in survivors of the 1999 Marmara, Turkey earthquake. *International Journal of Stress Management, 13*(3), 291.

Lazrove, S. (1994, November). *Integration of fragmented dissociated traumatic memories using EMDR.* Paper presented at the 10th annual meeting of the International Society for Traumatic Stress Studies, Chicago, IL.

Lazrove, S., & Fine, C. G. (1996). The use of EMDR in patients with dissociative identity disorder. *Dissociation, 9*, 289–299.

Lipke, H. (2000). *EMDR and psychotherapy integration.* Boca Raton, FL: CRC Press.

Luber, M. (in press). *Eye Movement Desensitization and Reprocessing (EMDR) scripted protocols: Special populations.* New York: Springer.

Madrid, A., Skolek, S., & Shapiro, F. (2006). Repairing failures in bonding through EMDR. *Clinical Case Studies, 5*, 271–286.

Marquis, J. N., & Puk, G. (1994, November). *Dissociative identity disorder: A common sense and cognitive-behavioral view.* Paper presented at the annual meeting of the Association for Advancement of Behavior Therapy, San Diego, CA.

Maxfield, L. (2007). Integrative treatment of intrafamilial child sexual abuse. In F. Shapiro, F. W. Kaslow, & L. Maxfield (Eds.), *Handbook of EMDR and family therapy processes* (pp. 344–364). Hoboken, NJ: Wiley.

Maxwell, J. P. (2003). The imprint of childhood physical and emotional abuse: A case study on the use of EMDR to address anxiety and lack of self-esteem. *Journal of Family Violence, 18*, 281–293.

Nadler, W. (1996). EMDR: Rapid treatment of panic disorder. *International Journal of Psychiatry, 2*, 1–8.

National Institute for Clinical Excellence (NICE). (2005). *PTSD clinical guidelines.* London, United Kingdom: NHS.

Paulsen, S. (1995). Eye movement desensitization and reprocessing: Its use in the dissociative disorders. *Dissociation, 8*, 32–44.

Popky, A. J. (2005). DeTUR, an urge reduction protocol for addictions and dysfunctional behaviors. In R. Shapiro (Ed.), *EMDR solutions: Pathways to healing* (pp. 167–188). New York: W. W. Norton.

Ray, A. L., & Zbik, A. (2001). Cognitive behavioral therapies and beyond. In C. D. Tollison, J. R. Satterhwaite, & J. W. Tollison (Eds.), *Practical pain management* (3rd ed., pp. 189–208). Philadelphia: Lippincott.

Ricci, R. J. (2006). Trauma resolution using eye movement desensitization and reprocessing with an incestuous sex offender: An instrumental case study. *Clinical Case Studies, 5*(3), 248.

Ricci, R. J., Clayton, C. A., & Shapiro, F. (2006). Some effects of EMDR treatment with previously abused child molesters: Theoretical reviews and preliminary findings. *Journal of Forensic Psychiatry and Psychology, 17,* 538–562.

Rouanzoin, C. (1994, March). *EMDR: Dissociative disorders and MPD.* Paper presented at the 14th annual meeting of the Anxiety Disorders Association of America, Santa Monica, CA.

Russell, M. (2006). Treating combat-related stress disorders: A multiple case study utilizing eye movement desensitization and reprocessing (EMDR) with battlefield casualties from the Iraqi war. *Military Psychology, 18,* 1–18.

Russell, M. (2008). Treating traumatic amputation-related phantom limb pain: A case study utilizing eye movement desensitization and reprocessing (EMDR) within the armed services. *Clinical Case Studies, 7*(2), 136–153.

Russell, A., & O'Connor, M. (2002). Interventions for recovery: The use of EMDR with children in a community-based project. *Association for Child Psychiatry and Psychology, Occasional Paper No. 19,* 43–46.

Russell, M. C., & Silver, S. M. (2007). Training needs for the treatment of combat-related posttraumatic stress disorder. *Traumatology, 13,* 4–10.

Russell, M. C., Silver, S. M., Rogers, S., & Darnell, J. (2007). Responding to an identified need: A joint Department of Defense-Department of Veterans Affairs training program in eye movement desensitization and reprocessing (EMDR) for clinicians providing trauma services. *International Journal of Stress Management, 14,* 61–71.

Schneider, J., Hofmann, A., Rost, C., & Shapiro, F. (2007). EMDR and phantom limb pain: Case study, theoretical implications, and treatment guidelines. *Journal of EMDR Science and Practice, 1,* 31–45.

Shapiro, F. (1991). Eye movement desensitization and reprocessing procedure: From EMD to EMDR: A new treatment model for anxiety and related traumata. *Behavior Therapist, 14,* 122–125.

Shapiro, F. (1994). Eye movement desensitization and reprocessing: A new treatment for anxiety and related trauma. In L. Hyer (Ed.), *Trauma victim: Theoretical and practical suggestions* (pp. 501–521). Muncie, IN: Accelerated Development Publishers.

Shapiro, F. (1995). *Eye movement desensitization and reprocessing: Basic principles, protocols and procedures.* New York: Guilford Press.

Shapiro, F. (1999). Eye movement desensitization and reprocessing (EMDR) and the anxiety disorders: Clinical and research implications of an integrated psychotherapy treatment. *Journal of Anxiety Disorders, 13*(1–2, Excerpt), 35–67.

Shapiro, F. (2001). *Eye movement desensitization and reprocessing: Basic principles, protocols and procedures* (2nd ed.). New York: Guilford Press.

Shapiro, F. (2004–2007). *Eye movement desensitization and reprocessing (EMDR) for Posttraumatic Stress Disorder (PTSD).* TherapyAdvisor.org. Retrieved February 19, 2009 from http://www.therapyadvisor.com/LocalContent/adult/Consumer-Shapiro-EMDR-PTSD.pdf

Shapiro, F. (2006). *EMDR: New notes on adaptive information processing with case formulation principles, forms, scripts and worksheets.* Watsonville, CA: EMDR Institute.

Shapiro, F., & Forrest, M. (1997). *EMDR the breakthrough therapy for overcoming anxiety, stress and trauma.* New York: Basic Books.

Shapiro, F., Kaslow, F. W., & Maxfield, L. (2007). *Handbook of EMDR and family therapy processes.* Hoboken, NJ: Wiley.

Shapiro, F., Vogelmann-Sine, S., & Sine, L. (1994). Eye movement desensitization and reprocessing: Treating trauma and substance abuse. *Journal of Psychoactive Drugs, 26,* 379–391.

Silver, S. M., Brooks, A., & Obenchain, J. (1995). Eye movement desensitization and reprocessing treatment of Vietnam war veterans with PTSD: Comparative effects with biofeedback and relaxation training. *Journal of Traumatic Stress, 8,* 337–342.

Silver, S. M., & Rogers, S. (2002). *Light in the heart of darkness: EMDR and the treatment of war and terrorism survivors.* New York: W. W. Norton.

Talan, B. S. (2007). Integrating EMDR and imago relationship therapy in treatment of couples. In F. Shapiro, F. W. Kaslow, & L. Maxfield (Eds.), *Handbook of EMDR and family therapy processes* (pp. 187–201). Hoboken, NJ: Wiley.

Tinker, R. H., & Wilson, S. A. (1999). *Through the eyes of a child: EMDR with children.* New York: W. W. Norton.

Tinker, R. H., & Wilson, S. A. (2006). The phantom limb pain protocol. In R. Shapiro (Ed.), *EMDR solutions: Pathways to healing* (pp. 147–159). New York: W. W. Norton.

Twombly, J. (2000). Incorporating EMDR and EMDR adaptations into the treatment of clients with dissociative identity disorder. *Journal of Trauma and Dissociation, 1,* 61–81.

Twombly, J. H. (2005). EMDR for clients with dissociative identity disorder, DDNOS, and ego states. In R. Shapiro (Ed.), *EMDR solutions: Pathways to healing* (pp. 88–120). New York: W. W. Norton.

United Kingdom Department of Health. (2001). *Treatment choice in psychological therapies and counselling evidence based clinical practice guideline.* London, England: Department of Health.

Vogelmann-Sine, S., Sine, L. F., Smyth, N. J., & Popky, A. J. (1998). *EMDR chemical dependency treatment manual.* New Hope, PA: EMDR Humanitarian Assistance Programs.

Wernik, U. (1993). The role of the traumatic component in the etiology of sexual dysfunctions and its treatment with eye movement desensitization procedure. *Journal of Sex Education and Therapy, 19,* 212–222.

Wilensky, M. (2006). Eye movement desensitization and reprocessing (EMDR) as a treatment for phantom limb pain. *Journal of Brief Therapy, 5,* 31–44.

Wilson, S. A., Becker, L. A., Tinker, R. H., & Logan, C. R. (2001). Stress management with law enforcement personnel. A controlled outcome study of EMDR versus a traditional stress management program. *International Journal of Stress Management, 8,* 179–200.

Wilson, S. A., Tinker, R., Becker, L. A., Hofmann, A., & Cole, J. W. (2000, September). *EMDR treatment of phantom limb pain with brain imaging (MEG).* Paper presented at the annual meeting of the EMDR International Association, Toronto, Canada.

Young, W. (1994). EMDR treatment of phobic symptoms in multiple personality. *Dissociation, 7,* 129–133.

Zweben, J., & Yeary, J. (2006). EMDR in the treatment of addiction. *Journal of Chemical Dependency Treatment, 8,* 115–127.

Acknowledgments

The genesis of this book took place in 2005 at an EMDR International Association Conference in Philadelphia, Pennsylvania, with an informal conversation with Arne Hofmann. Growing out of an EMDR Supervisory Training Manual that I had created and assembled to conduct Facilitator and Supervisory Trainings in Germany in the late 1990s and then in Israel, Arne asked me to "manualize" Francine Shapiro's protocols from her text, *Eye Movement Desensitization and Reprocessing: Basic Principles, Protocols and Procedures* for the first Trainer's Training that was to occur the following year in Kassel, Germany. I accepted the challenge. I would like to acknowledge Arne for the initial push and his contributions to this project.

In fact, scripting protocols has been my way of helping myself assimilate new material that I have learned from the early days of my professional career. The chapters in this book represent the accumulated knowledge of my many colleagues and friends in the EMDR community and my continuing interest in turning their ideas into scripts that would inspire and assist other therapists to work with their material. I would like to thank them for their contribution, hard work, and continuing interest in using EMDR in their practices to address and resolve the issues of their particular client population. I would particularly like to acknowledge the patience of these authors as they allowed me to engage them in the process of scripting their work. This was no small endeavor and I would like each one of them to know how appreciative I am of their willingness to respond to my numerous e-mails and to my litany of urgent requests with grace as they took time away from their already busy schedules.

Beyond this, one of the greatest joys for me has been to get to know so many of my colleagues more fully during the course of this work.

I would also like to acknowledge those members of this vast community of EMDR practitioners who use EMDR on a regular basis with their clients.

Special thanks goes to Robert Gelbach, the Executive Director of EMDR HAP, who suggested that I find a publisher for the book and pushed me in the direction of the Springer booth at the 2007 EMDR International Association Conference in Dallas, Texas; Victoria Britt, who helped me write my book proposal; Howard Wainer, who guided me in the mysterious ways of book publishing; Sheila Bender, Zona Scheiner, and Bennet Wolper, who engaged in helping me think about how to organize the content of the book; Louise Maxfield, who helped me think about critical points concerning EMDR; Francine Shapiro, Roger Solomon, Barbara Hensley, Nancy Errebo, and Bennet Wolper, who read and critiqued portions of this manuscript; Donald Nathanson, who has been a stalwart supporter of my writing; Catherine Fine and Richard Goldberg, who have been friends, colleagues, and supporters of my evolution as a clinician and writer; A. J. Popky, who introduced me into the EMDR community; and Shirley Luber, my mother, for her support and understanding.

With a great deal of irony, I would like to acknowledge my computer and the Internet. Despite countless crashes, blue screens, and runaway cursors, without the use of the computer and the Internet, this book would have taken much longer and resulted in the destruction of many more trees than necessary. In fact, contact with my contributors who came from all over the United States, Canada, South and Central America, Europe, Australia, and the Middle East was facilitated by the possibility of sending drafts through the international access of the Internet computer-to-computer. To my computer savior, Lew Rossi, I would like to acknowledge his coming out on a Friday night—without knowing me—to find my draft that had disappeared and continuing to tirelessly tackle the unique difficulties of my computer so that I could finish this book.

I would like to thank the Springer staff, especially my editor, Sheri Sussman, for her help and support.

I would particularly like to thank Robbie Dunton for her never-ending support and heart-felt compassion throughout my EMDR career.

To Francine Shapiro, I am forever grateful that she shared her dream with me by creating a way of addressing the trauma in the world, and asking me to support and nurture the learning of EMDR internationally. It has truly been a spectacular journey, way beyond that first walk in the park.

PART 1

Client History

In Phase 1 or the Client History Phase of the 8-Phase EMDR protocol, practitioners are responsible for gathering the information that will inform how the treatment of clients will unfold. Acquiring the information that is needed is a crucial step in Case Conceptualization and becomes the organizing foundation for practitioners' thinking. In the training of mental health practitioners, this subject is a standard staple in the art of becoming a professional in the field.

Eliciting a client history from an EMDR-informed approach is a seminal way to insure that the basic components of solid EMDR practice are obtained. It can also be a training ground to teach clients the basics of an Adaptive Information Processing (AIP) approach. The key to history taking is understanding the background of clients in the form of the developmental, familial, interpersonal, medical, work or school, psychological histories, and so forth.

Conceptualizing the best and parsimonious treatment plan entails the following:

- Understanding the ability of the client to contain affect and to achieve stabilization in the face of distressing material in the environment or internally. Sometimes, the client will need to learn stabilization and skill building—because of the nature of the problem—even before Phase 1 is completed.
- Assessing the client's attachment style especially concerning his ability to work in collaboration with the therapist.
- Checking on medical issues that might require special consideration.
- Making sure that the timing for the EMDR session is optimal concerning life events and the availability of the client and therapist for follow-up.

When all of the above criteria are in place, clients are ready to move on to the desensitization and reprocessing phases of EMDR. Crucial to this endeavor is to understand the nature and history of the presenting problem by having an idea about the full measure of the problem as well as the types of associations that might occur. Although by the very nature that maladaptive information is held in the brain, every moment of the client's history will not be known, even with the most detailed history, nor is it necessary. What is needed is a "map" of the territory and this includes the knowledge of the 3-prong approach that addresses the full measure of the problem along the developmental experience of the client. To accomplish this goal it is helpful to elicit the important elements (i.e., images, negative cognitions, positive cognitions, emotions, and sensations) of the presenting problem(s) during the history taking and then connecting them—if possible or appropriate—to the earliest event connected to the problem (Touchstone Event). There are certain populations and situations, however, that call for beginning the desensitization phase with the second or third prong (see below and Luber, in press). The second prong of the 3-prong approach is to recognize and ultimately address the current triggers or conditioned responses that are often the causes for clients to seek counsel in the first place.

This highlights the strength of the EMDR model as it targets the issue clients entrust to us from many different aspects and throughout the time line of their lives. This allows us to be thorough in our ability to access the problem, stimulate the information-processing system and move the information to an adaptive resolution.

In order to be complete concerning the reprocessing of the problem(s), it is important to address the desired treatment goals. EMDR accomplishes this through a future, positive outcome template that enables clinicians to address the possible concerns and anxieties that clients encounter related to how the presenting problem could manifest for them in the future. It also reveals the need for skill building that is often necessary for success.

In this way, a clear, concise, and targeted history taking enables practitioners to capture all aspects of the client's problem(s), teaches the client how to think and conceptualize the issue, and supports the success of the clinical treatment.

In this section, the authors include different ways to gather this data. The first chapter by the editor is a one-page sheet that summarizes basic information salient to EMDR psychotherapy to ensure the therapist a quick way to remember the pertinent facts of a client's history. The time line is another resource to assist both therapists and clients to understand the nature of the positive and negative life events and where they fall along their life's trajectory. The targeting sequence is a helpful way to conceptualize information according to the AIP model and the EMDR-Accelerated Information Resourcing Protocol (EMDR-AIR) assists us in rapidly gaining information about clients, especially concerning familial patterns and legacies.

EMDR Summary Sheet

Marilyn Luber

This author has been interested in the idea of consolidating information in an accessible form throughout her career. The EMDR Summary Sheet was the result of a need on her part to have access to all of the relevant information concerning client information and EMDR interventions at a glance. This EMDR Summary Sheet is a way to consolidate important client information quickly and succinctly.

EMDR Summary Sheet

NAME: _____ DIAGNOSIS: _____

MEDICATIONS: _____

PAPER AND PENCIL TEST RESULTS:

IES-R _____ DES _____ BDI-II _____ Other _____

GOALS

1. _____ 2. _____ 3. _____

PRESENTING PROBLEM-PP #A PP #B PP #C

A. _____ B. _____ C. _____

TOUCHSTONE EVENT

A. _____ B. _____ C. _____

EXPERIENCES   EXPERIENCES

Birth—12 years of age (Childhood)

1. _____ 1. _____ 1. _____ 1. _____
2. _____ 2. _____ 2. _____ 2. _____
3. _____ 3. _____ 3. _____ 3. _____

13 years through 19 years (Adolescence)

4. _____ 4. _____ 4. _____ 4. _____
5. _____ 5. _____ 5. _____ 5. _____
6. _____ 6. _____ 6. _____ 6. _____

20 years and higher (Adulthood)

7. _____ 7. _____ 7. _____ 7. _____
8. _____ 8. _____ 8. _____ 8. _____
9. _____ 9. _____ 9. _____ 9. _____
10. _____ 10. _____ 10. _____ 10. _____

Present Triggers

1. _____ 1. _____ 1. _____ 1. _____
2. _____ 2. _____ 2. _____ 2. _____
3. _____ 3. _____ 3. _____ 3. _____

Future Template/Anticipatory Anxiety

1. _____ 1. _____ 1. _____ 1. _____
2. _____ 2. _____ 2. _____ 2. _____

MAJOR THEMES/COGNITIVE INTERWEAVES

Safety/Survival

1. _____ 1. _____ 1. _____ 1. _____
2. _____ 2. _____ 2. _____ 2. _____

Self-Judgment/Guilt/Blame (Responsibility)

1. _____ 1. _____ 1. _____ 1. _____
2. _____ 2. _____ 2. _____ 2. _____

Self-Defective (Responsibility)

1. _____ 1. _____ 1. _____ 1. _____
2. _____ 2. _____ 2. _____ 2. _____

Choice/Control

1. _____ 1. _____ 1. _____ 1. _____
2. _____ 2. _____ 2. _____ 2. _____

PRESENT RESOURCES

Safe Place   Mastery

1. _____ 1. _____
2. _____ 2. _____

Attachment   Symbols

1. _____ 1. _____
2. _____ 2. _____

History Taking: The Time Line

Arne Hofmann and Marilyn Luber

Client history taking is an important part of well-prepared clinicians' understanding of their clients. The Time Line Script (Hofmann, 2004) is based on a number of personal communications with other EMDR clinicians. The forms are a way of eliciting the material crucial to preparing for future work in EMDR.

The Time Line Script Notes

Start with the best events and ask for the negative events in the session. This is especially important when working with unstable clients.

Continue to gather this information and put it into the form so that you can put it in your client's chart and see the important memories and resources easily. Also, when you complete processing, there is a place to put that (new) SUD score.

You can use the questions below to gather the rest of the information. When all of the memories are gathered, it is helpful to plot them onto a "Positive and Negative Memories Map" (Beere, 1997; Shapiro, 2006). This Map allows for a visual presentation along the time line of the client's life and offers a window into what the important landmarks of the client's life were for the clinician and client to see together. Often, just seeing the events in a visual chronological pattern helps both of you to see the gestalt of the client's life experience, the themes, the clusters, the gaps in memory, and the positives—or lack of positives—along the way.

You can use the form below or create your own time line on a larger piece of paper so that there is more room.

Part of the EMDR clinician's understanding of the client is to understand the future concerns and anticipated triggers that are connected to the presenting problem(s) or any other issues of concern that the client has revealed during the history-taking process. These future concerns or anticipated triggers can be added to the form throughout the course of treatment.

The Time Line Script

Say, *"Today, I am going to ask you to remember the best and the worst memories that you have had and we will put it into this chart. We can start with about five and if there are more or less, that is fine. Where would you like to start?"*

_____

_____

Okay, *"What is the first _____ (worst or best) memory that you can remember throughout the whole time line of your life? You do not have to go into all of the details because we will do that later."*

_____

_____

Say, *"How old were you when you had that _____ (worst or best) experience?"*

_____

_____

Only ask for the subjective units of disturbance (SUD) scale for the worst memories.

Say, *"On a scale of 0 to 10, where 0 is no disturbance or neutral and 10 is the highest disturbance you can imagine, how disturbing does it feel now?"*

0   1   2   3   4   5   6   7   8   9   10
(no disturbance)   (highest disturbance)

Create the "Positive and Negative Memories Map" with the client.

Say, *"Now that we have talked about the memories that are the most important to you in your life, let's create a Map. We can put the positive or best ones on top of the 'Age' line and we can put the negative or worst ones under the Age line. I have found it very helpful to see the important events in a person's life along the time line. Where would you like to start?"*

_____

_____

Say, *"Do you have any thoughts about the time line of your life now that we can see it? What do you think about what has happened in your life?"*

_____

_____

_____

_____

Say, *"Are there any particular themes that are clearer to you now that you can 'see' the important memories of your life in front of you. Or, does anything jump out to you of importance?"*

_____

_____

_____

_____

Elicit the current situations/events/stimuli that trigger the client and enter them on the form.

Say, *"Memories from the past are important, but, it is also important to think about what situations/events/stimuli trigger or bother you in the present. What have you noticed really gets you upset when it happens in your day-to-day life? Sometimes, it is the way your boss talks to you, or how your spouse gives you 'that look' _____ (state examples pertinent to your client). Other times, it is a certain song or smell. What have you noticed that triggers you recently?"*

_____

_____

_____

_____

Identify the client's future concerns, anticipated problems or other situations/events/stimuli that you think might trigger you in the future and enter into them into the chart.

Say, *"Now that we know about your positive and negative memories and some of the situations/events/stimuli that trigger you have in your daily life, it is helpful for us to identify the kinds of future concerns or anticipated problems or situations/events/stimuli that might trigger you and that you have been thinking about. What comes to mind for you, especially the ones connected to the problem(s) we have been talking about?"*

_____

_____

_____

_____

Say, *"Now that we have these memories and concerns mapped out, we can talk about how we want to proceed in our work together. With all of this in mind, what are your current thoughts about our objectives and goals for treatment?"*

_____

_____

_____

_____

Best or Positive and Worst or Negative Memories

List the best or positive memories and the worst or negative memories.

Best/Positive Memories

	Memories	Age
1.		
2.		
3.		
4.		
5.		
6.		
7.		
8.		
9.		
10.		

Worst/Negative Memories

	Memories	Age	SUD	SUD Post Processing
1.				
2.				
3.				
4.				
5.				
6.				
7.				
8.				
9.				
10.				

Positive and Negative Memory Map

Fill in the positive/best memories above the Age line and the negative/worst memories below the Age line:

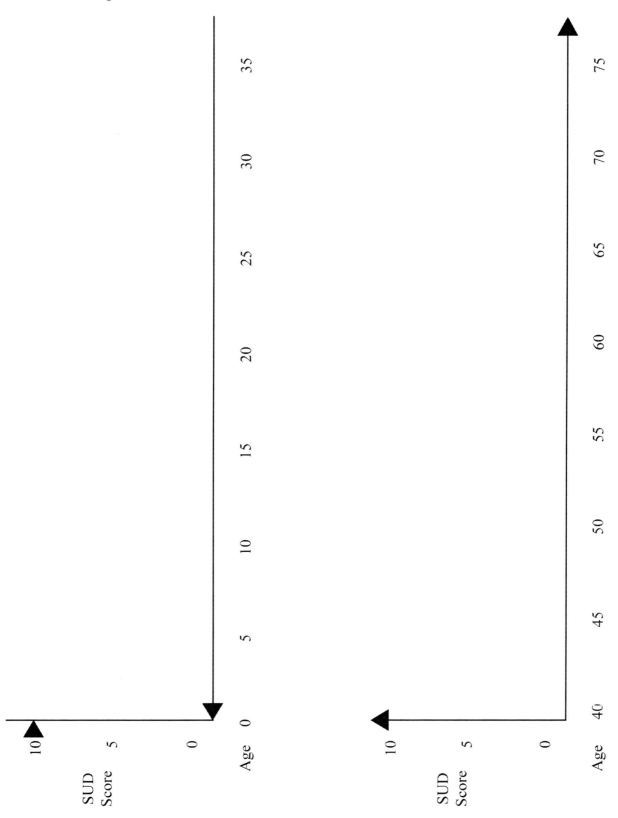

Positive and Negative Memory

Present and Future Situations/Events/Stimuli
That Are Triggers or Concerns

List the present situations/events/stimuli that are triggers and the future situations/events/stimuli that are triggers or concerns.

	Present Trigger List	SUD	SUD Post Processing
1.			
2.			
3.			
4.			
5.			
6.			
7.			
8.			
9.			
10.			

	Future Triggers or Concerns List	SUD	SUD Post Processing
1.			
2.			
3.			
4.			
5.			
6.			
7.			
8.			
9.			
10.			

Simple or Comprehensive Treatment Intake Questionnaire and Guidelines for Targeting Sequence

Roy Kiessling (Scripted by Marilyn Luber)

With the experience of teaching EMDR to many mental health practitioners over a number of years, increasingly it has become clear how important history taking is to the whole process of learning how to frame a client's information into a precise and relevant conceptualization of who the person who is sitting in front of you is, and a way to think about the problem(s) presented.

The following Intake Questionnaire, the guidelines for creating a Targeting Sequence Plan, and the Worksheets are invaluable tools in assisting therapists in gathering the client's information, and for the client to incorporate the tenets of adaptive information processing into the understanding of their own issues.

Simple or Comprehensive Treatment Script Notes: Treatment Planning Guide

Clients' presenting problems may present as either being a simple issue or in need of a more complex or comprehensive treatment formulation. Simple issue cases are typically defined by a single event, one dominant cluster or symptom, and often lend themselves well in time-limited, brief treatment settings. Comprehensive treatment, on the other hand, typically involves numerous issues, longer treatment time, and consistent client contact is necessary. Regardless of the client presentation, the cluster-focused targeting sequence planning strategies in the next section may be helpful in addressing the client treatment goals.

Simple Event, Single Cluster Treatment Planning

The reason for developing a targeting sequence outline is to help clients realize how disturbing incidents can cluster around a common denominator such as a belief, emotion, body sensation, issue, symptom, person, and so forth. Once clustered into a targeting sequence plan, the client and clinician have a targeting sequence to consider. Additionally, once the Touchstone Event associated with that cluster is targeted and reprocessed (SUD = 0, VoC = 7, clean Body Scan), often many of the other identified experiences within the targeting sequence will be reprocessed due to the generalization effect.

It is important to use clinical judgment when gathering history to determine whether the client or the client's environment is appropriate for gathering this type of focused history. Additionally, it is important that the clinician pace the information gathering process in such a way as to provide a safe and supportive environment for the client.

Belief-Focused Approach

When using the dominant belief as the common denominator, all the identified experiences will resonate with this belief. Ideally, the outline will include the touchstone (earliest recalled experience) event and any significant additional past incidents, additional present triggers, and future concerns. If the client is unable to identify a dominant negative belief, consider using the dominant issue as the strategy to develop the appropriate targeting sequence plan.

If clients are still unable to identify any childhood incidents, consider the "Float-Back" exercise (Browning, 1999; Young, Zangwill, & Behary, 2002) where the negative thought or schema is used as the focal point to float back to earlier experiences that are connected to the negative belief. The negative belief is used to remind the client of the feelings and the location of those feelings associated with the schema.

If the Float-Back Technique does not result in identifying the Touchstone Event, consider the Affect Scan, an adaptation of the Watkins and Watkins (1997) Affect Bridge. This approach elicits the affect associated with the incident or image to help the client bridge back to those earlier times where that same affect occurred.

Caution. Because it is the intent of history taking to identify, not access or activate past events, care should be taken when using the Float-Back or Affect Scan as they may flood some clients.

Issue or Symptom-Focused Clusters

Another way to develop a targeting sequence plan, especially when a dominant belief is not present, is to identify the dominant presenting issue or symptom: dominant emotion, body sensation, odor, taste, sound, person, place, and so forth. Once identified, the issue or symptom becomes the clustering agenda around which the targeting sequence plan is constructed. As such, each incident associated with that symptom may have a different set of negative and positive cognitions. Therefore, a different targeting sequence plan strategy is used. First identify each incident, where the symptom occurred in the past and in the present situations, as well as when it is expected to occur in the future. Next, identify the positive and negative belief associated with each incident (note that these may differ from incident to incident).

Where to Start: Touchstone Event or Some Other Incident?

While it is important to understand the client's clinical landscapes, the symptom clusters of the presenting problem, and its associated Touchstone Event, determining the appropriate initial target requires clinical judgment and an informed decision from the client. The adaptive information processing model suggests the most effective and efficient treatment approach is to initially target the Touchstone Event. However, in situations of acute stress or when the client has a strong preference, other targets may be chosen for reprocessing. In these situations, it is essential to discuss with the client how feeder memories are to be addressed should they come up during reprocessing.

If the client agrees to allow feeder memories to arise, then the standard reprocessing procedures are appropriate. However, it should not be assumed that by targeting another incident, the Touchstone Event will be reprocessed, consequently, the client may not achieve the full treatment effects.

When the client does not wish to allow free association that may bring up feeder memories, additional Preparation Phase resources will be necessary to ensure the client's abilities to contain other memories and to stay focused on the agreed upon target (see resource development chapters). Additionally, contained reprocessing techniques will be needed to ensure that no feeder memories arise. These techniques should only be attempted by fully trained EMDR clinicians.

Comprehensive Treatment

As noted earlier, while many clients present with simple, single event or issue cases, many do not. For those more complex cases a comprehensive therapy approach is necessary. Consequently, comprehensive presentations are not suited for time-limited, brief EMDR interventions. These cases require a very comprehensive treatment plan that may need to address issues such as attachment deficits, affect tolerance, extended preparation and stabilization, and developmental deficits. Within this type of treatment plan, however, the targeting sequence strategies listed above may be very effectively interwoven with additional psychotherapy interventions. As these clients usually present with multiple issues, each issue may be identified and a past and present targeting sequence plan constructed. Clients may be given the option as to whether to start with the worst or the least disturbing issue or symptom. When using the Issue or Symptom-Focused approach, reprocess each issue or symptom's past incidents (ideally starting with the touchstone) and present triggers. Once all of these have been reprocessed, run future templates associated with the client's concerns.

Another targeting strategy is to simply target and reprocess disturbing incidents along a chronological time line (developed from the psychosocial intake interview, genogram, and additional, more specific, questioning strategies). When using this approach, target and reprocess all past incidents, any remaining present triggers and then complete treatment by running future templates that address the client's desired future behaviors and responses.

Intake Questionnaire Script

General Information

Say, *"I am going to ask you some general information. Before we start, are there any questions that you want to ask me?"*

_____

_____

_____

Note the client's gender and ethnicity

Male _____ Female _____ Ethnicity _____

Say, *"What is your relationship status?"*

Married _____ Partnered _____ Single _____ Divorced _____ Widowed _____

Say, *"What are your living arrangements?"*

_____

_____

Say, *"Do you have a career?"*

_____

_____

Or say, *"What are you doing currently to occupy your time?"*

_____

_____

Say, *"How is your health?"*

Excellent _____ Good _____ Fair _____ Poor _____

Say, *"Do you have any medical concerns?"*

_____

_____

Say, *"What are the medications that you are currently taking?"*

_____

_____

_____

_____

Say, *"Do you smoke? If so, how much and how often?"*

_____

_____

Say, *"Do you drink? If so, what do you drink, how much and how often?"*

_____

_____

Say, *"Do you take any type of nonprescriptive drugs? If so, how much and how often?"*

_____

_____

Say, *"Are there any other types of addictive behaviors in which you engage that you or significant others in your life are concerned about?"*

_____

_____

Say, *"Let's move on to some questions about your family of origin. Are your parents still married, or are they divorced or widowed?"*

_____

_____

Say, *"What is your relationship like with them?"*

_____

_____

Say, *"If your parents are divorced or if one is widowed, do you have any stepparents in your life?"*

_____

_____

Say, *"What is your relationship like with him, her, or them?"*

_____

_____

Say, *"What is or was your father's parenting style?"*

_____

_____

Say, *"What is or was your father's major characteristics?"*

_____

_____

Say, *"What is or was your mother's parenting style?"*

_____

_____

Say, *"What is or was your mother's major characteristics?"*

_____

_____

Say, *"Do you have siblings or are you an only child?"*

_____

_____

Say, *"What is the birth order of you and your siblings?"*

_____

_____

Say, *"What was your religious upbringing?"*

_____

_____

Say, *"Are you still practicing?"*

_____

_____

Positive Experiences

Say, *"Let's talk about the significant childhood experiences that you have had. Let's start with your good, happy, or positive experiences. Tell me about the ones that you value the most and how old you were when they occurred."*

_____

_____

_____

_____

_____

_____

_____

_____

_____

_____

Negative Experiences

Say, *"Now, let's talk about the bad, negative, sad, or disturbing experiences that you have had. Tell me about the ones that have impacted you the most and how old you were when they occurred."*

_____

_____

_____

_____

_____

_____

_____

_____

_____

Presenting Problem

Questioning is targeted at the presenting problem as follows:

Say, *"What is the problem that is bringing you into therapy today? When was the last time that you remember experiencing, thinking, or reacting like this?"*

_____

_____

_____

_____

_____

_____

_____

_____

_____

_____

Say, *"What image represents the worst part of that experience?"*

_____

_____

Say, *"What goals do you have for your work with me?"*

_____

_____

_____

_____

Say, *"When did this problem begin? What triggered it?"*

_____

_____

Say, *"What are the symptoms?"*

_____

_____

Say, *"How long have the symptoms existed?"*

_____

_____

Say, *"Have there been any changes in the symptoms. Have they gotten better, worse, or have they just remained the same?"*

_____

_____

Clustering

Look for primary clusters by beliefs, emotions, physical sensations, and so forth, associated with the client's presenting issue(s). Elicit these clusters in the following manner.

Belief

Say, *"When you are experiencing your presenting problem(s), have you noticed that you have been thinking about yourself in a particularly persistent, negative, or irrational way(s)?"*

_____

_____

Emotion

Say, *"When you are experiencing your presenting problem(s), have you noticed any dominant emotion(s) or anxiety(ies) lately?"*

_____

_____

Physical Sensation

Say, *"When you are experiencing your presenting problem(s), have you noticed any dominant physical sensations lately?"*

_____

_____

Other

Say, *"When you are experiencing your presenting problem(s), have you noticed other dominant foci in your life such as on a particular place, thing, smell, taste, and so forth?"*

_____

_____

Targeting Sequence for Dominant Belief Script

1. Restate the dominant belief.

   Say, *"You told me earlier about your problem* _____ (give brief synopsis of your understanding of the problem) *that is concerning you. Is that accurate?"*

   _____

   _____

2. Note the onset.

   Say, *"When did it start?"*

   _____

   _____

3. Ask about the duration.

   Say, *"I would also like to know how long it has been going on?"*

   _____

   _____

4. Note the severity of the problem.

   Say, *"How bad or difficult has all of this been for you?"*

   _____

   _____

   Say, *"What has the impact been on your daily functioning?"*

   _____

   _____

5. Ask about future concerns.

   Say, *"How are you perceiving or thinking about your future?"*

   _____

   _____

From the above information, a targeting sequence plan outline is formulated according to the dominant primary negative belief cluster. You are helping the client learn about the different components of a memory according to the adaptive information processing approach.

6. Identify the negative belief that goes with the problem.

   Say, *"What is the primary negative belief that resonates for you or you think about when you are in the midst of your problem?"*

   _____

   _____

7. Identify the positive belief that goes with the problem.

   Look for the adaptive positive belief. The therapist is looking for an adaptive positive belief with an "internal locus of control."

   Say, *"Can you think about or figure out what belief about yourself would be better to have instead?"*

   _____

   _____

8. Identifying the Touchstone Event

   Identify the image and the negative cognition associated with the present event or future concern. Sometimes, it is possible to have a clear recollection of earlier events by asking either of the following two questions (Shapiro, 2006, p. 48).

   Say, *"When was the first time you remember thinking about yourself that way?"*

   _____

   _____

   Say, *"When is the first time you learned _____ (state the negative belief)?"*

   _____

   _____

   Further questions to elicit the targeting sequence are as follows.

9. Identify additional incidents triggered by the same negative belief.

   Say, *"What other times in your life have you experienced that same negative belief _____ (state the negative belief) about yourself?"*

   _____

   _____

   _____

   _____

   Say, *"Are there any incidents that happened in your family that resonate or connect with that thought _____ (state negative belief)? Often, remembering these early events are very helpful."*

   _____

   _____

   _____

   _____

   If clients are still unable to identify any childhood incidents, consider the Float-Back exercise, and/or the Affect Scan.

Float-Back Technique

Say, *"Now, please bring up that picture of _____ (repeat client's disturbing image) and those negative words _____* (state the negative cognition). *Now, notice what feelings are coming up for you, and where you are feeling them in your body, and just let your mind float back to an earlier time in your life—don't search for anything—just let your mind float back and tell me the earliest scene that comes to mind where you had similar thoughts of _____* (repeat negative cognition), *and feelings of _____* (repeat emotions), *and where you feel it in your body* (based on Shapiro, 2006, p. 48).

_____

_____

_____

_____

Check to make certain the negative cognition reinforces or increases negative emotions. If not, concentrate only on sensations.

Affect Scan

Identify the upset, emotions, and body sensations that resonate with the dominant negative belief that has been experienced. Once identified, have the client scan back to the last time of the upset.

Say, *"Bring up the last time you felt upset* (or had that emotion). *Hold the image in your mind and the thoughts that come up about it."*

Then ask: *"Where do you feel it in your body?"*

_____

_____

Say, *"Hold in mind the image, emotion, and the sensation, and let your mind scan back to the earliest time you remember feeling that way."*

_____

_____

Say, *"Now that you have remembered the earliest memory that is related to your problem, the Touchstone Event, what are your future concerns about this problem?"*

_____

_____

_____

_____

Targeting Sequence Planning for Belief-Focused Cluster Worksheet

Belief-Focused Cluster

Presenting Problem or Issue

_____

_____

Dominant Negative Belief: _____

Dominant Positive Belief: _____

Targeting Plan Outline

Touchstone Event

_____

_____

Past Incidents

Incident   **Age**

_____

_____

_____

_____

Present Triggers

_____

_____

_____

_____

_____

_____

Future Concerns

_____

_____

_____

_____

_____

_____

_____

Targeting Sequence for Issue or Symptom-Focused Clusters Script

The key to developing a well-formed targeting sequence plan for issue or symptom-focused clusters is to start by understanding the presenting problem.

1. Identify the dominant issue cluster.

   Say, *"The issue that we are working with is* _____ (state the symptom or issue). *There is usually a symptom that is associated with that* _____ (state the symptom or issue). *Notice that that symptom may be an emotion, a body sensation, an odor, a taste, a specific person, a place, or thing. What is the symptom that is most problematic for you?"*

   _____

   _____

2. Define the cluster by the emotion, sensation, person, place, or other dominant concern.

   Say, *"Okay. The cluster that we are going to work on today is* _____ (state the symptom or issue). *Is that correct?"*

   _____

   _____

3. Note the onset.

   Say, *"When did this* _____ (state the symptom or issue) *begin?"*

   _____

   _____

4. Ask about the duration.

   Say, *"How long have you had this problem with* _____ (state the symptom or issue)?"

   _____

   _____

5. Note the severity of the problem.

   Say, *"On a scale of 0 to 10 where 0 = no problem at all and 10 = the most severe problem, what is the severity of this problem for you?"*

   0   1   2   3   4   5   6   7   8   9   10
   (no problem)   (severe problem)

6. Figure out what situations, events. or stimuli trigger the symptom.

   Say, *"What situations, events, or stimuli trigger* _____ (state the cluster)?"

   _____

   _____

   _____

   _____

7. Find out its impact on daily functioning.

Say, *"How does it impact your daily life and functioning?"*

_____

_____

8. Ask about any future concerns.

Say, *"How will _____ (state the symptom or issue) affect your future and do you have any concerns about this?"*

_____

_____

_____

_____

From the above information, a targeting sequence plan outline is formulated according to the history of the client.

9. Identify past disturbing incidents related to that dominant issue.

Say, *"Let's talk about any disturbing events from your past that seem to connect to _____ (state the symptom or issue).*

_____

_____

10. Find the Touchstone Event; the earliest incident the client recalls when that disturbing symptom was experienced.

Say, *"What was the first time you remember experiencing this _____ (state the symptom or issue)?"*

_____

_____

11. Identify additional present incidents triggered by that dominant symptom.

Say, *"As you think of your presenting problem and its dominant symptom, what other situations, events, or stimuli trigger those same symptoms?"*

_____

_____

_____

_____

12. The Negative and Positive Cognitions are often different for each incident. Identify the NC and PC for each present trigger, past issue, and future concerns and write them on the targeting sequence plan.

Say, *"Now let's go over each of those experiences and identify a negative and positive belief for each one. Let's start with the situations, events, or stimuli that trigger you, after that we can look at all the past incidents and do the same."*

Present Stimuli That Trigger the Disturbing Memory or Reaction

1. Elicit the NC for each situation, event, or stimulus that is a present trigger.

   Say, *"What words best go with the picture that express your negative belief about yourself now?"*

   _____

   _____

2. Elicit the PC for each situation, event, or stimulus that is a present trigger.

   Say, *"When you bring up that picture or incident, what would you like to believe about yourself now?"*

   _____

   _____

Past Incidents

1. Do the same for the past incidents.

   Say, *"Let's start with the earliest incident (the Touchstone) and work our way forward."*

   _____

   _____

2. Elicit the NC for each past incident.

   Say, *"What words best go with the picture that express your negative belief about yourself now?"*

   _____

   _____

3. Elicit the PC for each past incident.

   Say, *"When you bring up that picture or incident, what would you like to believe about yourself now?"*

   _____

   _____

Future Incidents

1. Do the same for future anticipated incidents.

   Say, *"Now let's look at the situations in the future that may cause you the same concern. Let's start with those coming up the soonest and work our way into the future."*

   _____

   _____

   _____

   _____

2. Elicit the NC for each anticipated incident.

Say, *"What words best go with the picture that express your negative belief about yourself now?"*

_____

_____

3. Elicit the PC for each anticipated incident.

Say, *"When you bring up that picture or incident, what would you like to believe about yourself now?"*

_____

_____

Targeting Sequence Planning for Symptom-Focused Cluster Worksheet

Symptom-Focused Cluster

Dominant Symptom: _____

Targeting Plan

Touchstone: _____

NC: _____ PC: _____

Past Incidents: _____

(Client will vary in how many past incidents they recall)

NC: _____ PC: _____

_____

_____

NC: _____ PC: _____

_____

_____

NC: _____ PC: _____

_____

_____

NC: _____ PC: _____

_____

_____

Present Triggers: _____

NC: _____ PC: _____

_____

_____

NC: _____ PC: _____

_____

_____

Future Concerns: _____

NC: _____ PC: _____

_____

_____

NC: _____ PC: _____

_____

_____

Where to Start: Touchstone Event or Some Other Incident?

In situations of acute stress or when the client has a strong preference, other targets may be chosen for reprocessing. In these situations, it is essential to discuss with the client how feeder memories are to be addressed should they come up during reprocessing.

> Say, *"When we will be working with the incident you have chosen to target, it is possible that you will make associations to other connected issues; would that be okay with you?"*

_____

_____

If the client agrees to allow feeder memories to arise, then the standard reprocessing procedures are appropriate. However, it should not be assumed that by targeting another incident, the Touchstone Event will be reprocessed, consequently, the client may not achieve the full treatment effects.

If the client agrees, go ahead with the standard processing.

If the client does not agree, say the following:

> Say, *"This will be a fine place to start, however, later when you are feeling that it would be okay, it would be important for us to check out some of those earlier incidents that we will not be processing today. The reason for that is we want to make sure that the processing of this issue is complete. Would that be okay with you?"*

_____

_____

When the client does not wish to allow free association that may bring up feeder memories, additional Preparation Phase resources will be necessary to ensure the client's abilities to contain other memories and to stay focused on the agreed-upon target (see resource development chapters). Additionally, contained reprocessing techniques will be needed to insure that no feeder memories arise. These techniques should only be attempted by fully trained EMDR clinicians.

Summary

This chapter has identified several approaches in helping a client develop an EMDR targeting sequence plan to address the presenting problem(s). As with all psychotherapy approaches, it is important to obtain a full clinical history to identify stabilization needs, environmental management skills, and symptoms where EMDR reprocessing will be appropriate.

Once the client has been assessed as being appropriate for EMDR treatment, developing a targeting sequence plan will generate a roadmap for treatment. The client's presentation may fall into either being simple or comprehensive. For simple presentations, several possible targeting sequence plans are possible, depending upon the client's dominant symptom. For those presenting with a dominant irrational belief, clustering all incidents within that belief will lend itself to a very efficient targeting sequence plan that addresses all 3 prongs, past incidents starting with the Touchstone Event, present triggers, and future issues anticipating anxieties. In situations where a dominant symptom is not defined as a belief, clustering around the common symptom will also provide an effective targeting sequence plan. For comprehensive presentations, multiple clusters may be identified, prioritized, and targeted through past and present, with future templates being run once all present symptoms have been adaptively resolved. For some clients, especially those that are difficult to cluster, targeting chronologically along a time line may be the most effective and efficient.

Throughout, however, it is always important for the clinician to exercise sound judgment when suggesting a targeting sequence plan. Additionally, it is important to help clients understand the pros and cons for following any specific targeting strategy so they may make an informed decision regarding their treatment and expected outcomes.

The EMDR-Accelerated Information Resourcing (EMDR-AIR) Protocol

Frances R. Yoeli and Tessa Prattos

History, Heritage, and Legacy

Definition and Purpose

The EMDR Accelerated Information Resourcing Protocol (EMDR-AIR Protocol©) is designed to accelerate the search for the resources necessary to resolve the client's current crisis or long-term issues. The idea evolved from the "Double-Hai" paradigm (Yoeli & Prattos, 2005), which is a short-term intervention for use with couples. The EMDR-AIR Protocol is designed to look for that learned generational reaction to trauma that the client is currently using to cope with the current situation while, at the same time, tapping into the historical strengths and resources that enabled survival. These resources are found through the rapid accessing of client history by using the Multi-Tiered Trans-Generational Genogram (MTTG).

Multi-Tiered Trans-Generational Genogram (MTTG)

The concept of multi-tiered history taking is useful both as a general tool and for time-limited crisis interventions. Recognizing the history enables both client and therapist to decipher and examine whether historical reactions are appropriate today. Examining multigenerational patterns assists both the client and the therapist, to recognize those possible historical sources of the presenting *dysfunctional* reactions. The client then can own his own reactions and release those that no longer are of service to him. This suggested genogram format and case conceptualization quickly highlights inherited weaknesses, strengths, and resources. This is the client's historical legacy. Through the use of this format the client gains perspective and recognizes that recovery, survival, and overcoming crises is possible.

The details on how to set up a genogram are beyond the scope of this chapter. If the therapist is not familiar with how to set up the genogram or wants a review, information is readily available on the Internet by searching the key word "genogram." Also, there are a number of books written on how to create a genogram (e.g., DeMaria, Weeks, & Hof, 1999; McGoldrick, Gerson, & Petry, 2008).

The EMDR-Air Protocol Script Notes

Objectives and Steps of the EMDR-AIR Protocol

The main objectives for the EMDR-AIR Protocol are the following:

- To identify trans-generational transmission of resources and strengths.
- To recognize potential stuck components in the EMDR processing that are related to trans-generationally transmitted behavioral and emotional patterns.
- To enable the client to step away from the crisis so as to begin the process of reprocessing with EMDR, with the chronologically most relevant Touchstone Event.

The EMDR-AIR Protocol has 4 steps. Each step generally takes 30 minutes of a 2-hour session.

Step 1: When client and therapist meet
Step 2: Intake, history taking; MTTG
Step 3: EMDR
Step 4: Resolution, understanding, closure.

The EMDR-AIR Protocol does not change the Standard EMDR Protocol. This protocol is an adjunct for Phase 1 (client history) of the Standard EMDR Protocol. This approach elicits core targets necessary for the case conceptualization and that are best able in the shortest time to resolve and or prevent posttraumatic stress disorder (PTSD) following any life crises.

The MTTG

The MTTG consists of the narrative and creating the genogram. It seeks to look at family history, birth dates, cultural information, transgenerational behavioral patterns, lifestyle, untold secrets, multi-tiered transgenerational trauma and sexual history, belief systems, historical events, and styles of celebration. The MTTG is used to assess and interpret the information that is transgenerationally relevant to the presenting issues. Through this genogram process, it is often possible to find similar behavior patterns of earlier generations. In this way, the most relevant target for the current presenting problem becomes apparent and empowers the client and enables and enhances the processing. It becomes clear how families pass on behavior patterns. The idea is to find similarities and differences of reactions between and within the generations. The importance is to recognize what the most effective current behavior patterns are for today's circumstances and life threats. Because any event triggers memories of past generation reactions, the MTTG highlights attention to both past and current behavior patterns, a form of dual attention. During the process of the MTTG, both the client and the therapist have begun to conceptualize the current situation from a different perspective. This new perspective enables the understanding of patterns that sustained survival of previous generations. By recognizing these inherited strengths, the client becomes aware of the ability to cope and knows that recovery is possible.

The genogram begins with the client's generation. It starts by taking an interest in the chosen names and birth dates of the individual family members. Asking with sincere interest and curiosity is the key to rapport, and leads to a more comprehensive understanding and conceptualization. There can be no interpretations without asking the types of questions below and no assumptions. This MTTG is looking for the same information over three to five generations. Generally the therapist is looking for historical information on a personal, societal, worldwide, and disaster level per person.

Naming children can be diagnostic in terms of family relationships and is indicative of religious belief systems, life views, attitudes, behavior patterns, expectations, decision-making processes, and demonstrates the lifestyle of the family when the child is born. The essence of the name is primary to understanding multigenerational transmissions of behavior patterns. Discussion around the name often elicits reactions, information around interactions, and lifestyle of the individual. Names are the history of generations and the legacy of families. The story in the naming of the child has in it the dreams and aspirations of the parents and the history of the generations. The meaning of the name is impacting. Names provide the story that often indicates where stuck points begin and enable the alleviation of those issues.

Asking about dates of birth is a rapid accessing of multi-tiered trans-generational history and information. The significance of these dates or nonsignificance is found in the life story of the individual from as early as five generations prior. For example, date constellations around specific seasons or holidays can be indicative of sexual lifestyle or religious considerations.

Therapist Skills

The EMDR-AIR Protocol is a joint effort of attunement and learning for both client and therapist. Guided by the EMDR-AIR Protocol, the well-attuned, attentive therapist can access, understand, and assess the dynasty of the client within a single extended session. To promote healing, both client and therapist need to be open to explore client history and trans-generational patterning.

Through observation of the client, while talking about basic, neutral information, the therapist begins to accumulate a rich source of information and can notice any resources that arise to be used for the benefit of the client during the therapy. The therapist is observing with special interest: body posture, facial expressions, attitude (angry, hostile, sad, self-pity, etc.), clothing, stance, mobility, carrying anything; details such as fingernails, skin color and tone, makeup, attire; and movements such as nervous gestures, leg movements, time sequencing, tissue usage, tear flow, tics, eye contact, and so forth. The therapist is also paying special attention to: use of language, tonal qualities, issues raised, and useful cues. How the client functions in a new setting with a new person gives the therapist a quick understanding of how the client reacts with this type of stress. This process of observing the client is part of the search for the answer to the key question: *What makes this client react this way and what made him or her come for help now?*

To successfully build this type of genogram the practitioner must be nonthreatening, respectful, genuine, interested, and fascinated with the historical and familial connections of the client.

The EMDR-AIR Protocol Script

Note: Be sure the client is able to listen and hear what you are saying. Notice how focused the client is. If the client is in a state of disturbance and cannot focus, your clinical judgment is needed as to when to continue with the following process.

Step 1: When Client and Therapist Meet

1. From the door to the chair: Observational attunement and interactions

Say, *"How did you do getting here?"*

_____

_____

Say, *"How is the weather?"*

_____

_____

Say, *"How was the traffic?"*

_____

_____

It is important to take extra time to make the client feel more comfortable.

Say, *"Do you need something to drink, perhaps you need the washroom? It is in this direction."*

When the basic amenities are met and completed, the therapist and client go to the therapy room.

2. Settling in: Accessing what the client wishes to present

The client is invited to sit, the therapist sits, and then introduces herself to the client.

Say, *"As a therapist, my focus is on the resolution of problems. My tool kit is rich. What has been useful for most issues are EMDR and a trans-generational family picture."*

Briefly explain the process of what is about to happen, general contract issues, and your style of working with clients.

Say, *"This is how the sessions work: _____ (Explain your contract issues, i.e., consent issues, time schedule, cost, cancellation policy, etc.)."*

Say, *"I need to be sure I am explaining clearly. Can you let me know what you heard me say?"* or *"Do you have any questions about the contract issues?"*

_____

_____

After contract issues are settled, introduce Step 2.

Say, *"It is easy to see you are quite upset about* _____ (choose your own words from your own observations). *Would you like to share what is troubling you now?"*

_____

_____

Once the client has described his presenting problem/s and is composed enough to proceed,

Say, *"The way to help you through this most quickly is to get a family picture so we can better understand how you came to this discomfort. Would that be okay for us to briefly look at your family? A genogram picture helps to remember details, such as names and dates and family hierarchy. This does not take much time."*

_____

_____

This helps to assess and interpret the information that is trans-generationally relevant to the presenting issues.

Step 2: Client History–MTTG

1. The narrative (listening, hearing, getting the story)

In emergency situations, it may be imperative to first listen to the story and the presenting problem, rather than proceed to the MTTG immediately.

Say, *"When you are ready, please share your story."*

_____

_____

_____

_____

_____

_____

_____

_____

_____

_____

While listening to the client, pay attention to the following: the emotional points in the narrative; the people involved; what types of behavior patterns are present (tissue use, tears, how the client describes familial reactions, do they cry? do they yell? do they go silent? etc.).

Ask questions to elicit maximum information.

Say, *"Who was with you at the time?"*

_____

_____

Say, *"What brought you to that situation?"*

_____

_____

Say, *"What happened before you went there?"*

_____

_____

Say, *"What did you see first?"*

_____

_____

Say, *"How did you get help?"*

_____

_____

_____

_____

This process of observing the client is part of the search for the answer to the key question; *What makes this client react this way and what made him come for help now?* Once this client is calm enough, then proceed to the MTTG.

With a new client—not in an acute emergency state—following the introductions and technical issues, it is possible to go directly to the MTTG.

2. The Multi-Tiered Trans-Generational Genogram

    a. How to prepare a Multi-Tiered Trans-Generational Genogram

Say, *"We are going to create a family picture now and note some of the information that we talk about on the family picture that we are creating together."*

When you begin, start with the client and work from there writing in the material on this family picture or genogram as you gather the relevant information.

Say, *"What is your full name and date of birth?"*

_____

_____

For each new person you add to the genogram, write their date of birth and, if the person is deceased, write down that date as well.

If relevant, say, *"Please tell me the name of your spouse and date of birth."*

_____

_____

If relevant, say, *"Tell me the names and dates of births of your children from oldest to youngest."* (Start from the left of the diagram.)

_____

_____

Say, *"Were there any adoptions, miscarriages, abortions, deaths, or divorces among these family members?"*

_____

_____

Say, *"Where was _____* (state the name of the person) *born?"*

_____

_____

Say, *"Where does _____* (state the name of the person) *now live? What is his or her marital status and occupation?"*

_____

_____

This information can generally be recorded on one page, and becomes a picture of three to five generations. Allow yourself to take an interest in what you are hearing and initiate questions that may come up for you. Notice the emotional state of the client as he talks about each person on the genogram.

For both the maternal and paternal grandparents and great grandparents as well as parental siblings, the same questions apply as above. The relevant information has to do with patterns of interfamilial relationships, for example, knowing the dates of births often indicate close familial relationships as does living physically close. To elicit this information:

Say, *"How often do you see this family member?"*

_____

_____

Say, *"What memories come up for you when you think about this person?"*

_____

_____

The therapist is looking at how family relations work. How many people move away; how many get married, how many have children and what kinds of interfamilial interactions are there; how holidays and special events are celebrated, and so forth.

You might want to ask the following types of questions.

Say, *"How does your family celebrate holidays, birthdays, special events?"*

_____

_____

_____

_____

_____

Say, *"What have you carried with you in your life patterns around events* (such as holidays, celebrations, births, deaths) *that remind you of your parents' culture, behavioral patterns, lifestyle?"*

_____

_____

_____

Say, *"How do you deal with traumatic events?"*

_____

_____

_____

Say, *"How do you deal with secrets?"*

_____

_____

_____

Say, *"How do you deal with family history?"*

_____

_____

_____

Say, *"How do you deal with family stories?"*

_____

_____

_____

Say, *"How do you deal with trauma and sexuality?"*

_____

_____

_____

Say, *"How do you deal with belief systems?"*

_____

_____

_____

Say, *"How do you deal with historical events?"*

_____

_____

_____

Write down as much trauma history and significant events per person such as: holocaust, family, natural disaster, war, children dying, renaming, lifestyle, migrations, and so forth.

Say, *"What do you think might have affected you from their history, as we talk about how it affected them, and which characteristics of these relatives have become trans-generationally transmitted and inherited by you?"*

_____

_____

b. Names

Discussion around the name often elicits important information about the individual and the family.

Say, *"How did you get your name?"*

_____

_____

Say, *"What does your name mean?"*

_____

_____

Say, *"What is the reason your parents chose that name for you?"*

_____

_____

Say, *"How do other people learn the name your parents chose? Is there a kind of ceremony in your culture to convey the name?"*

_____

_____

Say, *"How do you and your family celebrate birthdays and other special days?"*

_____

_____

c. Dates

Dates tell stories about patterns of behavior, lifestyles, religious beliefs, rituals and celebrations, political situations, disasters, emigrations, and immigrations. Within these stories the current trauma reaction patterns often can be unmasked.

Say, *"What is the date you were born?"*

_____

_____

Say, *"What kind of day was that for your parents?"*

_____

_____

Say, *"What kind of birth?"*

_____

_____

Say, *"How did your parents and family welcome you into the world?"*

_____

_____

Significant dates are dates of births, illnesses, deaths, marriages, divorces, and life transitions. These speak of relationships, parenting, coupling, and lifestyles. Mistakes or knowledge of some birth dates as opposed to others is indicative of the kinds of relationships and needs to be looked at. Errors in dating things are often significant in terms of trauma. Immigration, for example, is a source of major trauma. Birth dates and name changes are often part of the process of immigration. Identity issues are often created in that flash moment of entering or leaving a country.

Say, *"Where were you born?"*

_____

_____

Say, *"Where were your parents born?"*

_____

_____

Say, *"Were there any name changes after you were born or familial name changes before you were born?"*

_____

_____

Behavior patterns in relation to significant life events such as special occasions, anniversaries, moves, connections with extended families, community, disasters, and even the political events of the times and places indicate resources or lack thereof. Getting the dates is the simpler aspect of this segment. Noticing reactions of the client who needs to provide the dates is a major significant factor and point for exploration.

Understanding culturally relevant dates such as 9/11, memorial days, and recognizing the tensions around events that are scheduled by dates is key to understanding the client in the here and now. Similarly, by working through the dates, the therapist can uncover how daily living, rules, schedules, rituals, customs, and traditions are handled.

Say, *"Are there any specific days you remember celebrating?"*

_____

_____

Say, *"How did your family celebrate holidays"* or *"What was it like at holiday time for you and your family?"*

_____

_____

Say, *"What was the atmosphere like around holidays, and major events?"*

_____

_____

Say, *"How did you celebrate events?"*

_____

_____

Say, *"What was it like in your family when major events happened outside of your family?"*

_____

_____

Say, *"How did people react to crises in your home, such as anything from breaking a glass or a leg, illnesses, death, or to watching 9/11 happen on TV?"*

_____

_____

Information about pets and the presence of other than immediate family, within the primary household, are relevant to the history of the individual.

Say, *"Did your family allow pets? What kind?"*

_____

_____

Say, *"What kind did you have?"*

_____

_____

Say, *"Were there other people outside of the immediate family living in your house?"*

_____

_____

Say, *"What was that like for you?"*

_____

_____

Say, *"Do you see any similarities in your current lifestyle to your familial lifestyle?"*

_____

_____

Say, *"Go ahead and describe what you have noticed."*

_____

_____

As the family tree grows and the patterns of the older generations become more apparent, information appears and often a client can suddenly sit up and say, *"Oh so that's where I got that from!"*

Once we have gone through the client's history, it is time to ask the following:

Say, *"When was the earliest time you remember feeling similar to the way you feel now?"*

_____

_____

Or say, *"Do you remember seeing someone else act like this?"*

_____

_____

This process leads the client and therapist to the chronologically earliest expression of an incident that produced the current reaction. This is what the therapist is looking at in the MTTG she has drawn up. When relevant, explore trauma and sexual history. This provides information and insight about: potential sexual abuse or other abuse leading to anxiety-provoking issues and unresolved traumas, unresolved grief and stuck points.

Often times, the therapist observes a small reaction in herself while listening to the client. This is the place where the therapist needs to look further into the client's statement that elicited that reaction in the therapist. It is often the key point of understanding the source of the client's present reaction and what is the focal point for EMDR.

Say, *"Are there any other events you might think of as traumatic that you might recall such as negative sexual experiences, or other volatile situations?"*

_____

_____

General questions to consider and be aware of when listening to the stories.

Say, *"Who else in the family background was involved or had something similar happen?"*

_____

_____

Say, *"Where and when did this situation begin?"*

_____

_____

Say, *"When was the first time this kind of reaction occurred?"*

_____

_____

Say, *"How do you think this was allowed to happen?"*

_____

_____

Say, *"Why do you think this might have happened?"*

_____

_____

d. Summing up

The Multi-Tiered Trans-Generational trauma history with all relevant information acknowledges the recognized resources. The therapist notes that survival is part of the trauma and is the most significant resource. To survive, one needs intuitiveness, belief in oneself, determination, skills, and so forth.

Say, *"Your intuitiveness and determination to rebuild and recover shows great courage. Thank you for sharing so much information about yourself and your family."*

The therapist has recognized issues with unresolved or left-over "heat."

Say, *"It does seem that there are still a few unresolved issues that perhaps might benefit from some EMDR work now. From what we have discussed what seems to have the most impact on you now?"*

_____

_____

_____

_____

This would be our entrance point (Touchstone Event) for beginning our work with EMDR.

Step 3: EMDR

1. Target selection

Through this MTTG format, the client has accessed the core issue(s) underlying the current presenting problem. Through this genogram, the client has taken a step away from the current issue and is able to recognize what has impacted his behavioral patterns over the generations. Essentially, the client has internalized a video system safely allowing distancing, reprocessing, rebuilding, and recovery.

The most relevant EMDR target is the Touchstone Event the client selects following this genogram, which has uploaded historical events impacting his life. Today's presenting issue is generally a replay of multigenerationally transmitted reactions to life events. Through the recounting of the client's history, the therapist has also noted resources that can be interwoven as needed at stuck points in the EMDR reprocessing.

> Say, *"It is not the symptom, it is not the behavior, it is the memory of the reactions to an historical event locked into the memory system that needs to be accessed via the MTTG and reprocessed with EMDR."*

Proceed with the EMDR Standard Protocol on the Touchstone Event the client has chosen following the MTTG.

Step 4: Resolution, Understanding, and Closure

Once the client has completed the EMDR reprocessing and has reached SUD = 0 and VoC = 7, it will be important to close the historical material and to help find meaning in the process that the client went through.

> Say, *"This has been a journey through time. How does that feel for you now?"*

_____

_____

> Say, *"Is there anything else that has come up that is still disturbing that you might want to work on next time?"*

_____

_____

> Say, *"Can you tell me what this process was like for you?"*

_____

_____

> Say, *"Can you remember where we started and see the path we took?"*

_____

_____

Finally, following standard safety processes for closure.

Say, *"Thank you for allowing me to be part of your process. Your appointment is* _____ (state the next appointment). *Goodbye."*

Summary

The MTTG is a format that brings life and new energy into your work with clients and into the life of your client. As the therapist and the client evolve the MTTG, the client teaches the therapist and himself about his richly textured history. Through the legacy of this history, the client gains clarity about his circumstances and an appreciation of life under the best and worst circumstances. Through the practitioner's interest and curiosity, the client learns the fascination that comes from viewing the dynamics of his family through the generations. The process creates a longer lasting effect, solidifying the results of the EMDR session.

EMDR, Trauma, and Adaptive Information Processing (AIP) Model Explanations

In the EMDR Procedural Step outline, Dr. Shapiro (2001) introduced the classic explanation that we have all used. Wording of the explanation of the EMDR method depends on the age, background, experience, and sophistication of the client. Her basic explanation of the adaptive information processing system, trauma, and what EMDR does, goes as follows:

> When a trauma occurs it seems to get locked in the nervous system with the original picture, sounds, thoughts, and feelings. The eye movements we use in EMDR seem to unlock the nervous system and allow the brain to process the experience. That may be what is happening in REM or dream sleep—the eye movements may help to process the unconscious material. It is important to remember that it is your own brain that will be doing the healing and that you are the one in control. (p. 431)

This explanation forms the bare bones of what is necessary to convey to our clients for them to understand what we are doing as clinicians. No doubt, there are any number of ways that creative EMDR clinicians have found to explain to their clients this process depending on their age, issue, concerns, diagnosis, and any other relevant variable that informs clinicians on how to respond to those who come to them for treatment. Dr. Daniel Siegel is a psychiatrist who has taken an interest in this question about EMDR. Also, he is an associate professor at the University of California–Los Angeles (UCLA), Director of the Mindsight Institute (www.mindsightinstitute.com), and codirector of the UCLA Mindful Awareness Research Center (www.marc.ucla.edu). This description of how EMDR works is taken from the *Handbook for EMDR Clients* (Luber, 2001):

> *The mind, which can be defined as the process that regulates the flow of energy and information, is encouraged to process memory and emotion in an efficient and therapeutic manner. As with other forms of psychotherapy, we do not yet know exactly how the healing process occurs in the mind or in the neural processes of the brain. Some authors have proposed that trauma involves an impairment in the integration of various forms of mental processes, such as memory, emotion, perception, and interpersonal communication, so that individuals may feel excessively constrained or at times flooded in the overall functioning of their minds. From a neural point of view, such an impairment in mental processes may be seen as due to a blockage in "neural integration," the manner in which the brain brings its circuitry into a functional whole.*
>
> *From this perspective, healing in psychotherapy would involve the development of the circuits that enable neural integration to occur in the brain. Areas such as the prefrontal cortex, the hippocampus, the corpus callosum, and the cerebellum are regions that may facilitate neural integration and thus are those that may be changing in effective therapy. EMDR may be particularly effective at promoting neural integration through the ways in which its phases activate distinctive processes in the brain, such as thoughts, emotions, memories, and bodily sensations. As the phases progress in EMDR, neural integration may be proposed to be the brain process that is being facilitated during the various phases of treatment. The result of effectively promoting neural integration would be both the alleviation of symptoms and the development of an enhanced sense of well-being internally as well as more rewarding experiences interpersonally.* (pp. 4–5)

This section includes how very experienced EMDR clinicians who have been using EMDR over a long period of time think about these issues and explain them to their clients. Each one has important information that may inform the way that you explain EMDR, trauma, and adaptive information processing to your clients from here on.

When Words and Pictures Fail: An Introduction to Adaptive Information Processing

Sheila Sidney Bender

As part of my discussion with my patients about their mind and the adaptive information processing (AIP) system, I find that patients are sometimes unable to find responses when asked about a picture representing the worst part of the event or what negative belief remains with them as a result of a life experience. It is my opinion that it is advantageous for the clinician to attempt to get all the pieces to the protocol and I recommend the following scripts as possible ways to do so. Tell them the following either during Phase 1 (history taking) or Phase 2 (preparation).

When Words and Pictures Fail Script

Phases 1 and 2: History Taking and Preparation

During the beginning introductions for Phases 1 and 2, I tell my patients about AIP and how it is thought to work by using metaphors that are designed to match the experiences and language of the patient.

> Say, *"I want to talk to you about how the adaptive information processing system and your mind work, especially concerning EMDR. If you want, you could think of the adaptive information processing system as your mind's immune system. When properly functioning, it is akin to your physical immune system's ability to fight disease. The adaptive information system can help you respond to an emotionally disturbing event with healthy resources."*

Continue with an explanation of what the system encompasses.

Say, *"Moment by moment, the system allows you to take in new information you receive through your senses and integrate it with what you have previously experienced so that your past informs the future. You are able to experience a fresh event not only through your senses, your eyes, your ears, your skin, your nose, and taste buds, but also from your sensorium, the components of the brain that interpret and label your experience. If the adaptive information system is functioning properly, you are able to behave proactively rather than merely reactively to the input. A simple example of this is for you to think now of a lemon. As you think of the lemon, you may have a picture of it and even feel the tart sensation in your mouth. You may even be salivating as you think of a lemon at this moment."*

You can give the patient further sensory experiences like the feel of warm sand or a cold drink to strengthen the point of sensory memory or any other examples that would be most relevant to your client.
Continue with the following:

Say, *"So you can see that your senses take in an event, what you see, hear, and feel, and you also can think about it, remember it, put words to it, and have beliefs about it and yourself."*

After you build the idea of senses, memory, beliefs, and potential triggers, you can begin to explain what happens when the adaptive information system becomes compromised.

Say, *"Comparable to your physical immune system being overwhelmed by a disease, your adaptive information processing system could be overwhelmed by a life event or a series of life events. Once exposed to a system compromise, the problem for many—and maybe for you—is that failure of one or more parts of the system either to register, or, if it does, to file or label the information effectively could have a wide range of consequences over your entire lifetime.*

What makes Dr. Shapiro's method of helping you with the situation that brings you to my office _____ (state the problem) as you previously experienced with the lemon (or whatever example you used) is that EMDR procedures enable you to consider not only the senses that assimilated (took in) the event, what you saw, heard, and felt, but also what you thought and said about what happened, the emotions you experienced, and the beliefs that you formed about yourself."

Continue as follows.

Say, *"When an event occurs, it is deconstructed in your memory and stored not as an entity but in parts. This means that sometimes when reconstructing the memory, you pull out a part from storage and it is connected to a part of another memory. It is like the magician's handkerchiefs that go separately into the hat and come out attached one to the next in a long stream.*

When you reprocess a memory it would be best to have as many aspects of mind available to separate the possible parts and then put them together in a way that could be thought of as healing or rebooting the adaptive information system. In the reprocess, you will keep all the information you need to keep and lose only the unhealthy clutter of old stories that were stored with body compromising memories or limiting thoughts and beliefs. You will also have an opportunity to develop healthier beliefs about yourself."

Give your patient an example of a negative belief that is relevant to him or use the following.

Say, *"For example, if you as a child were told by an important adult in your life that you were stupid or no good, not because you were either, but because the adult was having a difficult time with life, you could grow up believing you were flawed and no amount of success could be enough to dissuade you of the belief."*

Phase 3: Assessment

Say, *"Therefore, when working with the next steps of EMDR (Assessment Phase of the protocol), it is important to find all the aspects of the experience: sensory images, cognitions, beliefs, emotions, and physical sensations."*

Note that this type of explanation paves the way for your asking further questions or giving additional metaphors for clarification when asking the assessment questions. It is particularly helpful when you get responses like *"I have no picture"* or *"I wasn't thinking."*

The basic questions of the Assessment Phase are the following.

The Picture (Image in Memory)

Say, *"What picture* (using all of your senses) *represents the most traumatic part of the incident?"*

_____

_____

_____

If the patient reports no picture, say the following:

Say, *"Even though it is hard to find a picture right now, the visual cortex is the largest part of the brain, something could possibly be there, if you check. As I explained earlier, our job is to bring all parts of the mind on board even if the role is small.*

Note: The following metaphor, or one you think is more in keeping with your patient's experience, could be used.

Say, *"Suppose you were baking a cake from a recipe and you were missing an ingredient, you could continue to bake the cake or you could try to get the ingredient. What if you had no experience baking cakes and you were missing the flour? You might figure out that since the flour was the main part of the cake, it couldn't be done without it. But, what if it were something that was in small measure that was missing? How could you know? You might want to knock on a neighbor's door to borrow the missing ingredient or substitute something you had on hand that might have some of the qualities of the missing ingredient. We don't know how important the picture, the belief, or the body sensation is for you, so we want to try to find them if there is any way to do so."*

You may also add the following if there is no picture.

Say, *"How do you find the event in your mind?"*

_____

_____

Say, *"How do you know about it?"*

_____

_____

If the patient says that a parent, relative, or friend recounted it to him, or he overheard a conversation, or he saw a photograph, the therapist can ask the following:

Say, *"What is the worst part of that? Could you hold that as a picture?"*

_____

_____

Say, *"What does that look like?"*

_____

_____

Say, *"What do you hear?"*

_____

_____

Say, *"What other senses are involved?"*

_____

_____

Now that you have the picture, ask the next question of the assessment phase.

Negative Cognition (NC)

Say, *"What words best go with the picture that express your negative belief about yourself now?"*

_____

_____

If the patient cannot tell you a belief about himself, once again, educate him about what may be useful for the AIP system.

Say, *"As we discussed earlier, it helps to put together as many of the possible ways the problem that brought you here _____ (state the problem) has impacted your thinking then and now. It may be that you are unaware of a negative thought or belief you have about yourself now as a result and how it has limited your present thinking, but it is useful to try to find one. After, we have the negative belief; we will find a more positive belief that will be more advantageous and healthier. Thoughts, beliefs, and language are a gift of being human and are valuable in forming solutions for life's problems."*

If still no negative cognition, make some suggestions about the negative cognitions you have noted in your history taking. You can also hand the patient the list of NCs and PCs.

> Say, *"Like we discussed earlier, it is helpful to have some words to frame your experience, how that has influenced your life, and what you believe about yourself despite the passage of time."*

Patients, by this time, understand how their thinking and feeling about a past event have influenced the present and are willing to find the required ingredients for the protocol. The rest of the assessment phase flows and follows the usual steps.

Positive Cognition (PC)

> Say, *"When you bring up that picture or incident, what would you like to believe about yourself, now?"*

_____

_____

Validity of Cognition (VoC)

> Say, **"When you think of the incident** (or picture) *how true do those words _____* (clinician repeats the positive cognition) *feel to you now on a scale of 1 to 7, where 1 feels completely false and 7 feels completely true?"*

>   1   2   3   4   5   6   7
>   (completely false)   (completely true)

Sometimes, it is necessary to explain further when the VoC seems very high and you suspect that the patient may be thinking rather than feeling his response.

> Say, *"Remember, sometimes we know something with our head, but it feels differently in our gut. In this case, what is the gut-level feeling of the truth of _____* (clinician states the positive cognition), *from 1 (feels completely false) to 7 (feels completely true)?"*

>   1   2   3   4   5   6   7
>   (completely false)   (completely true)

Emotions

> Say, *"When you bring up the picture* (or incident) *and those words _____* (clinician states the negative cognition), *what emotions do you feel now?"*

_____

_____

Subjective Units of Disturbance (SUD)

> Say, *"On a scale of 0 to 10, where 0 is no disturbance or neutral and 10 is the highest disturbance you can imagine, how disturbing does it feel now?"*

>   0   1   2   3   4   5   6   7   8   9   10
>   (no disturbance)   (highest disturbance)

Location of Body Sensation

Say, *"Where do you feel it* (the disturbance) *in your body?"*

_____

_____

Phase 4: Desensitization

Say, *"Bring up the picture, the negative belief* (state negative belief), *notice where you're feeling it in your body, and follow my fingers."*

Case Example

This case example illustrates how to address unrecalled or missing assessment ingredients with the client.

Presenting Problem: Fear of Flying

A 57-year-old, married male executive employed in New York City had just completed a formal program aimed at fear of flying, but he was unable to complete the final step that was to actually go on a flight. The program leader had suggested EMDR. The patient described several other programs he had gone through with no success. His work required travel, so he arranged for meetings to be on Mondays and he would take a train on the weekend when the trip was to the Midwest. With this scheduling limitation, he could only travel comfortably as far as Chicago, and had managed with great difficulty to avoid any trip to California. He said he had always been afraid of planes and had never been on one. When asked for any history about the fear, he claimed that there was none.

A history was taken and he described himself as the only child of an intact marriage, he had a normal childhood, normal school experiences, and he was normal in all aspects of his life. He was very successful in his job and his only problem was traveling a distance requiring more than a full-day train trip.

Therapist:	*"What picture represents the worst part of the flying?"*
Client:	"I don't have a picture. I'm not very good at remembering pictures."
Therapist:	*"When we reprocess a memory, it would be best to have as many aspects of your mind and how you think of and remember information available. The more parts on board, the more opportunity we have to reprocess this event compromising your life. Perhaps your picture is more auditory, or kinesthetic; perhaps there's a feel to it. Describe it the best you can."*
Client:	"It's just dark. I can hear my heart."
Therapist:	*"So you see dark?"*
Client:	"Yes, but I also am imagining what's happening."
Therapist:	*"And what is that like?"*

Client: "I just see myself, the plane has crashed, and I'm lying there dead."

Therapist: *"And when you think of that picture, can you think of a time when you heard such a story whether in the news or on television?"*

Client: "Probably."

Therapist: *"Tell me about it."*

Client: "I must have; it's always on the news."

Therapist: *"And as you think about it, do you notice anything in your body?"*

Client: "I'm getting antsy."

Therapist: *"Is that familiar?"*

Client: "Only when I was a kid."

Therapist: *"Anything then, when you were a kid?"*

Client: "When I was a kid, I remember a story my mother told me about a plane."

Therapist: *"Tell me about it."*

Client: "My dad was in the service, and the plane was to take him and everyone home. My father missed the plane and it crashed. He was okay and he came on another plane."

               [Note that the patient told this story without a cognitive glimmer of its possible relevance.]

Therapist: *"What picture represents the worst part of hearing that story?"*

Client: "I don't know if this is real, but I can remember seeing a plane crashing and everyone but my dad on it."

Therapist: *"I'm going to ask for the negative thought that you still carry or have now because part of your thoughts in the present keep you trapped thinking about the crash."*

Client: "I was just scared."

Therapist: *"I can understand you were just scared, but what are your negative thoughts now about yourself because 'I was scared.'"*

Client: "I could die."

Therapist: *"When you think or believe 'I could die,' what do you believe about yourself today?"*

Client:	"I am not safe."
Therapist:	*"And as you think of that picture and the belief 'I am not safe,' what do you want to believe about yourself now?"*
Client:	"I am okay."
Therapist:	*"On a scale of 1 to 7, where 1 feels absolutely untrue and 7 feels as true as possible, how true do the words 'I am okay' feel to you right now?"*
Client:	"Not very."
Therapist:	*"For the purposes of our work, can you give me a number for the 'not very' from 1 to 7?"*
Client:	"Sure, maybe 2."

We finished up the assessment with his expressed emotions being "scared," 8 SUD, and reported sensations throughout his body. Eye movements were used for the desensitization. The session time nearly up, we closed according to protocol for incomplete session and scheduled for 1 week on a Tuesday again. His departing words were, "I think I feel very different about planes, but I don't think I'll be going on a plane for awhile."

Monday evening, he called and cancelled for the next day. His excuse, he was in Los Angeles. He had had to fly there early that morning and he did. When I pointed out that he had held the same job for more than 6 years and had managed to get out of every situation that required him to fly, he laughed and said, "Maybe I finally realized my dad had gotten on a plane that had taken him home." I never saw the patient again because as he said, "I probably have other stuff to take care of, but my flying problem is over so the other stuff will just have to wait."

Introducing Adaptive Information Processing (AIP) and EMDR: Affect Management and Self-Mastery of Triggers

Gene Schwartz

It is helpful to introduce the concept of Adaptive Information Processing, to help your clients understand the nature of how our brains work. To do this, you can use a metaphor concerning the front and back of the brain.

Metaphor: The Front and Back of the Brain Script

Say, *"People can only juggle a few ideas in the front of the brain. Every-thing else is in the back. For an exercise, I would like you to think of your car; while doing that, think of your favorite food; now add where you work to the car and food; now think of those and try to also think of where you went to school. The more things I add for you to remember, the more difficult it gets. It is because very few people can keep more than several thoughts in the front of the brain at any given time. The rest is in the back. Does that make sense to you?"*

The Purpose of Arousal

Say, *"The brain is very protective and is always looking for things in the current environment that represent information stored in the back of the brain that may need attention. The back of the brain talks to the front of the brain by arousal. For instance, if you walk into your home and something is not right, how long does it take for you to notice?"*

_____

_____

Say, *"It's almost instantaneous, right?"*

_____

_____

Say, *"How do you know something is not right?"*

_____

_____

Say, *"You feel it in your body and the words we use are body feeling words such as I have a feeling something isn't right. What's going on?"*

"We feel something isn't right. We ask, 'What is going on?' If the other person says nothing, the back of the brain raps on the front harder and you feel more arousal because you can't fool the back of the brain. If the person tells you what is going on, your arousal goes down, if it doesn't have anything to do with you."

"Another way to explain this is, when you are driving and see a ball roll out into the street a block away, the front of the brain sees the ball and you think there may be a kid and slow down. If the ball rolls right out in front of you, your foot hits the brake without your thinking about it. After the car stops, you start to shake and then the front of the brain catches up and you say to yourself 'I almost hit the kid!!!!' "

The Importance of the Body Scan

Say, *"Please scan through your body, notice what you feel, you don't need to even tell me. Now think about* _____ (state something from their assessment, treatment goals, or history that will raise affect) *and run a tape of it, stopping at the worst part. Now scan your body and notice what you feel."*

_____

_____

Say, *"Now notice the difference in what you feel between the first scan and when you brought up the unpleasant thought. Old learned negative experiences are stored in the back of the brain. Notice how quickly the emotions and sensations are accessed just by being asked to think about them."*

Then, it is important to make sure the client is grounded in the present and arousal is down.

Say, *"Okay. How are you feeling now?"* For this, just have the client feel the floor and look around the room to come into the present.

Say, *"The brain is always protective and scanning for sensory input such as sight, sound, smell, taste, or physical sensation that reminds the brain of past things it needs to be aware of so it can fire up arousal to protect the person if need be.*

Why Zebras Don't Get Ulcers

Say, *"I would like to tell you about the work of Robert Sapolsky, who wrote* Why Zebras Don't Get Ulcers *in 1993. Sapolsky is one of the foremost researchers of stress and has a lot to say about nature.*

Do you ever watch TV shows about nature where there is a water hole with lots of animals drinking? The animals are calm. The camera pans over to a lion and then back. All the animals are on alert, muscles vibrating ready to run. The camera shows the lion move, and all the animals run like hell. If you're the slowest zebra, what happens? He gets eaten. But the rest run until they are safe.

Sapolsky says the only thing the zebra needs while running is the large muscle groups, an increase of blood circulation, and maybe to break down a little fat to fuel the large muscles. All your other systems start to go off-line like your immune, digestive, and reproductive systems, and so forth. When the zebra stops running and starts eating grass, everything goes back online and he doesn't develop an ulcer.

People, though, are different. Do you know why? In thousands of years we developed this big part of our brain (point to your head); *we also developed something the zebra can't do. The zebra needs to see, hear, or smell the lion to fire up his arousal system, or he just sees all of his friends start to run and says to himself, 'If they are out of here, so am I.'"*

The Difference Between People and Zebras

Say, *"Isn't it interesting that people, with our great brains, only have to imagine a lion to get the same arousal response and get ready to run?"*

"Look around my office and see if you see any real lions. Don't pay attention to arousal, just look for a lion. Do you see one?"

_____

_____

This author has never yet had a person see a lion in his office!

Thank Your Brain!

Say, *"So, here is the secret to starting to control your arousal. If you feel arousal, and don't see a lion, it's most likely a lion is living in the back of your head! THANK YOUR BRAIN for trying to take care of you, but tell your brain that it doesn't need the arousal right then because there is no real lion. You can use various techniques to bring your arousal down such as deep breathing, grounding, and so forth. Now, this idea about thanking the brain must sound really silly, however, on the contrary, it is really important and I will tell you why."*

Say, *"The brain does not like negatives, so when you are thanking that part of your brain that is looking after you, it keeps you from blocking your thoughts. What we have found is that the more that you try not to think about something, the more the brain thinks about it! So, thanking your brain will let your brain rest concerning that particular arousal."*

Finding Your Lions

Say, *"So, are you interested in how to find your lions? Triggers are things in the environment that the brain pays attention to that represent lions in the back of the brain. These are the things that cause you distress on a daily basis. Can you list some of the lions or triggers that you have in your life?"* (I have them list ones they might know.)

_____

_____

_____

_____

Say, *"You can see that it is easy to find them. One way to help you with your lions is by doing a Body Scan. Can you start doing the Body Scan during the day? It is helpful to do it about six times a day; when you wake up, in midmorning, at lunch, in midafternoon, at dinner, and at bedtime. Actually, no one ever does it that much but you can learn a lot, feel better, and help your therapy move along faster if you do it at least a few times. If you wake up, check the scan, and feel okay, just note it.*

Later, if you scan during midmorning and notice a change in arousal or mood, you should assume your brain detected a lion. You may know what it was. Maybe, it was a fight with your boss or the mean look someone gave you. But, if you don't know, you then can try to find out by running the tape of the time period back and forth. For example, you might say, 'I felt okay when I woke up but I don't now. I was okay on the way to work. I do remember that an hour ago I felt bad.' If you keep running the tape back and forth, there is a good chance you will be able to isolate the trigger event. When you find it, note it, so we can use it as an EMDR target.

If you find it, you can also think about lions and ask yourself, 'Is there a real lion in the room?' If the answer is no, you can thank your brain for making you alert. Then, you can calm yourself, because it is a memory lion in your brain, not one that can hurt you now. If you can't find the trigger, you can look around for a lion. If you don't see one, it is in your head and we can do something to help reduce your arousal."

People respond well to this technique and often report that the *lion in the room* idea is very helpful. Clients are able to start to decrease and manage their affect. It is very helpful to therapy. When a client knows or finds a trigger by this method, you can then include it in the list of targets that you have for your case conceptualization for processing with the Standard EMDR Protocol.

Case Example: The Combat Veteran and *Being on Time* Events

Many combat veterans are reactive to being on time. They often report family fights over children who are late, or they become very angry if their spouses are late, or if they cause the veterans to be late.

Starting with the time event and the negative cognition involved, often a float-back went back to a combat situation where someone was killed or was almost killed because of time, usually because someone was late.

In individual therapy, using EMDR on the time event is very helpful. Because of the number of veterans with this trigger, they were taught to master this trigger with arousal management. Step 1 was to make them aware of the increase of arousal around time and where they felt it in their body. Step 2 was to teach them to start associating the time and arousal sensation with specific grounding routines.

One scenario might be the following: "I am in Baltimore, the date is 2008, I don't see a real lion. I am not in a combat situation. I have a discharge from the service. No one is trying to kill me or my family. The sensations I am feeling are real but not necessary now. Thank you brain for alerting me but I don't need to pay attention now." They are trained to use the grounding even before a time event starts for practice and prevention. If they practice, they will get relief right away and master the time trigger in a few months.

This is one of the many ways that this explanation can assist you in helping your client understand the nature of adaptive information processing and EMDR.

PART III

Creating

Resources

The second phase of EMDR is called the Preparation Phase. When EMDR first started, practitioners often went from Phase 1–Client History Taking to Phase 3–Assessment Phase with just a brief moment to introduce the client to the specifics such as the mechanics of EMDR, including bilateral stimulation (BLS), sitting position, stop signals, and the metaphor of "sitting on the train and watching the scenery going by." For some clients, this has worked well, however, as time went on, practitioners often reported that something more was needed before beginning desensitization and reprocessing.

The idea of tapping into the client's natural resources began within the Standard EMDR Protocol itself. Francine Shapiro (1989a, 1995, 2001) incorporated a positive cognition to stimulate the positive neural networks in the brain, as a way to nudge adaptive information processing (AIP) toward positive resolution. While the purpose of the Installation Phase was to link the positive cognition (PC) (or the "preferred" cognition, as it was known earlier [Shapiro, 1989b]), with the new gestalt of the target issue or problem and check to see if there was more dysfunctional material that needed to be processed, for some client populations this did not supply enough stability. In what has become the hallmark of the EMDR community, practitioners came up with new solutions.

Early on in the history of EMDR, Dr. Neal Daniels, a clinical psychologist working at the Veterans Administration Hospital in Philadelphia, Pennsylvania, found that the veterans with whom he worked were in need of stabilization and affect containment measures before descending into their trauma. To counteract the vets reexperiencing the emotional devastation of their traumatic memories, he built in the central idea of the "Safe Place." The results were so positive that one of the highlights that Francine Shapiro noted when reminiscing about Dr. Daniels was concerning this contribution to EMDR: "His reports on the use of the Safe Place exercise with the veterans supported and inspired its implementation as part of EMDR standard care" (Luber, 2006). Susan Del Maestro, as a member of Dr. Daniels's PTSD Clinical Team, elaborates further, "Neal was the creator of pairing eye movement with safe place imagery, and did this so that we could introduce EMDR to our patients in the least threatening manner. He taught us to begin with a safe place and to return to this calming image when patients' images or affect became overwhelming, unmoving" (Luber, 2006). In this section, there are several renditions of the Safe Place exercises.

Using positive experiences from our past is a natural occurring phenomenon to which we can all connect. Thinking about the time that you passed the test with flying colors, or when you learned to swim or ride a bike are among the many memories that we can draw out and think of in times of pride or in sorrow. One of the findings in this editor's dissertation research on peak and positive experiences in children and adolescence was that some children naturally pulled out their positive experiences during times of difficulty to self-soothe without ever being instructed (Luber, 1986). In the field of psychology, many of these resources began as ego-strengthening techniques developed by therapists working with hypnosis. Looking into the hypnosis literature, especially the work of Milton Erickson and those he inspired, will result in a number of resourcing strategies.

The basic structure in the chapters on resources in this book often follows—but not exclusively—the following format: find an image for the resource; connect it with the felt emotions and sensations; enhance the experience through words; incorporate bilateral stimulation; add a cue word; teach the client how to use the cue word to self-cue without disturbance and then with disturbance; and then encourage the client to practice using the resource during the week. This is a simple format that can result in many positive resources for your client.

Robbie Dunton, a brilliant Educator and Learning Disabilities Specialist, met Francine Shapiro in 1987, just as Dr. Shapiro was developing her early work on EMD. She was so enthused about EMDR that she and Francine founded the EMDR Institute. Mrs. Dunton developed the first specialty that was taught at EMDR Institute trainings on "EMDR with Children and Adolescents." During her trainings, she noted that one of the first things that she did was to ask the child or adolescent that she was seeing to think about something positive that happened to them and then she would use eye movements to install the experience. This began the session in a positive, proactive way and helped her young clients be ready for whatever work ensued. In this section, there are a number of resource-building exercises that either were derived from this early use of resources with eye movement or were independently created by observation or necessity.

One of the earliest innovators was Ron Martinez, a psychologist who wrote a regular column in the "Network Newsletter: Eye Movement Desensitization and Reprocessing," the original newsletter of the EMDR Institute, called "Innovative Uses." It was in this newsletter and the early EMDR Institute–sponsored Annual Conferences that many original ideas for resourcing were published or presented (Greenwald, 1993a, 1993b; Martinez, 1991; Wildwind, 1992).

A. J. Popky, another early pioneer of EMDR, applied the idea of "internal resource states" to his work on addictions and paired this with eye movements. Next, Dr. Popky had the client think of a "positive treatment goal." The client created an image of "how s/he would look being successful and fully functional, having attained his/her goal." Dr. Popky thought that the positive goal should be stated in positive terms, and time-related so that it could be achievable in the near future. It was important that this goal describe how clients see themselves coping and functioning successfully in their own words. The goal should also be "attractive, magnetic and compelling" (Popky, 1994, 2005). He went on to associate the positive state with the positive goal, building the positive associations so clients had a strong sense of the positive future to which they were moving. Dr. Popky's work has been an inspiration to others and has been incorporated into some of the protocols that follow (see Knipe's [in press] work on dysfunctional positive affect; and Pillai-Freedman's [in press] work on sexual dysfunction).

Steve Lazrove, when faced with clients who could not start with the Standard EMDR Protocol for trauma, simply asked the client to focus on a positive target and reprocessed this. Although there was a possibility that this could move into negative material, often the client was able to reinforce the positive material. Lazrove and other colleagues had good success using this process.

Jennifer Lendl and Sam Foster began using EMDR to transform their work in coaching. In 1995, they published their preliminary findings in the *Journal of Applied Sport Psychology* (Foster & Lendl, 1995) and then went on to create their manual, *EMDR Performance Enhancement for the Workplace: A Practitioner's Manual* (Lendl & Foster, 1997), which has been an important contribution to the work on performance enhancement.

In the face of man-made or natural catastrophes, practitioners have found that building resources are essential aspects of working with recent trauma, especially for children. Lucina Artigas and Ignacio Jarero's *The Butterfly Hug* (Artigas & Jarero, in press); as well as Brurit Laub and Esti Bar-Sade's "The Imma Group Protocol" (chapter 30, this volume) built on the Butterfly Hug concept to help children work through these types of trauma.

In 1995, Andrew Leeds (1995) went on to develop the concept of resources more formally and created a term "Resource Development and Installation (RDI)" to describe a more in-depth protocol to help clients establish resources that are needed, especially in relation to mastery, attachment, and symbols or metaphors. In 2002, Deborah Korn and Andrew Leeds cited preliminary evidence that RDI can be effective in the stabilization phase in the treatment of patients with complex post-traumatic stress disorder (PTSD).

At the turn of the millennium, the EMDR community was enthralled with resource development and it seemed like clinicians were spending a great deal of time focusing on building resources versus trauma processing. In 2003, on an Institute staff listserv (Shapiro, 2003) and later in her 2004 EMDRIA Conference Plenary, Dr. Shapiro (2004) reminded EMDR practitioners that the purpose of Phase 2 was to ensure that the client can process without "fear of the fear" and can maintain one foot in the present and one in the past. It is important to remember that the safe place or resource development are state change techniques and do not result in the reprocessing of the traumatic material. Emotions such as rage stem from unprocessed material and need to be fully processed to change. Without this understanding, it would be easy to fall back on monitoring state change rather than full processing. At the 2004 EMDRIA conference, Korn, Weir, and Rozelle (2004) went on to show the results of their well-controlled EMDR study where eight sessions were conducted with adult PTSD subjects, including childhood onset PTSD. They found that less than 5% of their subjects needed RDI, and those who did only needed one session. In 2006, Leeds (2006) also reported—in his paper presented at the EMDR International Conference in Philadelphia—that EMDRIA-approved consultants were noting informally that very few clients presenting with PTSD were in need of RDI before using EMDR to reprocess disturbing memories.

It is important to keep the organizing principle of EMDR treatment in mind during the Preparation Phase: To fully process the memories that contain the negative affects and overcome the developmental arrests or symptoms.

The goals of the Preparation Phase are:

- To prepare clients who have been assessed as appropriate EMDR clients to move on to the Assessment Phase;
- To form a bond between the therapist and the client;

- To assess the clients' abilities to self-soothe and manage their own affect;
- To develop stabilization or affect modulating skills as needed;
- To introduce the process of EMDR, including bilateral stimulation; Safe Place Exercise;
- To address any fears or concerns clients may have.

The protocols that follow have been developed by a number of creative practitioners of EMDR to address the need for clients to develop self-efficacy, an ability to modulate affect, and to self-soothe in the face of difficulty. The first is the "Developing a Safe Place" exercise taken from Dr. Shapiro's (2006) *EMDR New Notes on Adaptive Information Processing with Case Formulation Principles, Forms, Scripts and Worksheets*.

Luise Reddemann has contributed her Safe Place exercise, the Inner Safe Place, which is part of a larger body of work called "Psychodynamic Imaginative Psychotherapy of Trauma" (2001, 2008). This work grew out of her work in the 1980s in Germany with traumatized women. She was one of the early pioneers in the trauma field, introducing the concept of trauma to her German colleagues throughout the German-speaking world.

Resources for adults in man-made and natural disasters include the "Four Elements Exercise for Stress Management" by Elan Shapiro; this is a simple, efficient and effective way to elicit fundamental resources while linking them to the basic elements. Dr. E. Shapiro went on to create the idea of "The Resource Map" to have a way to quickly elicit and note a client's resources.

As part of his work with the Humanitarian Assistance Program, Roy Kiessling developed a number of resourcing techniques that have become staples in the EMDR practitioner's repertoire such as "Managing the 'Fear of the Fear,'" "Resource Strengthening," "Extending Resources Exercise," and "The Wedging Technique," building on the basic structure mentioned above to address many of the typical situations faced by clients.

Brurit Laub's (Laub, 2001; Laub & Weiner, 2007) contribution, the "Resource Connection," is particularly interesting as she has found a way to collect resources throughout the Standard EMDR Protocol by emphasizing the dialectical healing movement between negatively and positively stored memories or resources; this enhances processing toward completion and integration.

The Safe/Calm Place Protocol

Marilyn Luber (Script From Francine Shapiro, 2006)

The idea of the *safe place* has been a staple in practices of Clinical Hypnosis practitioners. The first known use of the Safe Place with EMDR was when Dr. Neal Daniels, an EMDR practitioner working at the Veterans Administration Hospital in Philadelphia, adopted this resource to assist the veterans with whom he worked to ground themselves and contain their affect before doing trauma work. Dr. Francine Shapiro saw the merit of this intervention and by 1995 included a formalized version into the first EMDR text.

The Safe/Calm Place Protocol Script

Use other affect if more appropriate for client (e.g., calm, control, courage).

Image

Say, *"I'd like you to think about some place you have been or imagine being that feels very safe or calm. Perhaps, being on the beach or sitting by a mountain stream."* (Pause)
Say, *"Where would you be?"*

_____

_____

Emotions and Sensations

Say, *"As you think of that safe* (or calm) *place, notice what you see, hear, and feel right now."* (Pause)
Say, *"What do you notice?"*

_____

_____

Enhancement

Say, "Focus on your safe (or calm) *place, its sights, sounds, smells, and body sensations. Tell me more about what you are noticing.*"

_____

_____

Bilateral Stimulation (BLS)

Say, "*Bring up the image of that place. Concentrate on where you feel the pleasant sensations in your body and allow yourself to enjoy them. Now concentrate on those sensations and follow my fingers* (or whatever BLS you use).*"

Use four to six sets.

Say, "*How do you feel now?*"

_____

_____

Repeat several times if the process has enhanced the client's positive feelings and sensations.
If positive, say, "*Focus on that.*"
Repeat BLS.

Say, "*What do you notice now?*"

_____

_____

Cue Word

Say, "*Is there a word or phrase that represents your safe* (or calm) *place?*"

_____

_____

Then say, "*Think of _____* (cue word) *and notice the positive feelings you have when you think of that word. Now concentrate on those sensations and the cue word and follow _____* (state BLS using).*"

Use short sets (four to six) of BLS with any positive responses.

Say, "*How do you feel now?*"

_____

_____

Repeat several times. Enhance positive feelings with BLS several times.

Self-Cuing

Say, "*Now I'd like you to say that word _____* (cue word) *and notice how you feel.*"

_____

_____

Cuing With Disturbance

Say, *"Now imagine a minor annoyance and how it feels."* (Pause)

Say, *"Now bring up your safe* (or calm) *place and notice any shifts in your body."*

_____

_____

Do BLS.

Guide the client through the process until he is able to experience the positive emotions and sensations. Repeat as often as necessary.

Self-Cuing With Disturbance

Say, *"Now I'd like you to think of another mildly annoying incident and bring up your safe* (or calm) *place by yourself again, especially noticing any changes in your body when you have gone to your safe* (or calm) *place."*

_____

_____

Practice

Say, *"I'd like you to practice using your safe place, between now and our next session, at any time you feel a little annoyed. Keep track of how things go and we'll talk about it next time we meet. Do you have any questions before we stop?"*

_____

_____

Note

Reprinted from *EMDR New Notes on Adaptive Information Processing with Case Formulation Principles, Forms, Scripts and Worksheets* by Francine Shapiro, PhD, with permission from The EMDR Institute, Copyright 2006.

The Inner Safe Place

Luise Reddemann

The Inner Safe Place Script Notes

The imagery of an "Inner Safe Place" is part of a body of work on stabilization techniques for trauma therapy called "Psychodynamic Imaginative Trauma Therapy (PITT)" (Reddemann, 2001). It is used within PITT to prepare clients for EMDR. However, it works very well as a resource for EMDR. It is important to know that clients who live in unsafe circumstances are often not able to develop the images and so seeing what happens while working on installing the inner safe place can tell us something about clients' external safety. If clients are able to create an inner safe place, the therapist can proceed with the exercise. If clients are unable to create and install a safe place, other stabilization work is used.

The Inner Safe Place Script

Say, *"This place can be on earth, but it does not have to be. It can also be outside the earth. . . . Let your thoughts, ideas, or images come into your mind of a place in which you feel completely safe and well cared for. Give this place a boundary of your own choice that is created so that only you can choose which being(s) should be there, or are allowed to be in this place, your place. You can, of course, invite beings that you would like to have in this place. If possible, I advise you not to invite any human being but perhaps dear inner companions or helpers, beings that give you love and support. If it pleases you, imagine your own inner helper with you in your safe place, however, if you prefer to be there alone, this is good as well. Your helper is with you, full of loving kindness and is helping you whenever you need assistance. If you would like, you can imagine your helper as your inner guide. Let your helper be a being from your imagination outside your day-to-day life.*

With all of your senses, check and notice if you feel good there. First, check whether that which you see with your eyes is really pleasing to the eye. If there is something that you do not like, then change it.

Now check whether the things you can hear are pleasing to the ear. If not, please change things so that everything you can hear is pleasant.

Is the temperature pleasant? If not, you can change it now.

Can you move your body so that you feel good, and can you get into any position in which you feel good?

If something is missing, change everything until everything is perfect for you.

Are the smells you can smell pleasant? You can also change these, until you feel really comfortable.

As soon as you are aware of how completely well you feel in your inner safe place, you can decide on a physical gesture and link it with your inner safe place. In the future, you can perform this gesture, and it will help you to reach this place quickly in your imagination. If you like, you can perform this gesture now.

To finish the exercise you can become conscious of the boundaries of your body again, carefully registering your body's contact with the ground. Then, come back into the room with your full awareness. I would like to invite you to be aware of how you feel after you have done this exercise."

Four Elements Exercise for Stress Management

Elan Shapiro

Four Elements Script Notes

The rationale behind the creation of "The Four Elements Exercise for Stress Management" is to address the cumulative effect of external and internal triggers that occur over the course of the day. Since we know that people cope better with stress when they stay within their arousal "window of tolerance" (Ogden & Minton, 2000), ways to lower stress—especially when under stress—are essential. An antidote to stress triggers is the frequent random monitoring of stress levels with simple stress reduction actions.

The heart of the exercise consists of four, brief, self-calming and self-control activities. The sequence of the four elements—Earth-Air-Water-Fire—is designed to follow the body up from the feet to the stomach and chest, to the throat and mouth, and up through the head. It begins with the ground to signify safety in the present reality and moves up to the imagination of recalled safety.

While learning to do the Four Elements Exercise for Stress Management, it is suggested that clients wear a four elements "bracelet" as a reminder to do the exercise. This can be a colored rubber band, string, or bracelet, something novel that clients will notice or already wear on a regular basis on their wrists. The idea is to take a quick reading of the current stress level using the simple 0 to 10 SUD scale (subjective units of disturbance scale) where 10 = the most stress and 0 = no stress at all. This can occur every time clients observe their bracelets. Then, clients do the exercises and the therapist takes another SUD reading to see the results of doing the Four Elements Exercises.

Sometimes, clients find it helpful to gently stretch the rubber band and release it each time to signal the beginning of the Four Elements Exercise, to stop negative thoughts and to ground quickly in the present.

An alternative to the rubber band is to place a small sticker or label on a frequently seen object that the client carries such as a watch, a mobile phone, for example.

By checking in with stress levels at random times throughout the day and also when stressful events are occurring, the exercise can aid in preventing the accumulation of stress and enables clients to stay within their window of tolerance. The modest goal is to reduce the stress level by 1 or 2 units each time the exercise is performed.

The original conceptualization of the Four Elements Exercise was that the first three elements could be a preparation for the Safe Place (or other resource exercise such as the Resource Connection), especially when there is an ongoing emergency situation or when it is difficult to find a Safe Place. Often, the fourth element is introduced at the following meeting, as the first three elements are enough to remember and practice in the beginning for clients.

Working on the Safe Place separately during the following session gives it more space and impact. It is then practiced with the bracelet reminder frequently, together with the other elements. It is also possible, depending on time and the needs of the client, to incorporate the creating of the Safe Place after the third element.

It is advisable to follow up on how the client practiced the four elements at the beginning of the next session and to ask them to show you how they do it. If necessary, demonstrate it again at the beginning of the first few sessions. This is a way of checking for compliance and readiness for EMDR as well as present level of stress and sense of safety with you in the room.

Four Elements Exercise for Stress Management Script

Introduction

Say, *"Okay. Let's begin the 'Four Elements Exercise for Stress Management.' The purpose of this exercise is to help you manage your stress throughout the day and stay within what we call your 'window of tolerance' for stress. If you can keep your stress level from accumulating throughout the day by this very brief exercise, you will notice the difference in your quality of life. Would you be interested in learning this skill for managing stress?"*

_____

_____

Say, *"First, let's start by finding a reminder that you might use. I have a* stone *(state whether you have a rubber band, bracelet, etc. It is important for the therapist to give this transitional object that will also remind the client of the safety of the therapist and the therapist's office). Or, I have some stickers here that you could put on your mobile phone if you prefer to do that. What would you like to choose?"*

_____

_____

Say, *"Let's take a current reading of your stress level where 0 is no stress or neutral and 10 is the highest stress you can imagine. How stressful does it feel now?"*

0   1   2   3   4   5   6   7   8   9   10
(no stress)   (highest stress)

Say, *"The exercise consists of four, brief, self-calming and self-control activities. The sequence of the four elements—Earth-Air-Water-Fire—is designed to follow the body up from the feet to the stomach and chest, to the throat and mouth and up through the head. Let's begin."*

The Four Elements for Stress Management

1. Earth: Grounding, Safety in the Present

Say, *"The first element is EARTH. The Earth represents the idea of grounding ourselves in the present and noticing that we are safe in the present. Take a minute or two to land—to be here now.*
Place both feet on the ground, feel the chair supporting you. Direct your attention outward. Look around and notice three new things that you see."

_____

_____

Say, *"Tell me what you hear."*

_____

_____

Say, *"Tell me what you smell."*

_____

_____

Note: Don't ask this if it draws attention to ongoing dangers, for example, if you are in a war zone and there are explosions still going on.

2. Air: Breathing for Strength, Balance, and Centering

Say, *"The element of AIR represents a feeling of strength, balance, and centering. If anxiety is excitement without oxygen and results in your stopping breathing, when you start noticing your breath and breathing deeply, your anxiety decreases. So, as you continue feeling the SECURITY NOW of your feet on the GROUND, take three or four deeper, slower breaths from your stomach to your chest, making sure to breathe all the way out to make room for fresh energizing air. As you breathe out, imagine that you are letting go of some of the stress and breathing it out, direct your attention inward to your center."*

3. Water: Calm and Controlled—Switch on the Relaxation Response

Say, *"Through the element of WATER, we can switch on the relaxation response and become calm and controlled. Notice if you have saliva in your mouth. Have you noticed that when you are anxious, or stressed, your mouth often 'dries' because part of the stress emergency response is to shut off the digestive system? This has to do with the Sympathetic Nervous System. When you start making saliva, you switch on the digestive system again or the parasympathetic nervous system and the relaxation response. This is the reason why people are offered water or tea or chew gum after a difficult experience.*

Sometimes, people find it helpful to imagine the taste of a lemon or something that makes their mouth 'water' in anticipation. When you make saliva, you can optimally control your thoughts and your body.

So, as you continue feeling the SECURITY NOW of your feet on the GROUND and feel CENTERED as you BREATHE in and out, direct your attention to making saliva."

Before moving on to the fourth element, it is important to decide whether the client would benefit from practicing the first three elements at the beginning or moving on to create the Safe Place after the third element is established.

If you decide to end with the third element, it is helpful to do the following:

Say, *"As you continue feeling the SECURITY NOW of your feet on the GROUND; and feel CENTERED as you BREATHE in and out; and feel CALM and in CONTROL as you produce more and more SALIVA";*
"Where do you feel it in your body?"

_____

_____

Say, *"Does it feel good?"*

_____

_____

Say, *"Then, direct your attention to feeling good in your body and go with* _____ *(whatever bilateral stimulation [BLS] you are using)."*

Install with brief, slow BLS or butterfly hugs.

Say, *"Now touch your bracelet* (or sticker, etc.), *and start by thinking first about the element of earth, then air, and then water."* (Pause)
Say, *"Have you done that?"*

_____

_____

Say, *"Great. Go with that as a way to install or connect your bracelet to the elements of earth, air, and water."*

Do BLS.

Say, *"Let's take a current reading of your stress level where 0 is no stress or neutral and 10 is the highest stress you can imagine. How stressful does it feel now?"*

0	1	2	3	4	5	6	7	8	9	10
(no stress)										(highest stress)

Say, *"The modest goal that we have is that you are able to reduce your stress level by at least one or two points. If you think it would be helpful, you can repeat the exercise."*
Say, *"It is recommended that you practice the exercise at least 10 times a day for the first 2 weeks and when you notice that your stress is high. Also, it is helpful to use these three elements when your stress levels are not so high in order to create the positive connection that will help you to use it more effectively. Do you have any questions?"*

_____

_____

The fourth element can be included directly after the third element is introduced or—for more power and impact—wait for the next session.

4. Fire: Light Up the Path of Your Imagination

Say, *"FIRE is the fourth element and is used in this exercise to light up the path of your imagination to access your SAFE PLACE or another resource that is positive for you."*
"I'd like you to think about some place you have been or imagine being that feels very safe or calm. Perhaps being on the beach or sitting by a mountain stream (or any other choice that would be appropriate for your client)." (Pause)
"Where would you be?"

_____

_____

Say, *"As you think of that safe* (or calm) *place, notice what you see, hear, and feel right now."* (Pause)
Say, *"What do you notice?"*

_____

_____

Say, *"Focus on your safe* (or calm) *place, its sights, sounds, smells, and body sensations. Tell me more about what you are noticing."*

_____

_____

Say, *"Bring up the image of that place. Concentrate on where you feel the pleasant sensations in your body and allow yourself to enjoy them. Now concentrate on those sensations and follow my fingers* (or whatever BLS you use)."*

Use four to six sets.

Say, *"How do you feel now?"*

_____

_____

Repeat several times if the process has enhanced the client's positive feelings and sensations.
If positive, say the following:

Say, *"Focus on that."*

Repeat BLS.

Say, *"What do you notice now?"*

_____

_____

Repeat several times. Enhance positive feelings with BLS several times. After installing the safe place, move on to the fourth element.

Say, *"Now that you have your safe place, we can continue with the Four Elements Exercise. So, as you continue feeling the SECURITY NOW of your feet on the GROUND of the Earth Element and feel CENTERED as you BREATHE in and out with the Air Element and feel CALM and in CONTROL as you produce more and more SALIVA for the Water Element, fire up your IMAGINATION for the Fire Element and bring up the image of your SAFE PLACE* (or some other positive RESOURCE). *Where do you feel it in your body?"*

_____

_____

Say, *"Does it feel good?"*

_____

_____

Say, *"Then, direct your attention to feeling good in your body and go with* _____ *(whatever BLS you are using)."*

Install with brief slow BLS or Butterfly Hugs.

Say, *"As you continue feeling the SECURITY NOW of your feet on the GROUND; and feel CENTERED as you BREATHE in and out; and feel CALM and in CONTROL as you produce more and more SALIVA; you can let the FIRE LIGHT the path to your IMAGINATION to bring up an IMAGE of a place where you feel SAFE or a memory in which you felt good about yourself. Do you have it?"*

_____

_____

Say, *"Go with that* ᲮᲢᲝᲜᲔ *(using whatever BLS)."*
Say, *"Now touch your bracelet* (or sticker, etc.), *and start by thinking first about earth, then air, then water, and then fire."* (Pause)
Say, *"Have you done that?"*

_____

_____

Say, *"Great. Go with that as a way to install or connect your bracelet to the elements of earth, air, water, and fire."*

Do BLS.

Say, *"Let's take a current reading of your stress level where 0 is no stress or neutral and 10 is the highest stress you can imagine. How stressful does it feel now?"*

0	1	2	3	4	5	6	7	8	9	10
(no stress)								(highest stress)		

Say, *"The modest goal that we have is that you are able to reduce your stress level by one or two points. If you think it would be helpful, you can repeat the exercise."*
"It is recommended that you practice the exercise at least 10 times a day for the first 2 weeks and when you notice that your stress is high. Also, it is helpful to use the Four Elements Exercise when your stress levels are not so high in order to create the positive connection that will help you to use it more effectively. Do you have any questions?"

_____

_____

Managing the "Fear of the Fear"

Roy Kiessling

Managing the "Fear of the Fear" Script Notes

For some clients finding a Safe/Calm Place is very difficult, either because of their life experiences or their difficulty in using their imagination. In cases such as these, construction of a container to hold traumatic material, both during desensitization and between sessions, may be an alternative strategy to help the client develop a sense of safety. Constructing a container follows the same basic setup protocol as establishing the Safe/Calm Place.

Managing "The Fear of the Fear" Script

Strategy

Image

Say, *"Imagine a container that could hold all your traumatic material. Tell me what you have constructed."*

_____

_____

Emotions and Sensations

Say, *"As you think of your container, notice what you see, hear, and feel right now."*

Pause.

Say, *"What do you notice?"*

_____

_____

Enhancement

Verbally enhance with soothing guided imagery suggestions until your client can feel the positive results of placing her traumatic memories into the container.

> Say, *"Focus on putting disturbing material into your container. Notice the positive sensations you are experiencing. What are you noticing?"*

_____

_____

Bilateral Stimulation (BLS)

> Say, *"Bring up the image of that container. Concentrate on where you feel the pleasant sensations in your body and allow yourself to enjoy them. Now concentrate on those sensations and follow my fingers* (or whatever BLS you use).*"*

Use four to six sets.

> Say, *"How do you feel now?"*

_____

_____

Repeat several times if the process has enhanced the client's positive feelings and sensations.

Cue Word

> Say, *"Is there a word or phrase that represents your container?"*

_____

_____

Self-Cuing

> Say, *"Now I'd like you to say that word* _____ (say cue word) *and notice how you feel. Go with that."*

Enhance with bilateral stimulation.

Cuing With Disturbance

> Say, *"Now imagine a minor annoyance and how it feels."*

Pause.

> Say, *"Now put it into your container and notice any shifts in your body."*

Guide the client through the process until she is able to experience the positive emotions and sensations. Repeat as often as necessary.

_____

_____

Self-Cuing With Disturbance

Say, *"Now, I'd like you to think of another mildly annoying incident and put it into your container by yourself. Again, noticing any changes in your body when you have put them in your container."*

Let your client place it in the container without your assistance.

Practice

Say, *"I'd like you to practice using your container, between now and our next session, any time you need to put something in the container. Keep track of how things go and we'll talk about it next time we meet. Do you have any questions?"*

_____

_____

Resource Strengthening

Roy Kiessling

Resource Strengthening Script Notes

When a client seems too overwhelmed by the trauma and, therefore, cannot focus on anything else, having them focus on positive things in their lives may help them regain a more appropriate and positive perspective. Once stabilized, clients may be ready to address the trauma with the Standard EMDR Protocol.

Resource Strengthening Script

Strategy

Image

Ask the client to think of something positive.

Say, *"Please think of something positive in your life."*

_____

_____

Enhancement

Enhance verbally, then, cautiously, add bilateral stimulation (BLS) to strengthen the positive experience, person, object, and so forth.

Say, *"Focus on _____ (state positive experience, person, or object), its sights, sounds, smells, and body sensations. Tell me what you are noticing."*

_____

_____

Bilateral Stimulation (BLS)

Say, *"Bring up that resource and notice what you are experiencing. Concentrate on where you feel the pleasant sensations in your body and allow yourself to enjoy them. Now, concentrate on those sensations and follow my fingers* (or whatever BLS you use)*."*

Use four to six sets.

Say, *"How do you feel now? Follow my fingers* (or other BLS)*."*

_____

_____

Add as many positive experiences as is helpful. Repeat the first three steps with each positive experience, person, object, and so forth that the client recalls.

If the client brings up a negative thought, redirect to the last positive thought and continue focusing on more positives. Repeat this process until the client feels strong enough to begin addressing the traumatic issue. This may take several sessions.

Extending Resources

Roy Kiessling

Extending Resources Script Notes

In a small number of clients, developing a calm place may increase levels of distress. For some clients, bilateral stimulation (BLS), paired with the development of the calm place, may quickly bring the client to intense negative affect. Therefore, it is helpful to find what skill, strength, or resource clients need and help them access those experiences to assist them in preparing for the trauma work.

Extending Resources Script

Strategy

Image

Identify a skill, strength, or resource clients feel will help with the issue.

> Say, *"Think about a skill, strength, or resource that you feel you will need to help you with your issue."*

_____

_____

Emotions and Sensations

Have the client focus on the image, feelings, and sensations associated with the corresponding skill, strength, or resource.

> Say, *"Focus on the image, feeling, and sensations associated with your _____ (state skill, strength, or resource). What do you notice and feel?"*

_____

_____

87

Enhancement

Verbally enhance with soothing guided imagery stressing positive feelings and sensations associated with the client's skill, strength, or resource.

> Say, *"Focus on your _____ (state skill, strength, or resource), its sights, sounds, smells, and body sensations. Tell me more about what you are noticing."*

_____

_____

Bilateral Stimulation (BLS)

Once enhanced, add several brief sets of bilateral stimulation (four to six passes or taps). Repeat several times if the process has enhanced the client's positive feelings and sensations.

> Say, *"As you think of _____ (state skill, strength, or resource), concentrate on where you feel the pleasant sensations in your body and allow yourself to enjoy them. Now concentrate on those sensations and follow my fingers (or whatever BLS you use)."*

Use four to six sets.

> Say, *"How do you feel now?"*

Cue Word

Have clients identify a single word that represents their skill, strength, or resource. Repeat several times, adding BLS with each experience.

> Say, *"What word or phrase best represents your _____ (state skill, strength, or resource)? Now concentrate on that word or phrase and the positive thoughts or sensations associated with it and follow _____ (state BLS)."*

Use short sets (four to six eye movements/tactile) of BLS with any positive response.
Repeat several times.

> Say, *"How do you feel now?"*

_____

_____

Self-Cuing

Instruct the client to repeat the procedure on their own, bringing up the image and its positive emotions and sensations.

> Say, *"Now think of the cue word on your own and what do you notice?"*

_____

_____

Cuing a Recent Disturbance (Rescripting)

Have clients think of a recent, mildly disturbing situation and the skill, strength, or resource that could have been used, then instruct them to imagine how the situation would have been different had they used their skill, strength, or resource and notice the difference in their feelings and sensations. Guide clients through the process until they are able to experience the positive emotions and sensations.

> Say, *"Think of a mildly disturbing situation where you could have used your* _____ (state skill, strength, or resource) *then imagine how the situation would have been different if you had used* _____ (state skill, strength, or resource). *Notice the difference in your feelings and sensations."*

_____

_____

Cuing an Anticipated Disturbance (Rehearsing)

Have the client think of a mildly disturbing situation that might come up in the near future. Then instruct the client to imagine how the situation may be different if this chosen skill, strength, or resource is used. Have the client notice the difference in the feelings and sensations associated with the skill, strength, or resource. Guide the client through the process until the positive emotions and sensations are experienced.

> Say, *"Think of a mildly disturbing situation that may come up in the near future where you can use your* _____ (state skill, strength, or resource); *now imagine how the situation will be different. Notice the difference in your feelings and sensations."*

_____

_____

Practice

> Say, *"I'd like you to practice using your* _____ (state skill, strength, or resource), *between now and our next session, any time you feel a little annoyed. Keep track of how things go and we'll talk about it next time we meet. Do you have any questions before we stop for today?"*

_____

_____

The Wedging Technique

Roy Kiessling

The Wedging Technique Script Notes

Some clients may be able to talk about their trauma; however, the thought of processing it with the Standard EMDR Protocol may seem too overwhelming. In cases such as these, having the client develop a resource to address the "fear of the fear" may reduce the anxiety of reprocessing the traumatic memory.

The Wedging Technique Script

Strategy

Skill or Strength

Say, *"What skill or strength do you feel would help you manage this trauma?"*

_____

_____

Image

Say, *"Think or imagine other times in your life when you have used this skill."*

_____

_____

Emotions and Sensations

Say, *"What feelings and sensations are you experiencing now, knowing that you have this skill available to help you?"*

_____

_____

Enhancement

Say, *"Experience the strength that you have and feel those feelings and sensations while you follow my fingers* (or whatever bilateral stimulation [BLS] you are using) *and what are you noticing?"*

_____

_____

Cue Word

Say, *"Think of a word that represents your strength or skill and feel those positive feelings and sensations as you follow my fingers* (or whatever BLS you are using)*."*

_____

_____

During Desensitization

Say, *"This skill is a resource that we may use while we are working with EMDR. Any time that you are overwhelmed, let me know and we can use your cue word to give you support. Do you have any questions?"*

_____

_____

Resource Connection Envelope (RCE) in the EMDR Standard Protocol

Brurit Laub

The Resource Connection Envelope (RCE) derives from the assumption that the dialectical healing movement between negative stored memories or problems and positive stored memories or resources is crucial for adaptive processing. The dialectical movement is enhanced when the dialectical poles are made more accessible (Laub & Weiner, 2007). The Assessment Phase in the Standard EMDR Protocol makes the problem, which is represented by the traumatic image or picture, more accessible for processing. The RCE aims to complement it by making the resource pole accessible as well.

Resource Connection Envelope Script Notes

The RCE procedure enables clients to get in touch with their unique resources that match the problem precisely. The RCE begins with a Past Resource Connection (PRC), collects the Present Resource Connection (PrRC) that comes up during processing, and ends with a Closing Resource Connection (CRC) chosen from the Present Resources or the Past Resource. Sometimes a Future Resource Connection (FRC) is added after the Closing Resource so that the resource envelope is expanded even further. The RCE provides a containment envelope for the processing of the traumatic memories. It also facilitates the dialectical movement between the problem and resource poles. This enhances the processing toward completion and integration.

In the Assessment Phase of the Standard EMDR Protocol, Compact Focusing is performed on a representative picture of the traumatic event (Sensory image, NC, Emotions, and Somatic sensations). The author coined the term *Compact Focusing* to describe a therapeutic technique of accessing the different modalities of an experience in concert: Sensory (images), Cognitive (thoughts, beliefs), Emotional (affect), and Somatic (heartbeats, trembling, getting warm, aches, etc.). Different therapeutic approaches have various techniques to enhance accessibility or do their own version of Compact Focusing.

The author suggests a complementary Compact Focusing on resources: A representative picture of the first resource (PRC) of the RCE as well as one of the closing resources. This suggestion stems from the hypothesis about the importance of the dialectical movement in adaptive processing. The four modalities are accessed by the suggestion of the therapist to relive the picture of the positive memory while referring to the different senses and later by relating to the emotions, body sensations, and thoughts.

The congruency between stating the issue or event and the immediate request to elicit a positive memory, as well as the indirect way of the request, provide an unconscious connection between the traumatic issue or event and the resource. The PRC is matched precisely to the problem. It is a reminder to the client, before starting the processing of the trauma, that he or she possesses some resourceful memories that connect him or her to inner strengths.

Note: When a strong resource appears at the end of the session, it is sometimes advisable to strengthen it immediately as a closing resource, even before the Installation Phase, so that it flows naturally.

Resource Connection Script: Past, Present, and Future

Phase 1: History Taking

Do Phase 1 according to the Standard EMDR Protocol.

Phase 2: Preparation

Do Phase 2 according to the Standard EMDR Protocol.

Phase 3: Assessment

Before you start the regular assessment, access the Past Resource Connection.

Past Resource Connection

After stating the issue (if there is no clear theme, after stating the traumatic event), proceed immediately to the recall of a positive memory.

> Say, *"The issue or event that we will be working on today is _____ (state the issue). Is that correct?"*

_____

_____

Recall a Positive Memory

Eliciting a positive memory *immediately* after the traumatic issue helps the client make an *unconscious* link between *the trauma and the resource(s) needed.*

> Say *"Before we start I would like you to recall a memory in which you felt good about yourself. This could be a time or a situation in which you felt really well and whole. It can be an early memory or a more recent one. It could be a memory that lasted a few moments or an extended period of feeling well. What is the first thing that comes to mind?"*

_____

_____

> Say, *"What feelings and body sensations go with the memory?"*

_____

_____

Compact Focusing

> Say, *"Please choose one image or picture that represents the good feelings of the positive memory."*

_____

_____

_____

> Say, *"Please close your eyes and reconnect with this picture."*

While tapping (or you may use any other form of BLS), say the following:

Say, *"Take all the time necessary to relive this picture with all your senses. Notice what you see, hear, touch, or smell. Allow your feelings, body sensations, and thoughts to emerge. Breathe into it and let yourself be there for a few moments. Go with that."*

Do short BLS (up to 14).

Say, *"Stay there as long as you need. You can do this even after the _____ (state BLS) has stopped."*
Then say, *"What came up?"* (inquire about the feelings, body sensations, and thoughts).

_____

_____

Say, *"Go with that."* Do BLS.

Repeat the procedure until there is no change.

If the partially positive past resource includes negative elements, suggest focusing on the positive aspects.

Say, *"Focus on those positive elements in your resource. Go with that."*

Do BLS.

It is diagnostic if the client can do it. If the client is unable to do it, you may suggest that he choose another resource.

Say, *"Okay. Can you think of another resource that is positive for you?"*

_____

_____

Proceed until the resource is enhanced optimally.

Say, *"Go with that."*

Do BLS.

Verbal Cue

Say, *"Please reconnect with the positive picture."*
While doing short BLS say, *"Now you may choose a name, a word, or a sentence that matches the picture."*

_____

_____

Say, *"This verbal cue is like an entrance to the positive memory and you will be able to call up the memory by using the word or sentence where ever you are."*

Suggestion

Say, *"This memory probably has some healing elements and is related to the issue you are working on today. Perhaps this will become clearer by the end of the session. Do you see any connection now?"*

_____

_____

Say, *"This resource has now become accessible and you may practice connecting to it and using it when suitable. It is like filling your empty car with gasoline."*

Phase 4: Desensitization

Do Phase 4 according to the Standard EMDR Protocol. The term Present Resource Connection (PrRC) refers to the resources that appear throughout the processing; they are distinct from the Past Resource Connection (PRC) just elicited and the last optional future resource. However, for simplicity, mark the PrRC as "R" in your notes. Present Resources include anything positive that comes up during processing and can be a thought, emotion, sensation, or combination of these. They may appear spontaneously or be elicited by Cognitive Interweaves. Again, the dialectical nature between the positive and the trauma processing are at work here.

Phase 5: Installation

Do Phase 5 according to the Standard EMDR Protocol. After installation, the client is requested to choose a closing resource, both for a complete and incomplete session. The Closing Resource replaces the Safe Place or any other relaxation exercises.

Choosing a Closing Resource

Say, *"Here are some of the resources that emerged during your processing* (list them). *Please choose one, or the original past resource that we used in the beginning (PRC) to close the session."*

_____

_____

Sometimes, at the end of processing, a strong, insightful, positive sentence comes up. Such a sentence, which the author calls a "power sentence," can be chosen as a new PC. It can also be expanded by Compact Focusing and become a Closing Resource. The client is instructed to focus on the sentence and to note if any image, emotion, or body sensation comes up while using BLS.

Say, *"Sometimes, since we are at the end of our processing for now, you become aware of a strong, positive sentence. Have you noticed something like that or is one of the other resources we were talking about more meaningful to you?"*

_____

_____

Compact Focusing

Say, *"Please reconnect to the resource with all your senses and notice your feelings, body sensations, and thoughts."*

Do short BLS.

Say, *"What came up?"* (Inquire about the feelings, body sensations, and thoughts).

_____

_____

Say, *"Go with that."* Do BLS.

Repeat the procedure until there is no change.

Verbal Cue

Say, *"Please reconnect with the resource."*
While doing short BLS say, *"Now you may choose a name, a word, or a sentence that matches the resource."*

_____

_____

Somatic Cue (Optional)

Say, *"Please choose a posture that matches the resource."*

Have the client demonstrate the posture.

Say, *"Now reconnect to the resource with the name and the posture. Go with that."*

Add BLS.

Suggestion for use of resources:

Say, *"Now that the resources have become accessible, you can connect to them in times of need in order to recharge your batteries."*

Future Resource Connection (FRC)

This is an optional step.

Eliciting a Future Resource

Say, *"Imagine how you would like to see yourself in the future."*

_____

_____

Compact Focusing

Say, *"Choose one positive picture of this future resource and notice any image that comes up, and the feelings, body sensations, and thoughts."*

Do short BLS.

Say, *"Tell me about the experience."*

_____

_____

Verbal Cue

While doing short BLS, say the following:

Say, *"Choose a cue word or a sentence that goes well with the image."*

_____

_____

Phase 6: Body Scan

Do the Body Scan according to the Standard EMDR Protocol.

Phase 7: Closure

Do Phase 7 according to the Standard EMDR Protocol. Safe Place or relaxation exercises are not needed due to the Closing Resource.

Phase 8: Reevaluation

Do Phase 8 according to the Standard EMDR Protocol.

The Resource Map

Elan Shapiro

The Resource Map Script Notes

The rationale for creating the Resource Map consists of the following:

- A structured format and record of the resources that have been identified and installed that can be collected and used again in the future.
- Multiple resources that empower the client.
- Level of Connection (LoC) scale, which is designed to overcome the limitations of trying to guess if the installation is working from qualitative signals. It is inspired by the validity of cognition (VoC) and attempts to better gauge progress in nonverbal domains.
- Extension of the Absorption Technique (Hofmann, in press)—which itself is basically an expanded Resource Installation—with some other additions.

The Resource Map Script

The Resource Map form can be used to write down the client's responses.

Issue

Say, *"What difficulty would you like to cope with better?"*

_____

_____

Resource Needed

Say, *"What characteristics or qualities would help you to cope better with it?"*
Ask for as many as clients can think of—up to five—and write them down in the boxes A, B, C, D, and E.

_____

_____

Say, *"For characteristic _____ (state characteristic or quality), can you remember a specific time in the last few years or earlier in which you experienced this quality at least partly?"*

_____

_____

The idea is to begin with a memory for characteristic A and proceed to get the information required in column A.

Picture

Say, *"What picture represents the memory?"*

_____

_____

Feeling

Say, *"What is the feeling you get when you recall this memory now?"*

_____

_____

Location of Body Sensation

Say, *"Where do you experience it in your body?"*

_____

_____

Level of Connection

Ask for the LoC (Level of Connection).

Say, *"How connected do you feel to that experience on a scale of 1 to 5, where 1 is no connection at all and 5 is the most connection you can imagine. How connected do you feel now?"*

1	2	3	4	5
(no connection)			(most connection)	

Say, *"Go with that."*

Use about six short sets of BLS.

Say, *"What is your LoC now?"*

1	2	3	4	5
(no connection)			(most connection)	

Check to see if the LoC is stronger.
Repeat a few times until it is the most strengthened.

Cue Word

Say, *"Is there a word or phrase that represents your resource?"*

_____

_____

Then say, *"Think of _____ (cue word) and notice the positive feelings you have when you think of that word. Now concentrate on those sensations and the cue word and follow _____ (state BLS)."*

Use short sets of four to six BLS with any positive responses. Repeat several times.

Say, *"How do you feel now?"* (PC is preferred as this is stronger.)

_____

_____

Say, *"Taking the _____ (state the PC or cue word) and think of the picture and experience the feelings and body sensations of this positive memory and go with that."*

Check LoC. If it is four or five, then you can stop.

Say, *"What is your level of connection?"*

1	2	3	4	5
(no connection)			(most connection)	

Somatic Cue

This step is optional.

Say, *"Pick a physical sign or anchor and follow my fingers (or any other BLS)."*

_____

_____

Do BLS several times.
Repeat above for Resources B, C, D, and E (see Figure 15.1).

RESOURCE MAP

ISSUE	A	B	C	D	E
RESOURCE					
Characteristics/Qualities Needed					
1. RESOURCE MEMORY					
2. PICTURE					
3. FEELING					
4. BODY SENSATION					
5. LoC 1.........5 Level of Connection Install	Short sets of BLS / BLS / BLS	BLS	BLS	BLS	BLS
6. PC or Cue Word	BLS / BLS	BLS	BLS	BLS	BLS
7. Somatic Cue (optional)	BLS / BLS	BLS	BLS	BLS	BLS
8. Check Final LoC 1.........5					

Figure 15.1 The Resource Map.

EMDR and Special Targeting

It is not an unusual phenomenon to begin to work with clients to select a target, only to find that no matter how you phrase questions, the target is hard to pin down. At this juncture, it is important to ascertain if this is a stalling technique indicating that clients are not ready to proceed. If so, it is important to find out what clients need before they move forward and complete the Assessment Phase.

In "The EMDR Drawing Protocol for Adults," drawing is used to assist clients in figuring out what their targets are and also their positive cognition(s). There is no exceptional artistic skill that is a prerequisite for this protocol, only a willingness to explore their elusive targets. Esly Carvalho continues the use of drawing throughout as a way of capturing the changes that occur as clients proceed through the protocol.

At other times, the target is so disturbing that clients are overwhelmed or even avoidant when approaching the issue represented by the target. Tanos Freiha, in his "The Image Director Technique," allows for a different approach by encouraging clients to be more in control by directing what is happening and by choosing their own starting point in their nightmare or trauma, allowing it to get worse where appropriate and stopping when or if they become overwhelmed.

These protocols give therapists another way to begin their Assessment Phases when clients are reluctant to begin.

The EMDR Drawing Protocol for Adults

Esly Regina Carvalho

EMDR Drawing Protocol Script Notes

At certain points in my clinical practice, after I began using EMDR consistently, I would have clients come in who could not describe a specific scene or image for us to use as the target, yet, they would usually have a clear negative cognition that they would give spontaneously ("I'm trash"). I am a very visual and artistic person and I used drawings in my psychodrama practice. As a result, when I began to use EMDR, it was a natural evolution for me to use drawings. I began to ask my adult clients to draw a picture that would illustrate the negative cognition. Sometimes, they would have feelings about themselves or self-perceptions that would also turn into drawings, and from these drawings, the Standard EMDR Protocol ensued. I usually ask for drawings when people come in with generalities and we need to pin down a specific target to work on. The Drawing Protocol for Adults can be helpful in narrowing down a target, using a metaphor or picture—which has a strong generalizable effect—instead of a concrete scene from the past.

When using this protocol, it is usually important to assure clients that most people cannot draw better than a 6-year-old and that this is not an evaluation of artistic talent.

EMDR Drawing Protocol for Adults Script

Phase 3: Assessment

Target or Memory

Say, *"Today we have decided to reprocess _____ (select the next incident to be targeted)."*

_____

_____

Picture

Say, *"Make a drawing of it—the image or 'photograph' of what you want to work on. Let's label it Drawing #1."*

_____

_____

Negative Cognition (NC)

Say, *"What words best go with the picture* (Drawing #1) *that express your negative belief about yourself now?"*

_____

_____

Positive Cognition (PC)

Say, *"When you bring up that picture or incident, what would you like to believe about yourself, now? Make a drawing of it and let's label it Drawing #2."*

_____

_____

Validity of Cognition (VoC)

Say, *"When you think of the incident* (or Drawing #2), *how true do those words _____* (clinician repeats the positive cognition) *feel to you now on a scale of 1 to 7, where 1 feels completely false and 7 feels completely true?"*

1   2   3   4   5   6   7
(completely false)   (completely true)

Put the drawing of the PC aside during the Desensitization Phase, because we want to concentrate on the negative drawing as it is the target for the desensitization.

Emotions

Say, *"When you bring up the picture* (or incident) *and those words _____* (clinician states the negative cognition), *what emotion do you feel now?"*

_____

_____

Subjective Units of Disturbance (SUD)

Say, *"On a scale of 0 to 10, where 0 is no disturbance or neutral and 10 is the highest disturbance you can imagine, how disturbing does it feel now?"*

0   1   2   3   4   5   6   7   8   9   10
(no disturbance)   (highest disturbance)

Location of Body Sensation

Say, *"What sensations in your body come up while you look at this drawing?"*

_____

_____

Phase 4: Desensitization

Say, *"Think about the drawing (#1) and the words _____ (state the NC), and watch my fingers* (or other bilateral stimulation).

_____

_____

_____

When the SUDs equal 0 or an ecological 1, pull out and check the positive drawing or PC (Drawing #2) to see if it is still appropriate or if a new drawing should be made. Confirm PC or change it.

Say, *"Does this picture still describe what you would like to think about yourself or would you like to draw another one?"*

_____

_____

This would be Drawing #3, if needed.

If a new drawing is to be made, say the following:

Say, *"Make a drawing of how you see yourself now. What words would you use to describe yourself now as you look at this drawing?"*

_____

_____

Phase 5: Installation

Say, *"How does _____ (repeat the PC) sound?"*

_____

_____

Say, *"Do the words _____ (repeat the PC) still fit, or is there another positive statement that feels better?"*

_____

_____

If the client accepts the original positive cognition, the clinician should ask for a VoC rating to see if it has improved.

Say, *"As you think of the incident, how do the words feel, from 1 (completely false) to 7 (completely true)?"*

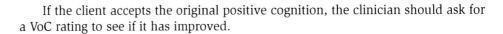

1   2   3   4   5   6   7
(completely false)   (completely true)

Say, *"Think of the event, and hold it together with the words _____ (repeat the PC)."*

Do a long set of BLS to see if there is more processing to be done.

Continue installation as long as the material is becoming more adaptive. If the client reports a 6 or 7, do BLS again to strengthen and continue until it no longer strengthens.

Phase 6: Body Scan

Say, *"Close your eyes and keep in mind the original memory and the positive cognition. Then bring your attention to the different parts of your body, starting with your head and working downward. Any place you find any tension, tightness, or unusual sensation, tell me."*

_____

_____

If any sensation is reported, do a set of BLS. If a positive or comfortable sensation is reported, do BLS to strengthen the positive feeling. If a sensation of discomfort is reported—reprocess until discomfort subsides.

Phase 7: Closure

Say, *"Things may come up or they may not. If they do, great. Write it down, and it can be a target for next time. If you get any new memories, dreams, or situations that disturb you, just take a good snapshot. It isn't necessary to give a lot of detail. Just put down enough to remind you so we can target it next time. The same thing goes for any positive dreams or situations. If negative feelings do come up, try not to make them significant. Remember, it's still just the old stuff. Just write it down for next time. Then use the tape or the Safe Place exercise to let as much of the disturbance go as possible. Even if nothing comes up, make sure to use the tape every day and give me a call if you need to."*

The Image Director Technique for Dreams

Tanos Freiha

The "Image Director Technique" was developed to target recurring nightmares or bad dreams and those targets that are directly related to a traumatic experience. Often, when patients are having nightmares or when they feel overwhelmingly out of control during a trauma, it is helpful to give them a way to be more in control of directing what might happen, even if it gets worse. Instead of utilizing the Standard Protocol that implies that you must follow wherever the associations the patient has led you, the Image Director Technique allows the patient to choose her own starting point in the nightmare or trauma and stop if she is overwhelmed. Again, the idea is to return to the Standard EMDR Protocol as soon as it is possible.

The Image Director Script Notes

This technique is a special module that is embedded in the Standard EMDR Protocol. The technique begins with the worst image of the dream and then accesses and measures it as in Phase 3 of the Standard EMDR Protocol that includes the image, cognitions, emotions, and sensations. This technique can also be considered an imagery exposure method that is based in systematic desensitization, a behavioral approach. In contrast to positively oriented imagery rehearsal methods, like the "Imagery Rehearsal" of Krakow and Krakow (2002), the Image Director Technique enables the client to imagine the worst that might happen. After that, the client might be able to look for solutions or alternatives, which usually end positively.

Cautions

The more horrifying the nightmare, the more the client tends to work with fragments or simple images. Clients are more likely to work with short clips or films if the subjective units of disturbance (SUD) of the target image is low. At the end, the clips will be connected together as a whole film as clients seem to want to reach an endpoint or wish to create an ending for the nightmare. When this does not occur spontaneously, the therapist can use interweaves as in normal EMDR reprocessing. Less motion in the target, or more stable image processing, is related to higher SUDs and that quality of "stuckness" or "being frozen" that accompanies trauma.

Often, clients prefer the tactile bilateral stimulation (BLS) because they can close their eyes in order to be visually undisturbed during the creation of the new images.

Developments That Might Occur During the Image Director Work

1. Simple positive development.
2. Complex negative development. Struggle and defense as abreactions, and then moves to a more positive development, the same as item 1 in this list.
3. Dissociative fragments or anticipated fears. Any new images might contain fragments from memories that were still hidden as a part of dissociation or as images of anticipated fears that are real or irrational. As these new images arise, the therapist can proceed with the normal caveats of an EMDR session. For instance, he could either stop and work with the dissociative process, if it is indicated, or work with the new images as if they were targets for a new channel of processing. It is because of these situations that it is suggested that the Image Director Technique be used only if the therapist has been fully trained in EMDR and feels confident and able to work with these types of difficulties.
4. Contraindication. If the client is not able to create new images, it is contraindicated to use the Image Director Technique.

The Image Director Technique Script

Phase 3: Assessment

Picture

Say, *"Today we are going to work on the worst image in the dream or nightmare that we were talking about. Usually, it is the last one before you woke up. What picture represents the worst image of this dream or nightmare?"*

_____

_____

Negative Cognition (NC)

Say, *"What words go best with that picture that express your negative belief about yourself <u>now</u>?"*

_____

_____

Positive Cognition (PC)

Say, *"When you bring up that picture or incident, what would you like to believe about yourself <u>now</u>?"*

_____

_____

Validity of Cognition (VoC)

Say, *"When you think of the incident* (or picture) *how true do those words _____* (clinician repeats the positive cognition) *feel to you now on a scale of 1 to 7, where 1 feels completely false and 7 feels completely true?"*

1	2	3	4	5	6	7
(completely false)				(completely true)		

Emotions

Say, *"When you bring up the picture* (or incident) *and those words _____* (clinician states the negative cognition), *what emotion do you feel now?"*

_____

_____

Subjective Units of Disturbance (SUD)

Say, *"On a scale of 0 to 10, where 0 is no disturbance or neutral and 10 is the highest disturbance you can imagine, how disturbing does it feel now?"*

0	1	2	3	4	5	6	7	8	9	10
(no disturbance)						(highest disturbance)				

Location of Body Sensation

Say, *"Where do you feel it* (the disturbance) *in your body?"*

_____

_____

Phase 4: Desensitization

A modification in the Standard EMDR Protocol is mainly made in Phase 4 or Desensitization Phase. The client is asked to focus on the target image from Phase 3, and then think about the negative cognition and the body sensation. As usual, the therapist begins bilateral stimulation.

Target

Say, *"Please focus on the image, the negative cognition, emotions, and body sensations. Go with that."*

Use BLS of choice. After the first set of eye movements or taps, the client reports about the experience.

Say, *"What do you notice?"*

_____

_____

The Image Director

The next step is where the Image Director Technique gets its name and changes the usual progression of the Desensitization Phase. The client is asked to think of or imagine the next image while using BLS. Usually, this is an image that the client, perhaps, knows or anticipates it. It can be considered as a spontaneous image. The important issue here is that the client begins to approach the catastrophe, but in a controlled and slow method.

Say, *"Can you imagine what the next image <u>might</u> look like during this next set of _____ (state BLS)? Your main work during this next set is to think about what the next image <u>could</u> be and just notice what it is. Go with that."*

Do BLS. After a BLS set of about 1 minute, or more if the client wishes, ask the following:

Say, *"What do you notice? Can you talk about the image or describe it?"*

_____

_____

_____

_____

During the next BLS, the client goes back to image one then to the next, then she stops, that is, she can talk about it. Every new image has to be created after imaging all previous images, while using BLS. It is similar to rehearsal.

Before the therapist begins with the third BLS set, he asks the client to go back to the first image and then to the second. This means the client connects or combines the first with the second image during the BLS, the client will come up with the third image. After each set of BLS, the client can talk about what is happening at that moment in her head. She might talk about the images, emotions, cognitions, body sensations, or whatever else she wants as in a standard EMDR session.

Say, *"Now before we begin the next set, please go back to the first image and then connect it to the second image. Go with that."*
Then say, *"What do you notice now?"*

_____

_____

Say, *"Now, with this new image in mind, continue and imagine the next possible image to continue the dream. Go with that."*

Do BLS.

Say, *"What do you notice now?"*

_____

_____

During the next stimulation, ask the client to connect image one to image two and three. This process is continued until the client creates neutral or positive images (see Figure 17.1). When this occurs, the therapist asks for the SUD. In most cases, the SUD is reduced to 0. If not, it is because the fear is real or there is a significant loss. In this case, work with problem solving with or without EMDR depending on what is clinically needed. When the SUD is 0, continue to the next phases of the Standard EMDR Protocol.

Say, *"Now before we begin the next set, please go back to the first image and then to the second, and then to the third and notice the image that you have now, continue your dream and go with that."*

Do BLS.

Say, *"What do you notice now?"*

_____

_____

If there is more to do with the images, say the following:

Say, *"Now before we begin the next set, please go back to the first image and then to the second, the third, and the fourth and notice the image that you have now, continue your dream and go with that."*

Do BLS.

Say, *"What do you notice now?"*

_____

_____

The "Image Director Technique" modifies Phase 4 as follows:

Focus on the target image

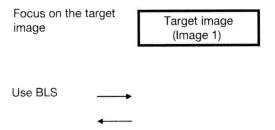

Use BLS

After BLS, the client can describe the experience.

The therapist asks the client to imagine the next image during the second set of bilateral stimulation.

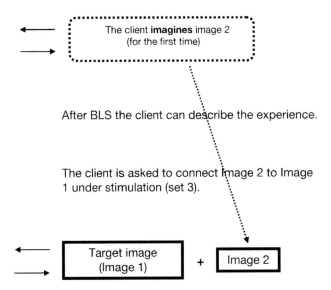

After BLS the client can describe the experience.

The client is asked to connect Image 2 to Image 1 under stimulation (set 3).

The client is asked to imagine (create) image 3 under Stimulation (set 4).

Figure 17.1   The Image Director Technique.

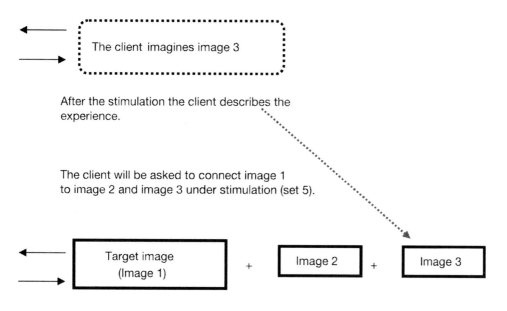

After the stimulation the client describes the experience.

The client will be asked to connect image 1 to image 2 and image 3 under stimulation (set 5).

After the stimulation, the client describes the experience.

The client is asked to imagine (create) image 4 under stimulation (set 6).

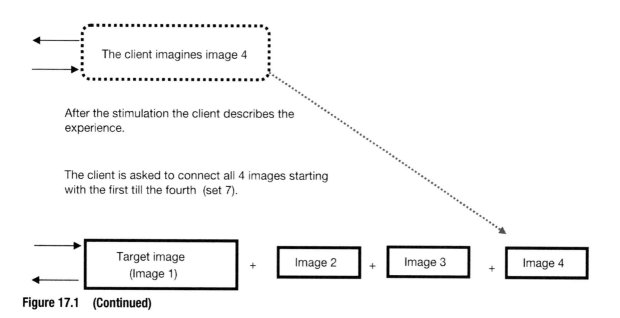

Figure 17.1   (Continued)

If needed, continue the dream and say the following:

Say, *"Now before we begin the next set, please go back to the first image and then to the second, the third, the fourth, and the fifth and notice the image that you have now, continue your dream and go with that."*

Do BLS.

Say, *"What do you notice now?"*

_____

_____

The client may need longer stimulation. The process of creating images has to be continued till the images become neutral or positive. When the SUD has decreased to 0, the therapist continues to Phases 5, 6, and 7.

If the client continues to produce images that have a negative cognitive or emotional character, then the therapist has to use one or more cognitive interweaves, depending on the topic, such as the following:

Say, *"Which color is needed for the next image?"*
Or, *"Can you imagine the next image without people in it?"*
Or, *"Can you imagine only the left part of the image?"*
Or continue with similar kinds of suggestions.

Sometimes, the patient will not have time to complete all of the processing and it will need to be reevaluated and then reprocessed during the next session. When the SUD is neutral and a positive shift occurs, continue through Phases 5, 6, and 7.

PART V

Francine Shapiro's Protocols Scripted

It is a source of constant fascination to this author and all of her fellow facilitators from the EMDR Institute with whom she has spoken that no matter how many times we take Francine Shapiro's training, we hear something we have not heard before, we see something that we have not seen before, or we feel something that we have not felt before. We walk away "getting it" in a much different way than when we first walked in. Whether it is the vicissitudes of life that cause us to see, hear, and feel in different ways or the sheer density of material to learn in what we now call the "EMDR Institute Basic Training" course, what is often the case—despite the ongoing changes and updating—is that material that seemed so new was there all along.

The protocols in Part IV form the heart of this work. The basic information for these protocols can be found in Dr. Shapiro's 2001 text, *Eye Movement Desensitization and Reprocessing: Basic Principles, Protocols and Procedures* (2nd ed.) and in her *EMDR: New Notes on Adaptive Information Processing With Case Formulation Principles, Forms, Scripts and Worksheets* (2006) text. This author has scripted them so that the language that is used reflects the Standard EMDR Protocol and the 11-Step Standard Procedure and so the complete protocol is accessible with all its component parts clearly stated. They can be copied and put in your client's chart or used as a guide so that you will have all the material that you need in one place.

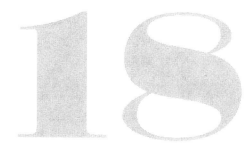

Single Traumatic Event

Scripted by Marilyn Luber
(Francine Shapiro, 2001, 2006)

Single Traumatic Event Script Notes

The following is a summary of the Single Traumatic Event Protocol (Shapiro, 2001, p. 223). For single traumatic events, the Standard EMDR Protocol should be applied to the following targets (assuming they are available).

Past Memories

1. Memory or image of the actual traumatic event.
2. Flashback scene (which may differ from the recalled image that represents the trauma).
3. Dream image, or most traumatic scene in a recurring nightmare.

Present Triggers

4. Present stimuli that trigger the disturbing memory or reaction (such as the sound of a car backfiring or being touched in a certain way).

Future Template

5. Create a future template.

Traumatic Event Protocol Script

Past Memories

1. Actual Traumatic Event

Begin with the memory or image of the actual traumatic event.

Incident

Say, *"The memory that we will start with today is _____ (select the next incident to be targeted).*

_____

_____

Say, *"What happens when you think of the incident or traumatic event?"*

_____

_____

_____

_____

Or say, *"When you think of the incident or traumatic event, what do you get?"*

_____

_____

Picture

Say, *"What picture represents the entire incident or traumatic event?"*

_____

_____

If there are many choices or if the client becomes confused, the clinician assists by asking the following:

Say, *"What picture represents the most traumatic part of the incident?"*

_____

_____

When a picture is unavailable, the clinician merely invites the client to do the following:

Say, *"Think of the incident."*

_____

_____

Negative Cognition (NC)

Say, *"What words best go with the picture that express your negative belief about yourself now?"*

_____

_____

Positive Cognition (PC)

Say, *"When you bring up that picture or incident, what would you like to believe about yourself, now?"*

_____

_____

Validity of Cognition (VoC)

Say, *"When you think of the incident or traumatic event* (or picture), *how true do those words _____* (clinician repeats the positive cognition) *feel to you now on a scale of 1 to 7, where 1 feels completely false and 7 feels completely true?"*

1   2   3   4   5   6   7
(completely false)   (completely true)

Sometimes it is necessary to explain further.

Say, *"Remember, sometimes we know something with our head, but it feels differently in our gut. In this case, what is the gut-level feeling of the truth of _____* (clinician states the positive cognition), *from 1 (completely false) to 7 (completely true)?"*

1   2   3   4   5   6   7
(completely false)   (completely true)

Emotions

Say, *"When you bring up the picture or traumatic event* (or incident) *and those words _____* (clinician states the negative cognition), *what emotion do you feel now?"*

_____

_____

Subjective Units of Disturbance (SUD)

Say, *"On a scale of 0 to 10, where 0 is no disturbance or neutral and 10 is the highest disturbance you can imagine, how disturbing does it feel now?"*

0 1 2 3 4 5 6 7 8 9 10
(no disturbance)   (highest disturbance)

Location of Body Sensation

Say, *"Where do you feel it* (the disturbance) *in your body?"*

_____

_____

Continue with Phases 4 through 7 for each incident.

2. Flashback Scene

The flashback scene may differ from the recalled image that represents the trauma.

Say, *"Is there a flashback scene that arises concerning the trauma?"*

_____

_____

Picture

Say, *"What picture represents the entire flashback scene?"*

_____

_____

If there are many choices or if the client becomes confused, the clinician assists by asking the following:

Say, *"What picture represents the most traumatic part of the flashback scene?"*

_____

_____

When a picture is unavailable, the clinician merely invites the client to do the following:

Say, *"Think of the flashback scene."*

_____

_____

Negative Cognition (NC)

Say, *"What words best go with the picture that express your negative belief about yourself now?"*

_____

_____

Positive Cognition (PC)

Say, *"When you bring up that picture or flashback scene, what would you like to believe about yourself, now?"*

_____

_____

Validity of Cognition (VoC)

Say, *"When you think of the flashback scene* (or picture), *how true do those words _____* (clinician repeats the positive cognition) *feel to you now on a scale of 1 to 7, where 1 feels completely false and 7 feels completely true?"*

1	2	3	4	5	6	7
(completely false)				(completely true)		

Sometimes it is necessary to explain further.

Say, *"Remember, sometimes we know something with our head, but it feels differently in our gut. In this case, what is the gut-level feeling of the truth of _____ (clinician states the positive cognition), from 1 (completely false) to 7 (completely true)?"*

1   2   3   4   5   6   7
(completely false)   (completely true)

Emotions

Say, *"When you bring up the picture (or flashback scene) and those words _____ (clinician states the negative cognition), what emotion do you feel now?"*

_____

_____

Subjective Units of Disturbance (SUD)

Say, *"On a scale of 0 to 10, where 0 is no disturbance or neutral and 10 is the highest disturbance you can imagine, how disturbing does it feel now?"*

0   1   2   3   4   5   6   7   8   9   10
(no disturbance)   (highest disturbance)

Location of Body Sensation

Say, *"Where do you feel it (the disturbance) in your body?"*

_____

_____

Continue with Phases 4 through 7 for each flashback scene.

3. Dream Image, or Most Traumatic Scene in a Recurring Nightmare

Target or Memory

Say, *"Is there a dream image or a recurring nightmare that occurs concerning the trauma?"*

_____

_____

Picture

Say, *"What picture represents the entire dream image or recurring nightmare?"*

_____

_____

If there are many choices or if the client becomes confused, the clinician assists by asking the following:

Say, *"What picture represents the most traumatic part of the dream image or recurring nightmare?"*

_____

_____

When a picture is unavailable, the clinician merely invites the client to do the following:

Say, *"Think of the dream image or recurring nightmare."*

_____

_____

Negative Cognition (NC)

Say, *"What words best go with the picture of the dream image or recurring nightmare that express your negative belief about yourself now?"*

_____

_____

Positive Cognition (PC)

Say, *"When you bring up that picture, dream image, or recurring nightmare, what would you like to believe about yourself now?"*

_____

_____

Validity of Cognition (VoC)

Say, *"When you think of the dream image or recurring nightmare* (or picture) *how true do those words* _____ (clinician repeats the positive cognition) *feel to you now on a scale of 1 to 7, where 1 feels completely false and 7 feels completely true?"*

1	2	3	4	5	6	7
(completely false)				(completely true)		

Sometimes it is necessary to explain further.

Say, *"Remember, sometimes we know something with our head, but it feels differently in our gut. In this case, what is the gut-level feeling of the truth of* _____ (clinician state the positive cognition), *from 1* (completely false) *to 7* (completely true)?*"*

1	2	3	4	5	6	7
(completely false)				(completely true)		

Emotions

Say, *"When you bring up the picture* (or dream image or recurring nightmare) *and those words* _____ (clinician states the negative cognition), *what emotion do you feel now?"*

_____

_____

Subjective Units of Disturbance (SUD)

Say, *"On a scale of 0 to 10, where 0 is no disturbance or neutral and 10 is the highest disturbance you can imagine, how disturbing does it feel now?"*

0   1   2   3   4   5   6   7   8   9   10
(no disturbance)   (highest disturbance)

Location of Body Sensation

Say, *"Where do you feel it* (the disturbance) *in your body?"*

_____

_____

Continue with Phases 4 through 7 for the dream or nightmare from above and any others.

Present Triggers

4. Present Stimuli That Trigger the Disturbing Memory or Reaction

List the situations that elicit the symptom(s). Examples of situations, events, or stimuli that trigger clients are the following: another traumatic incident, the sound of a car backfiring, or being touched in a certain way.

Say, *"What are the situations, events, or stimuli that trigger your trauma _____ (state the trauma)? Let's process these situations, events, or stimuli that trigger you one-by-one."*

Situations, Events, or Stimuli Trigger List

_____

_____

_____

_____

_____

_____

Target or Memory

Say, *"What situation, event, or stimulus that triggers you would you like to use as a target today?"*

_____

_____

Picture

Say, *"What picture represents the _____ (state the situation, event, or stimulus) that triggers you?"*

_____

_____

If there are many choices or if the client becomes confused, the clinician assists by asking the following:

Say, *"What picture represents the most traumatic part of the* _____ (state the situation, event, or stimulus) *that triggers you?"*

_____

_____

When a picture is unavailable, the clinician merely invites the client to do the following:

Say, *"Think of the* _____ (state the situation, event, or stimulus) *that triggers you."*

_____

_____

Negative Cognition (NC)

Say, *"What words best go with the picture that express your negative belief about yourself now?"*

_____

_____

Positive Cognition (PC)

Say, *"When you bring up that picture or the* _____ (state the situation, event, or stimulus) *that triggers you, what would you like to believe about yourself now?"*

_____

_____

Validity of Cognition (VoC)

Say, *"When you think of the* _____ (state the situation, event, stimulus, or picture that triggers you), *how true do those words* _____ (clinician repeats the positive cognition) *feel to you now on a scale of 1 to 7, where 1 feels completely false and 7 feels completely true?"*

1   2   3   4   5   6   7
(completely false)   (completely true)

Sometimes it is necessary to explain further.

Say, *"Remember, sometimes we know something with our head, but it feels differently in our gut. In this case, what is the gut-level feeling of the truth of* _____ (clinician state the positive cognition), *from 1 (completely false) to 7 (completely true)?"*

1   2   3   4   5   6   7
(completely false)   (completely true)

Emotions

Say, *"When you bring up the picture* _____ (state the situation, event, or stimulus) *that triggers you and those words* _____ (clinician states the negative cognition), *what emotion do you feel now?"*

_____

_____

Subjective Units of Disturbance (SUD)

Say, *"On a scale of 0 to 10, where 0 is no disturbance or neutral and 10 is the highest disturbance you can imagine, how disturbing does it feel now?"*

0	1	2	3	4	5	6	7	8	9	10

(no disturbance)   (highest disturbance)

Location of Body Sensation

Say, *"Where do you feel it* (the disturbance) *in your body?"*

_____

_____

Continue with Phases 4 through 7 for the situation, event, or stimulus that triggers you from above and any others.

Future Template

5. Incorporate a Detailed Template for a Trauma-Free Future Action (Shapiro, 2006)

Say, *"I would like you to imagine yourself coping effectively with* _____ (state the goal) *in the future. With the positive belief* _____ (state the positive belief) *and your new sense of* _____ (state the quality, i.e., strength, clarity, confidence, calm), *imagine stepping into this scene.*
Notice what you see and how you are handling the situation.
Notice what you are thinking, feeling, and experiencing in your body."

_____

_____

_____

Again, here is the opportunity to catch any disturbance that may have been missed.

Say, *"Are there any blocks, anxieties, or fears that arise as you think about this future scene?"*

_____

_____ _____

_____

If yes, say the following:

Say, *"Then focus on these blocks and follow my fingers* (or any other bilateral stimulation [BLS])."

Say, *"What do you get now?"*

_____

_____

_____

If the blocks do not resolve quickly, evaluate if the client needs any new information, resources, or skills to be able to comfortably visualize the future coping scene. Introduce needed information or skills.

Say, *"What would you need to feel confident in handling the situation?"*
Or say, *"What is missing from your handling of this situation?"*

_____

_____

If the block still does not resolve and the client is unable to visualize the future scene with confidence and clarity, use direct questions, the Affect Scan, or the Float-Back Technique to identify old targets related to blocks, anxieties, or fears. Remember, the point of the 3-Prong Protocols is not only to reinforce positive feelings and behavior in the future, but to catch any unresolved material that may be getting in the way of an adaptive resolution of the issue(s) again. Use the Standard EMDR Protocol to address these targets before proceeding with the template (see worksheets in Appendix A).

If there are no apparent blocks and the client is able to visualize the future scene with confidence and clarity, say the following:

Say, *"Please focus on the image, the positive belief, and the sensations associated with this future scene and follow my fingers (or any other BLS)."*

_____

_____

Process and reinforce the positive associations with BLS. Do several sets until the future template is sufficiently strengthened.

Say, *"Go with that."*

_____

_____

Then say, *"Close your eyes and keep in mind the image of the future and the positive cognition. Then bring your attention to the different parts of your body, starting with your head and working downward. Any place you find any tension, tightness, or unusual sensation, tell me."*

_____

_____

If any sensation is reported, do BLS.

Say, *"Go with that."*

If it is a positive or comfortable sensation, do BLS to strengthen the positive feelings.

Say, *"Go with that."*

If a sensation of discomfort is reported, reprocess until the discomfort subsides.

Say, *"Go with that."*

When the discomfort subsides, check the VoC.

Say, *"When you think of the incident* (or picture), *how true do those words _____* (clinician repeats the positive cognition) *feel to you now on a scale of 1 to 7, where 1 feels completely false and 7 feels completely true?"*

1   2   3   4   5   6   7
(completely false)   (completely true)

Continue to use BLS until reaching the VoC = 7 or there is an ecological resolution. When the image as future template is clear and the PC true, move on to the movie as future template.

Movie as Future Template or Imaginal Rehearsing

During this next level of future template, clients are asked to move from imagining this one scene or snapshot to imagining a movie about coping in the future, with a beginning, middle, and end. Encourage clients to imagine themselves coping effectively in the face of specific challenges, triggers, or snafus. Therapists can make some suggestions of things in order to help inoculate them with future problems. It is helpful to use this type of future template after clients have received needed education concerning social skills and customs, assertiveness, and any other newly learned skills.

Say, *"This time, I'd like you to close your eyes and play a movie, imagining yourself coping effectively with _____* (state where client will be) *in the future. With the new positive belief _____* (state positive belief) *and your new sense of _____* (strength, clarity, confidence, calm), *imagine stepping into the future. Imagine yourself coping with ANY challenges that come your way. Make sure that this movie has a beginning, middle, and end. Notice what you are seeing, thinking, feeling, and experiencing in your body. Let me know if you hit any blocks. If you do, just open your eyes and let me know. If you don't hit any blocks, let me know when you have viewed the whole movie."*

_____

_____

If the client hits blocks, address as above with BLS until the disturbance dissipates.

Say, *"Go with that."*

If the material does not shift, use interweaves, new skills, information, resources, direct questions, and any other ways to help clients access information that will allow them to move on. If these options are not successful, usually it means that there is earlier material still unprocessed; the Float-Back and Affect Scan are helpful in these cases to access the material that keep clients stuck.

If clients are able to play the movie from start to finish with a sense of confidence and satisfaction, ask them to play the movie one more time from beginning to end and introduce BLS.

> Say, *"Okay, play the movie one more time from beginning to end. Go with that."*

Use BLS.

In a sense, you are installing this movie as a future template.

After clients have fully processed their issue(s), they might want to work on other positive templates for the future in other areas of their lives using the above future templates.

Current Anxiety and Behavior

Scripted by Marilyn Luber
(Francine Shapiro, 2001, 2006)

Current Anxiety and Behavior Script Notes

This protocol is for clients with anxieties not related to major trauma. The focus here is the Standard EMDR Protocol. This is a summary of the Current Anxiety and Behavior Protocol (Shapiro, 2001, p. 224). For current anxiety and behavior problems, the Standard EMDR Protocol should be applied to the following targets (assuming they are available).

Past Memories

1. Initial memory.

Present Triggers

2. Most recent or most representative example of a present situation that causes anxiety.

Future Template

3. Future projection of a desired emotional and behavioral response. Work with any disturbances that arise subsequently when the client encounters the target situation in the real world.

Current Anxiety and Behavior Protocol Script

Past Memories

1. Initial Memory

Say, *"When was the first time you experienced your fear or anxiety?"*

_____

_____

Incident

Say, *"The memory that we will start with today is* _____ (select the next situation that caused the fear or anxiety to be targeted).*"*

_____

_____

Say, *"What happens when you think of the* _____ (state the situation that caused fear or anxiety)*?"*

_____

_____

Or say, *"When you think of* _____ (state the situation that caused fear or anxiety), *what do you get?"*

_____

_____

_____

Picture

Say, *"What picture represents the entire* _____ (state the situation that caused fear or anxiety)*?"*

_____

_____

If there are many choices or if the client becomes confused, the clinician assists by asking the following:

Say, *"What picture represents the most traumatic part of the* _____ (state the situation that caused fear or anxiety)*?"*

_____

_____

When a picture is unavailable, the clinician merely invites the client to do the following.

Say, *"Think of* ____ (state the situation that caused fear or anxiety).*"*

_____

_____

Negative Cognition (NC)

Say, *"What words best go with the picture that express your negative belief about yourself now?"*

_____

_____

Positive Cognition (PC)

Say, *"When you bring up that _____ (state the situation that caused fear, anxiety, or picture), what would you like to believe about yourself now?"*

_____

_____

Validity of Cognition (VoC)

Say, *"When you think of the _____ (state the situation that caused fear, anxiety, or picture), how true do those words _____ (clinician repeats the positive cognition) feel to you now on a scale of 1 to 7, where 1 feels completely false and 7 feels completely true?"*

1 2 3 4 5 6 7
(completely false)   (completely true)

Sometimes it is necessary to explain further.

Say, *"Remember, sometimes we know something with our head, but it feels differently in our gut. In this case, what is the gut-level feeling of the truth of _____ (clinician states the positive cognition), from 1 (completely false) to 7 (completely true)?"*

1 2 3 4 5 6 7
(completely false)   (completely true)

Emotions

Say, *"When you bring up the picture _____ (or state the situation that caused fear or anxiety) and those words _____ (clinician states the negative cognition), what emotion do you feel now?"*

_____

_____

Subjective Units of Disturbance (SUD)

Say, *"On a scale of 0 to 10, where 0 is no disturbance or neutral and 10 is the highest disturbance you can imagine, how disturbing does it feel now?"*

0 1 2 3 4 5 6 7 8 9 10
(no disturbance)   (highest disturbance)

Location of Body Sensation

Say, *"Where do you feel it* (the disturbance) *in your body?"*

_____

_____

Continue with Phases 4 through 7 for the initial memory.

Present Triggers

2. Most Recent or Most Representative Example of a Present Situation That Causes Anxiety or Recent Anxiety

Current Situation, Events, or Stimuli Triggers

List the situations that elicit the symptom(s). Examples of situations, events, or stimuli that trigger clients are the following: another trauma, the sound of a car backfiring, or being touched in a certain way.

Say, *"Are there any other disturbances that you have noticed before, during or after you encountered the old _____* (state the fear, or anxiety), *in your day-to-day life?"*

_____

_____

Process any stimuli or triggers associated with the anxiety.

Say, *"What are the situations, events, or stimuli that trigger _____* (state the situation that caused fear or anxiety)? *Let's process these situations, events, or stimuli that trigger you one-by-one."*

Situations, Events, Stimuli That Trigger Fear or Anxiety List

_____

_____

_____

_____

_____

_____

Target or Memory

Say, *"What situation, event, or stimulus that triggers you would you like to use as a target today?"*

_____

_____

Picture

Say, *"What picture represents the _____* (state the situation, event, or stimulus) *that triggers you?"*

_____

_____

If there are many choices or if the client becomes confused, the clinician assists by asking the following:

Say, *"What picture represents the most traumatic part of the* _____ (state the situation, event, or stimulus) *that triggers you?"*

_____

_____

When a picture is unavailable, the clinician merely invites the client to do the following:

Say, *"Think of the* _____ (state the situation, event, or stimulus) *that triggers you."*

_____

_____

Negative Cognition (NC)

Say, *"What words best go with the picture that express your negative belief about yourself now?"*

_____

_____

Positive Cognition (PC)

Say, *"When you bring up that picture* _____ (state the situation, event, or stimulus) *that triggers you, what would you like to believe about yourself now?"*

_____

_____

Validity of Cognition (VoC)

Say, *"When you think of the* _____ (state the situation, event, or stimulus or picture that triggers you)*, how true do those words* _____ (clinician repeats the positive cognition) *feel to you now on a scale of 1 to 7, where 1 feels completely false and 7 feels completely true?"*

1   2   3   4   5   6   7
(completely false)   (completely true)

Sometimes it is necessary to explain further.

Say, *"Remember, sometimes we know something with our head, but it feels differently in our gut. In this case, what is the gut-level feeling of the truth of* _____ (clinician states the positive cognition), *from 1 (completely false) to 7 (completely true)?"*

1   2   3   4   5   6   7
(completely false)   (completely true)

Emotions

Say, *"When you bring up the picture* _____ (state the situation, event, or stimulus) *that triggers you and those words* _____ (clinician states the negative cognition), *what emotion do you feel now?"*

_____

_____

Subjective Units of Disturbance (SUD)

Say, *"On a scale of 0 to 10, where 0 is no disturbance or neutral and 10 is the highest disturbance you can imagine, how disturbing does it feel now?"*

0   1   2   3   4   5   6   7   8   9   10
(no disturbance)   (highest disturbance)

Location of Body Sensation

Say, *"Where do you feel it* (the disturbance) *in your body?"*

_____

_____

Continue with Phases 4 through 7 for the situation, event, or stimulus that triggers you from above and any others.

Future Template

3. Future Projection of a Desired Emotional and Behavioral Response

Image as Future Template: Imagining Positive Outcomes
(Francine Shapiro, 2006)

Imagining positive outcomes seems to assist the learning process. In this way, clients learn to enhance optimal behaviors, to connect them with a positive cognition and to support generalization. The assimilation of this new behavior and thought is supported by the use of bilateral stimulation (BLS) into a positive way to act in the future.

Say, *"I would like you to imagine yourself coping effectively with* _____ (state the goal) *in the future. With the positive belief* _____ (state the positive belief) *and your new sense of* _____ (state the quality, i.e., strength, clarity, confidence, calm), *imagine stepping into this scene.*
Notice what you see and how you are handling the situation.
Notice what you are thinking, feeling, and experiencing in your body."

_____

_____

_____

Again, here is the opportunity to catch any disturbance that may have been missed.

Say, *"Are there any blocks, anxieties, or fears that arise as you think about this future scene?"*

_____

_____

_____

If yes, say the following:

Say, *"Then focus on these blocks and follow my fingers* (or any other BLS).*"*
Say, *"What do you get now?"*

_____

_____

_____

If the blocks do not resolve quickly, evaluate if the client needs any new information, resources, or skills to be able to comfortably visualize the future coping scene. Introduce needed information or skills.

Say, *"What would you need to feel confident in handling the situation?"*
Or say, *"What is missing from your handling of this situation?"*

_____

_____

If the block still does not resolve and the client is unable to visualize the future scene with confidence and clarity, use direct questions, the Affect Scan, or the Float-Back Technique to identify old targets related to blocks, anxieties, or fears. Remember, the point of the 3-Prong Protocols is not only to reinforce positive feelings and behavior in the future, but again to catch any unresolved material that may be getting in the way of an adaptive resolution of the issue(s). Use the Standard EMDR Protocol to address these targets before proceeding with the template (see worksheets in Appendix A).

If there are no apparent blocks and the client is able to visualize the future scene with confidence and clarity, say the following:

Say, *"Please focus on the image, the positive belief, and the sensations associated with this future scene and follow my fingers* (or any other BLS).*"*

_____

_____

Process and reinforce the positive associations with BLS. Do several sets until the future template is sufficiently strengthened.

Say, *"Go with that."*

_____

_____

Then say, *"Close your eyes and keep in mind the image of the future and the positive cognition. Then bring your attention to the different parts of your body, starting with your head and working downward. Any place you find any tension, tightness, or unusual sensation, tell me."*

_____

_____

If any sensation is reported, do BLS.

Say, *"Go with that."*

If it is a positive or comfortable sensation, do BLS to strengthen the positive feelings.

Say, *"Go with that."*

If a sensation of discomfort is reported, reprocess until the discomfort subsides.

Say, *"Go with that."*

When the discomfort subsides, check the VoC.

Say, *"When you think of the incident* (or picture), *how true do those words _____* (clinician repeats the positive cognition) *feel to you now on a scale of 1 to 7, where 1 feels completely false and 7 feels completely true?"*

1	2	3	4	5	6	7
(completely false)				(completely true)		

Continue to use BLS until reaching the VoC = 7 or there is an ecological resolution. When the image as future template is clear and the PC is true, move on to the movie as future template.

Movie as Future Template or Imaginal Rehearsing

During this next level of future template, clients are asked to move from imagining this one scene or snapshot to imagining a movie about coping in the future, with a beginning, middle, and end. Encourage clients to imagine themselves coping effectively in the face of specific challenges, triggers, or snafus. Therapists can make some suggestions of things in order to help inoculate them with future problems. It is helpful to use this type of future template after clients have received needed education concerning social skills and customs, assertiveness, and any other newly learned skills.

Say, *"This time, I'd like you to close your eyes and play a movie, imagining yourself coping effectively with _____* (state where client will be) *in the future. With the new positive belief _____* (state positive belief) *and your new sense of _____* (strength, clarity, confidence, calm), *imagine stepping into the future. Imagine yourself coping with ANY challenges that come your way. Make sure that this movie has a beginning, middle, and end. Notice what you are seeing, thinking, feeling, and experiencing in your body. Let me know if you hit any blocks. If you do, just open your eyes and let me know. If you don't hit any blocks, let me know when you have viewed the whole movie."*

_____

_____

If the client hits blocks, address as above with BLS until the disturbance dissipates.

Say, *"Go with that."*

If the material does not shift, use interweaves, new skills, information, resources, direct questions, and any other ways to help your clients access information that will allow them to move on. If these options are not successful, usually it means that there is earlier material still unprocessed; the Float-Back and Affect Scan are helpful in these cases to access the material that keep clients stuck.

If clients are able to play the movie from start to finish with a sense of confidence and satisfaction, ask them to play the movie one more time from beginning to end and introduce BLS.

Say, *"Okay, play the movie one more time from beginning to end. Go with that."*

Use BLS.

In a sense, you are installing this movie as a future template.

After clients have fully processed their issue(s), they might want to work on other positive templates for the future in other areas of their lives using the above future templates.

If new material comes ups during the Reevaluation Phase after the current anxiety and behavior were processed, target this material as soon as possible to make sure that the whole event, its past issues, current triggers, and future issues have been fully reprocessed.

Recent Traumatic Events Protocol

Scripted by Marilyn Luber
(Francine Shapiro, 2001, 2006)

Recent Traumatic Events Script Notes

The following is a summary of the Recent Traumatic Events Protocol (Shapiro, 2001, p. 225). For single traumatic events, the Standard EMDR Protocol should be applied to the following targets (assuming they are available).

Past Memories

1. Obtain a *narrative* history of the event, that is, each separate disturbing aspect or moment of the memory. Treat each separate aspect or moment as a separate target with the EMDR Standard Procedure and installation of positive cognition (PC).
2. Target the *most disturbing* aspect or moment of the memory (if necessary) otherwise target events in chronological order.
3. Target the *remainder* of the narrative in chronological order.
4. Have client visualize the *entire sequence* of the event with *eyes closed* and reprocess it as any disturbance arises. The client should have a full association with the material as it is being reprocessed. If there is disturbance, the client should stop and inform the clinician. Then, the EMDR Procedure including the negative cognition (NC) and positive cognition (PC) is implemented. Repeat until the entire event can be visualized from start to finish without emotional, cognitive, or somatic distress.
5. Have client visualize the event from start to finish with eyes open, and install the PC.
6. Conclude with the Body Scan. Only do Body Scan at the end of the processing of *all* of the targets.

Present Triggers

7. Process *present stimuli* that may cause a startle response, nightmares, and other reminders of the event that the client still finds disturbing, if necessary.

Future Template

8. Create a future template.

Note: For clients whose *earlier history* contains unresolved events that are associated with lack of safety and control, a longer treatment may be required.

Recent Traumatic Event Protocol Script

Past Memories

1. Narrative History

Obtain a narrative history of the event, such as each separate aspect or moment of the event. Treat each separate aspect or moment as a separate target with the full Standard EMDR Procedure and Protocol and installation of the PC. Do not do a Body Scan until all targets are processed.

> Say, *"Please tell me every important detail of the event that occurred to you. We will treat each separate moment that stands out as a target for EMDR."*

_____

_____

_____

_____

_____

_____

_____

_____

_____

_____

_____

2. Target: Most Disturbing Aspect or Moment of the Memory

Target the most disturbing aspect or moment of the memory (if necessary), otherwise target events in chronological order.

> Say, *"What was the most disturbing aspect or moment of the memory of the event?"*

_____

_____

Picture

> Say, *"What picture represents the disturbing aspect or moment of the event?"*

_____

_____

If there are many choices or if the client becomes confused, the clinician assists by asking the following:

Say, *"What picture represents the most traumatic moment of the event?"*

_____

_____

When a picture is unavailable, the clinician merely invites the client to do the following:

Say, *"Think of the disturbing aspect or moment of the event."*

_____

_____

Negative Cognition (NC)

Say, *"What words best go with the picture that express your negative belief about yourself now?"*

_____

_____

Positive Cognition (PC)

Say, *"When you bring up that disturbing aspect or moment of the event, what would you like to believe about yourself now?"*

_____

_____

Validity of Cognition (VoC)

Say, *"When you think of the disturbing aspect or moment of the event (or picture)* how true do those words _____ (clinician repeats the positive cognition) *feel to you now on a scale of 1 to 7, where 1 feels completely false and 7 feels completely true?"*

1	2	3	4	5	6	7
(completely false)				(completely true)		

Sometimes it is necessary to explain further.

Say, *"Remember, sometimes we know something with our head, but it feels differently in our gut. In this case, what is the gut-level feeling of the truth of _____ (clinician state the positive cognition), from 1* (completely false) *to 7* (completely true)?"

1	2	3	4	5	6	7
(completely false)				(completely true)		

Emotions

Say, *"When you bring up the picture or the disturbing aspect or memory of the event and those words _____ (clinician states the negative cognition), what emotion do you feel now?"*

_____

_____

Subjective Units of Disturbance (SUD)

Say, *"On a scale of 0 to 10, where 0 is no disturbance or neutral and 10 is the highest disturbance you can imagine, how disturbing does it feel now?"*

0	1	2	3	4	5	6	7	8	9	10
(no disturbance)										(highest disturbance)

Location of Body Sensation

Say, *"Where do you feel it* (the disturbance) *in your body?"*

_____

_____

Continue with Phases 4 through 5. Phases 6 through 7 are completed after the final segment of the memory has been reprocessed and all of the targets have been treated. It is at that point that the body tension can dissipate.

3. Target: Remainder of the Narrative in Chronological Order

Picture

Say, *"Now let's target the first stand-out moment of the event and go from there."*

_____

_____

If there are many choices or if the client becomes confused, the clinician assists by asking the following:

Say, *"What picture represents the most traumatic part of this stand-out moment?"*

_____

_____

When a picture is unavailable, the clinician merely invites the client to do the following:

Say, *"Think of the stand out moment."*

_____

_____

Negative Cognition (NC)

Say, *"What words best go with the picture of this stand out moment that express your negative belief about yourself now?"*

_____

_____

Positive Cognition (PC)

Say, *"When you bring up that picture or stand out moment, what would you like to believe about yourself now?"*

_____

_____

Validity of Cognition (VoC)

Say, *"When you think of the stand out moment* (or picture), *how true do those words* _____ (clinician repeats the positive cognition) *feel to you now on a scale of 1 to 7, where 1 feels completely false and 7 feels completely true?"*

1   2   3   4   5   6   7
(completely false)   (completely true)

Sometimes it is necessary to explain further.

Say, *"Remember, sometimes we know something with our head, but it feels differently in our gut. In this case, what is the gut-level feeling of the truth of* _____ (clinician states the positive cognition), *from 1* (completely false) *to 7* (completely true)*?"*

1   2   3   4   5   6   7
(completely false)   (completely true)

Emotions

Say, *"When you bring up the picture* (or stand-out moment) *and those words* _____ (clinician states the negative cognition), *what emotion do you feel now?"*

_____

_____

Subjective Units of Disturbance (SUD)

Say, *"On a scale of 0 to 10, where 0 is no disturbance or neutral and 10 is the highest disturbance you can imagine, how disturbing does it feel now?"*

0   1   2   3   4   5   6   7   8   9   10
(no disturbance)   (highest disturbance)

Location of Body Sensation

Say, *"Where do you feel it* (the disturbance) *in your body?"*

_____

_____

Continue with Phases 4 through 5. Phases 6 through 7 are completed after the final segment of the memory has been reprocessed and all of the targets have been treated. It is at that point that the body tension can dissipate.

Note: Repeat the sequence above for each moment that stands out in chronological order.

4. Visualize Entire Sequence of Event With Eyes Closed

Have the client visualize the entire sequence with eyes closed and reprocess it as any disturbance arises. The client should have a full association with the material as it is being reprocessed. If there is disturbance, the client should stop and inform the clinician. Repeat until the entire event can be visualized from start to finish without emotional, cognitive, or somatic distress.

Say, *"Please visualize the entire sequence of the event with eyes closed. If there is any disturbance, please open your eyes and we will reprocess the material together. Let me know when your disturbance decreases."*

_____

_____

Repeat this until the client can visualize the entire event from start to finish without distress.

If or when there is no disturbance, visualize the entire sequence of the event with eyes open. See the following section.

5. Visualize Entire Sequence of Event With Eyes Open and Install

Positive Cognition (PC)

Have the client visualize the event from start to finish with *eyes open*, and install the PC.

Say, *"Please visualize the entire sequence of the event with your eyes open and think of _____ (state the positive cognition). Scan the videotape mentally—even though the images will not be clear—and give the stop signal when you are finished. Go with that (or any other bilateral stimulation [BLS] you are using)."*

Use a long set of BLS.

6. Body Scan

Conclude with Body Scan. Only do Body Scan at the end of the processing of *all* of the targets or moments of the event.

_____

_____

Say, *"Close your eyes and keep in mind the original memory and the _____ (repeat the selected positive cognition). Then bring your attention to the different parts of your body, starting with your head and working downward. Any place you find any tension, tightness, or unusual sensation, tell me."*

_____

_____

If any sensation is reported, do BLS.

Say, *"Go with that."*

If a positive or comfortable sensation, do bilateral stimulation to strengthen the positive feeling.

Say, *"Go with that."*

If a sensation of discomfort is reported, reprocess until discomfort subsides.

Say, *"Go with that."*

Present Triggers

7. Present Stimuli or Triggers

Process *present stimuli* that may cause a startle response, nightmares, and other reminders of the event that the client still finds disturbing, if necessary.

Target or Memory—Startle Response

Say, *"Are you having any startle responses to situations, events, or stimuli that are related to this event?"*

LIST FOR SITUATIONS AND EVENTS THAT TRIGGER A STARTLE RESPONSE

_____

_____

_____

Picture

Say, *"What picture represents the situation or event where the startle response occurs?"*

_____

_____

_____

Say, *"What are the images that are coming up from the situation or event where the startle response occurs?"*

_____

_____

Say, *"What picture represents the most traumatic part of the situation or event where the startle response occurs?"*

_____

_____

Negative Cognition (NC)

Say, *"What words best go with the picture that express your negative belief about yourself now?"*

_____

_____

Positive Cognition (PC)

Say, *"When you bring up that picture, situation, or event where the startle response occurs, what would you like to believe about yourself now?"*

_____

_____

Validity of Cognition (VoC)

Say, *"When you think of the startle response* (or picture) *how true do those words _____* (clinician repeats the positive cognition) *feel to you now on a scale of 1 to 7, where 1 feels completely false and 7 feels completely true?"*

1	2	3	4	5	6	7
(completely false)				(completely true)		

Sometimes, it is necessary to explain further.

Say, *"Remember, sometimes we know something with our head, but it feels differently in our gut. In this case, what is the gut-level feeling of the truth of _____* (clinician states the positive cognition), *from 1* (completely false) *to 7* (completely true)?"

1	2	3	4	5	6	7
(completely false)				(completely true)		

Emotions

Say, *"When you bring up the picture* (the situation or event where the startle response occurs) *and those words _____* (clinician states the negative cognition), *what emotion do you feel now?"*

_____

_____

Subjective Units of Disturbance (SUD)

Say, *"On a scale of 0 to 10, where 0 is no disturbance or neutral and 10 is the highest disturbance you can imagine, how disturbing does it feel now?"*

0	1	2	3	4	5	6	7	8	9	10
(no disturbance)							(highest disturbance)			

Location of Body Sensation

Say, *"Where do you feel it* (the disturbance) *in your body?"*

_____

_____

Continue with Phases 4 through 7 for the situation, event, or stimulus that triggers you from above and any others. After processing the first situation that results in a startle response, check to see if any of the others mentioned are still active; if not, proceed to the next question. If there are more startle responses that need to be processed, go ahead and reprocess that experience.

Target or Memory—Nightmare Image

Say, *"Are you having any nightmares concerning this event?"*

NIGHTMARE TRIGGER LIST

_____

_____

_____

Picture

Say, *"What picture represents the nightmare?"*

_____

_____

_____

Say, *"What picture represents the most traumatic part of the nightmare?"*

_____

_____

Negative Cognition (NC)

Say, *"What words best go with the picture that express your negative belief about yourself now?"*

_____

_____

Positive Cognition (PC)

Say, *"When you bring up that picture or nightmare, what would you like to believe about yourself now?"*

_____

_____

Validity of Cognition (VoC)

Say, *"When you think of the nightmare* (or picture), *how true do those words* _____ (clinician repeats the positive cognition) *feel to you now on a scale of 1 to 7, where 1 feels completely false and 7 feels completely true?"*

1	2	3	4	5	6	7
(completely false)				(completely true)		

Sometimes, it is necessary to explain further.

Say, *"Remember, sometimes we know something with our head, but it feels differently in our gut. In this case, what is the gut-level feeling of the truth of* _____ (clinician states the positive cognition), *from 1 (completely false) to 7 (completely true)?"*

1	2	3	4	5	6	7
(completely false)				(completely true)		

Emotions

Say, *"When you bring up the picture* (or nightmare) *and those words* _____ (clinician states the negative cognition), *what emotion do you feel now?"*

_____

_____

Subjective Units of Disturbance (SUD)

Say, *"On a scale of 0 to 10, where 0 is no disturbance or neutral and 10 is the highest disturbance you can imagine, how disturbing does it feel now?"*

0	1	2	3	4	5	6	7	8	9	10
(no disturbance)								(highest disturbance)		

Location of Body Sensation

Say, *"Where do you feel it* (the disturbance) *in your body?"*

_____

_____

Continue with Phases 4 through 7 for the dream or nightmare from above. After processing the first nightmare, check to see if any of the others mentioned are still active, if not, proceed to the next question. If there are more nightmares that need to be processed, go ahead and reprocess that experience.

Other Reminders of the Recent Event

Process any situation, event, or stimulus that triggers your association with the recent event.

Say, *"What are the other reminders of the* _____ (state the situation, event, or stimulus) *that triggers you and that you still find disturbing?"*

OTHER REMINDERS TRIGGER LIST

_____

_____

_____

_____

Target or Memory

Say, *"What* _____ (state the situation, event, or stimulus) *that triggers should we use first?"*

_____

_____

Picture

Say, *"What picture represents the most traumatic part of* _____ (state the situation, event, or stimulus) *that triggers you?"*

_____

_____

Negative Cognition (NC)

Say, *"What words best go with the picture that express your negative belief about yourself now?"*

_____

_____

Positive Cognition (PC)

Say, *"When you bring up that picture or* _____ (state the situation, event, or stimulus) *that triggers you, what would you like to believe about yourself now?"*

_____

_____

Validity of Cognition (VoC)

Say, *"When you think of the* _____ (state the situation, event, or stimulus) *that triggers you* (or picture), *how true do those words* _____ (clinician repeats the positive cognition) *feel to you now on a scale of 1 to 7, where 1 feels completely false and 7 feels completely true?"*

1	2	3	4	5	6	7
(completely false)				(completely true)		

Sometimes, it is necessary to explain further.

Say, *"Remember, sometimes we know something with our head, but it feels differently in our gut. In this case, what is the gut-level feeling of the truth of* _____ (clinician states the positive cognition), *from 1* (completely false) *to 7* (completely true)?"

1	2	3	4	5	6	7
(completely false)				(completely true)		

Emotions

Say, *"When you bring up the picture or* _____ (state the situation, event, or stimulus) *that triggers you and those words* _____ (clinician states the negative cognition), *what emotion do you feel now?"*

_____

_____

Subjective Units of Disturbance (SUD)

Say, *"On a scale of 0 to 10, where 0 is no disturbance or neutral and 10 is the highest disturbance you can imagine, how disturbing does it feel now?"*

0	1	2	3	4	5	6	7	8	9	10
(no disturbance)										(highest disturbance)

Location of Body Sensation

Say, *"Where do you feel it* (the disturbance) *in your body?"*

_____

_____

For clients whose earlier history contains unresolved events that are associated with lack of safety and control, a longer treatment may required.

Say, *"Are there any other earlier unresolved events that are associated with lack of safety and control? If so, we can work with them now."*

_____

_____

Future Template

8. Create a Future Template

Continue with the Standard EMDR Protocol for targets that need reprocessing.

Although in the summary for the Protocol for Recent Traumatic Events (Shapiro, 2001, p. 225), Dr. Shapiro does not mention the use of any future templates, in fact, the use of the future template is implicit in all EMDR work. Furthermore, the future template is part of the recent event protocol that is taught in the EMDR training to address avoidance, adaptation, and actualization in the future (R. Solomon, personal communication, February, 2009). See Appendix A.

Phobia Protocol

Scripted by Marilyn Luber
(Francine Shapiro, 2001, 2006)

Phobia Protocol Script Notes

Dr. Shapiro distinguishes between two types of phobias.

1. Simple Phobia is defined as "fear of an object (e.g., a spider) that is circumscribed and independent of the client's actions." The fear is generated by the sight of the object and is independent of further participation. Many times, these phobias are easily handled by steps 1 to 3 below.

2. Process Phobia is defined as "fear of a situation in which the client must actively participate." For instance, a phobia of flying requires the participation of the client. In order to be in the feared situation the client must purchase tickets, drive to the airport, and get in the airplane. Therefore, when targeting a process phobia, the clinician must address all the pertinent aspects of the experience, including the decision-making and anticipatory anxiety. These are handled by steps 4 to 6 below. However, if a deliberate interaction with any feared object is needed in daily activity (e.g., approaching a dog at a neighbor's house or cleaning a spider-filled attic), or in research (e.g., touching a snake in a Behavioral Avoidance Test [BAT]), the full procedures should be used for simple phobias as well (De Jongh, Ten Broeke, & Renssen, 1999; Shapiro, 1999). It should be remembered that the phobia diagnosis is given because of the avoidance that debilitates the client's current life. Although the procedures for the simple phobia may eliminate the client's self-perceived fear, they may not overcome (without the full steps) the evolutionary biases (such as disgust of spiders or discomfort around snakes) challenged by a BAT. Although the Simple Phobia Protocol may be sufficient in many instances, some phobia researchers believe that the division is not useful and that the Process Phobia Protocol should be used exclusively (De Jongh et al., 1999).

The following is The Phobia Protocol Summary (Shapiro, 2001, p. 228). Use the Standard EMDR Protocol for targets elicited below.

1. Teach self-control procedures to handle the "fear of fear"

Past Memories

2. Target and reprocess the following:

   a. Antecedent or ancillary events that contribute to the phobia
   b. The first time the fear was experienced
   c. The most disturbing experiences
   d. The most recent time it was experienced

Present Triggers

   e. Any associated present stimuli
   f. The physical sensations or other manifestations of fear, including hyperventilation

Future Template

3. Incorporate a positive template for fear-free future action
4. Arrange contract for action
5. Run mental videotape of full sequence and reprocess disturbance
6. Complete reprocessing of targets revealed between sessions

To do the full Phobia Protocol, all 6 steps should be included.

The Phobia Protocol Script

Client History Taking

These are the questions to ask during Phase 1 of history taking.

1. Say, *"What is the phobia that has brought you in?"*

   _____

   _____

2. Say, *"When was the first time that you experienced your phobia?"*

   _____

   _____

3. Say, *"What was happening to you just prior to your experiencing this fear for the first time?"*

   _____

   _____

4. Say, *"What was happening to you and around you during this first experience of your phobia?"* (You are looking for anything in the history that might constitute secondary gain.)

   _____

   _____

5. Say, *"Was there ever a time that you experienced the same types of feelings or sensations in your body before your phobia started?"*

   _____

   _____

6. Say, *"When was the most disturbing time that you experienced your phobia?"*

   _____

   _____

7. Say, *"Does this remind you of any earlier memories that might be related to your phobia?"*

   _____

   _____

8. Say, *"When was the last time that you experienced your phobia?"*

   _____

   _____

9. Say, *"What other situations, events, or stimuli trigger you concerning your phobia?"* Or, *"What else triggers your fear response?"*

   _____

   _____

10. Say, *"What are the physical sensations or other internal experiences that you have of your fear, including the hyperventilation that you experience when you*

become fearful or think of your phobia?" (The ability to identify the sensations implicitly allows the client to perceive himself as larger than the fear, since he can cognitively separate himself from it and place it under his control.)

_____

_____

11. Say, *"What would you be able to do if you no longer had your phobia?"*

_____

_____

12. Say, *"What would you not be able to do if you no longer had your phobia?"*

_____

_____

13. Say, *"Has your phobia generalized to any other areas?"*

_____

_____

14. Say, *"Do you have any other phobias?"*

_____

_____

Say, *"It is important for you to know that there will be no pressure to perform or conform to any outside standard. Giving up this fear does not mean that you must engage in any particular activity. For instance, relinquishing a fear of snakes does not force you to take up camping; losing a fear of heights does not necessitate skydiving. The right to choose what you do is yours and your actions need not be motivated—or mandated—by either the fear or its absence."* (Shapiro, 2001)

Step 1: Teach Self-Control Procedures to Handle the Fear of the Fear

Say, *"I am going to teach you several ways to handle the fear of your fear, and you can choose the one or ones that work best for you. We will practice them until you feel that you have mastered them and can use some or all of them to handle your anxiety and fear with a measure of confidence."*

The therapist can choose as many or as few of the following techniques depending on the needs and style of the client.

The Light Stream Technique

The Light Stream Technique is very useful with acute pain.

Say, *"I would like you to scan your whole body now and to tell me where you notice any unpleasant body sensations or tensions."*

_____

_____

Say, *"I'd like you to imagine that those sensations were energy. If the energy had a _____ (state each of the attributes below) what would it be?"*

Shape: _____

Size: _____

Color: _____

Temperature: _____

Texture: _____

Sound: _____

Say, *"What color does your body need today to heal?"*

_____

_____

Say, *"Imagine that this favorite colored light is coming in through the top of your head and directing itself at the shape in your body. Let's pretend that the source of this light is the infinite cosmos so the more you use, the more you have available. <u>Allow the soothing, healing light to come in more and more, and direct itself at the shape. As it does so, let the light resonate and vibrate in and around it, more and more. And as it does, what happens to the shape?"</u>*

_____

_____

If the client gives feedback that it is changing in any way, continue repeating the underlined portion and asking for feedback, until the shape is completely gone. This usually correlates with the disappearance of the upsetting feeling.

Say, *"Continue to allow the light to flow into your head, neck, and shoulders. Let it flow into your chest and down your arms and out your fingertips. Let the soothing, healing light flow through your torso into your legs and out through your feet. Let the light flow into every part of your body. Imagine saying to yourself the positive words you most need to hear right now."*

Say, *"Then, as I count upward from one to five, I'd like you to bring yourself back here in the room, and as you do, I would like you to bring your whole and complete self here. (Pause) So, bringing your whole and complete self back in the room now, one, two (rising intonation), three, four, and five."*

The Spiral Technique

Say, *"Please remember a disturbing memory and concentrate on the body sensations that go with that disturbance. Remember, this is a visualization exercise, so there are no right or wrong answers."*

Say, *"When you bring up the memory, on a scale of 0 to 10, where 0 is no disturbance or neutral and 10 is the highest disturbance you can imagine, how disturbing does it feel now?"*

0   1   2   3   4   5   6   7   8   9   10
(no disturbance)   (highest disturbance)

Say, *"Where do you feel it in your body?"*

_____

_____

Say, *"Please concentrate on the feelings in your body. Now let's pretend that the feelings are energy and if the sensation were going in a spiral, what direction would it be moving in? Clockwise? Or, counterclockwise?"*

_____

_____

Whatever the client answers, respond, *"Good."*

Say, *"Okay, now with your mind, let's change direction and move the spiral _____ (state, "clockwise" or "counterclockwise" to indicate the opposite direction). Just notice what happens as it moves in the opposite directions."*
Say, *"What happens?"*

_____

_____

If the technique works, the client will report that moving in the opposite direction will cause the feelings to dissipate and the subjective units of disturbance (SUD) to drop. If the client says the spiral doesn't change, doesn't move, nothing happens, then you can choose another technique.

Say, *"You can also use this on your own."*

Inner Voice

Say, *"Who is your favorite cartoon character?"*

_____

_____

Say, *"Imagine that critical voice that you always hear speaking with the voice of your favorite cartoon character. What is that like for you?"*

_____

_____

Usually this intervention changes the client's perception of the critical voice that he is hearing.

Relaxation Cue

Say, *"Think of a relaxing image or phrase. Please use whatever image or phrase is most helpful for you. What is it?"*

_____

_____

Say, *"Now take a deep breath and hold it. If you hear sound as you are breathing, you are breathing too quickly. Just allow yourself to breathe deeply as you think of your relaxing image or phrase."*
Say, *"Now, as you are thinking of that relaxing image or phrase, touch your hand to your chest (or any other part of the body that feels comfortable to you) and breathe in and then out, feeling the deep*

sense of relaxation that comes as you experience your relaxing image or phrase."

Say, *"During the next days, weeks, or months, each time that you have the experience of something that brings you this sense of relaxation, you can anchor it by touching your chest* (or any other part of the body that feels comfortable to you) *so that each time you touch your chest* (or other body part), *you will experience this deep sense of relaxation."*

Say, *"Please practice these techniques at home so that you can use them in all types of situations."*

Breathing Shift

Say, *"Think of a good, happy, or positive memory. Please use whatever feeling is most helpful for you. What is it?"*

_____

_____

Say, *"Notice where your breath is starting and put your hand over that location in your body. Please take a moment to take several breaths and notice how it feels."*

Say, *"Now, bring up a memory with a low level of disturbance and notice how your breath changes. Please put your hand over that location in your body? Now, change your hand to the location you touched earlier and deliberately change your breathing pattern to the earlier pattern."*

This should cause the disturbance to dissipate. Teach it to your client for self-use.

Say, *"This is a way to help the disturbance diminish. You can use this at home. The best thing to do is to practice it several times a day. Any questions?"*

_____

_____

Past Memories

Step 2: Target and Reprocess

A. ANCILLARY OR ANTECEDENT EVENTS THAT CONTRIBUTE TO THE PHOBIA

The next step is to process the ancillary or antecedent events (see questions 2 and 3 above in the "Client History Taking" section) that contribute to the phobia using the Standard EMDR Protocol, which is an event with similar feelings and sensations that predated the phobia.

Say, *"Today, we have decided to reprocess* _____ (state the target memory or incident to work on). *When you think of the incident what do you get?"*

_____

_____

Incident

Say, *"The memory that we will start with today is _____ (select the next incident to be targeted)."*

_____

_____

Say, *"What happens when you think of the _____ (state the event/issue)?"*

_____

_____

Or say, *"When you think of the _____ (state the event or issue), what do you get?"*

_____

_____

Picture

Say, *"What picture represents the entire _____ (state the event or issue)?"*

_____

_____

If there are many choices or if the client becomes confused, the clinician assists by asking the following:

Say, *"What picture represents the most traumatic part of _____ (state the event or issue)?"*

_____

_____

When a picture is unavailable, the clinician merely invites the client to do the following.

Say, *"Think of _____ (state the event or issue)."*

_____

_____

Negative Cognition (NC)

Say, *"What words best go with the picture that express your negative belief about yourself now?"*

_____

_____

Positive Cognition (PC)

Say, *"When you bring up that picture or _____ (state the event or issue), what would you like to believe about yourself now?"*

_____

_____

Validity of Cognition (VoC)

Say, "When you think of the _____ (state the event, issue, or picture), *how true do those words* _____ (clinician repeats the positive cognition) *feel to you now on a scale of 1 to 7, where 1 feels completely false and 7 feels completely true?*"

1	2	3	4	5	6	7
(completely false)				(completely true)		

Sometimes, it is necessary to explain further.

Say, "*Remember, sometimes we know something with our head, but it feels differently in our gut. In this case, what is the gut-level feeling of the truth of* _____ (clinician states the positive cognition), *from 1* (completely false) *to 7* (completely true)?"

1	2	3	4	5	6	7
(completely false)				(completely true)		

Emotions

Say, "*When you bring up the picture* (state the event or issue) *and those words* _____ (clinician states the negative cognition), *what emotion do you feel now?*"

_____

_____

Subjective Units of Disturbance (SUD)

Say, "*On a scale of 0 to 10, where 0 is no disturbance or neutral and 10 is the highest disturbance you can imagine, how disturbing does it feel now?*"

0	1	2	3	4	5	6	7	8	9	10
(no disturbance)							(highest disturbance)			

Location of Body Sensation

Say, "*Where do you feel it* (the disturbance) *in your body?*"

_____

_____

Continue with Phases 4 through 7 for this antecedent or ancillary event and any others.

B. FIRST TIME FEAR EXPERIENCED

Process the first time the fear was experienced.

Incident

Say, "*The memory that we will start with today is* _____ (the first time the fear was experienced)."

_____

_____

Say, *"What happens when you think of the _____ (the first time the fear was experienced)?"*

_____

_____

Or say, *"When you think of the _____ (the first time the fear was experienced), what do you get?"*

_____

_____

Picture

Say, *"What picture represents the entire first time you experienced fear?"*

_____

_____

Say, *"What picture represents the most traumatic part of the first time you experienced fear?"*

_____

_____

Negative Cognition (NC)

Say, *"What words best go with the picture that express your negative belief about yourself now?"*

_____

_____

Positive Cognition (PC)

Say, *"When you bring up that picture or the first time you experienced fear, what would you like to believe about yourself now?"*

_____

_____

Validity of Cognition (VoC)

Say, *"When you think of the first time you experienced fear (or picture), how true do those words _____ (clinician repeats the positive cognition) feel to you now on a scale of 1 to 7, where 1 feels completely false and 7 feels completely true?"*

1	2	3	4	5	6	7
(completely false)				(completely true)		

Sometimes, it is necessary to explain further.

Say, *"Remember, sometimes we know something with our head, but it feels differently in our gut. In this case, what is the gut-level feeling of the truth of _____ (clinician states the positive cognition), from 1 (completely false) to 7 (completely true)?"*

> 1   2   3   4   5   6   7
> (completely false)   (completely true)

Emotions

> Say, *"When you bring up the picture* (or first time you experienced fear) *and those words* _____ (clinician states the negative cognition), *what emotion do you feel now?"*

> _____

> _____

Subjective Units of Disturbance (SUD)

> Say, *"On a scale of 0 to 10, where 0 is no disturbance or neutral and 10 is the highest disturbance you can imagine, how disturbing does it feel now?"*

> 0   1   2   3   4   5   6   7   8   9   10
> (no disturbance)   (highest disturbance)

Location of Body Sensation

> Say, *"Where do you feel it* (the disturbance) *in your body?"*

> _____

> _____

> Continue with Phases 4 through 7 for the first time that the fear was experienced.

C. MOST DISTURBING EXPERIENCE

Process the most disturbing phobic experience.

> Say, *"The memory that we will start with today is* _____ (the most disturbing phobic experience).*"*

> _____

> _____

> Say, *"What happens when you think of the* _____ (the most disturbing phobic experience)*?"*

> _____

> _____

> Or say, *"When you think of the* _____ (the most disturbing phobic experience), *what do you get?"*

> _____

> _____

Picture

> Say, *"What picture represents the entire incident concerning the most disturbing experience of* _____ (state the phobia)*?"*

> _____

> _____

Say, *"What picture represents the most traumatic part of the most disturbing experience of* _____ (state the phobia)*?"*

_____

_____

Negative Cognition (NC)

Say, *"What words best go with the picture that express your negative belief about yourself now?"*

_____

_____

Positive Cognition (PC)

Say, *"When you bring up that picture or the most disturbing experience of* _____ (state the phobia), *what would you like to believe about yourself now?"*

_____

_____

Validity of Cognition (VoC)

Say, *"When you think of the incident or the most disturbing experience of* _____ (state the phobia), *how true do those words* _____ (clinician repeats the positive cognition) *feel to you now on a scale of 1 to 7, where 1 feels completely false and 7 feels completely true?"*

1	2	3	4	5	6	7
(completely false)				(completely true)		

Sometimes, it is necessary to explain further.

Say, *"Remember, sometimes we know something with our head, but it feels differently in our gut. In this case, what is the gut-level feeling of the truth of* _____ (clinician states the positive cognition), *from 1 (completely false) to 7 (completely true)?"*

1	2	3	4	5	6	7
(completely false)				(completely true)		

Emotions

Say, *"When you bring up the picture or the most disturbing experience of* _____ (state the phobia) *and those words* _____ (clinician states the negative cognition), *what emotion do you feel now?"*

_____

_____

Subjective Units of Disturbance (SUD)

Say, *"On a scale of 0 to 10, where 0 is no disturbance or neutral and 10 is the highest disturbance you can imagine, how disturbing does it feel now?"*

0	1	2	3	4	5	6	7	8	9	10
(no disturbance)							(highest disturbance)			

Location of Body Sensation

> Say, *"Where do you feel it* (the disturbance) *in your body?"*

_____

_____

Continue with Phases 4 through 7 for the most disturbing time that the fear was experienced.

D. MOST RECENT TIME EXPERIENCED

Process the most recent time that the fear was experienced.

Incident

> Say, *"The memory that we will start with today is _____* (select the most recent time that the fear was experienced)*."*

_____

_____

_____

> Say, *"What happens when you think of _____* (the most recent time that the fear was experienced)*?"*

_____

_____

_____

> Or say, *"When you think of the _____* (the most recent time that the fear was experienced), *what do you get?"*

_____

_____

_____

Picture

> Say, *"What picture represents the entire _____* (the most recent time that the fear was experienced)*?"*

_____

_____

> Say, *"What picture represents the most traumatic part of _____* (the most recent time that the fear was experienced)*?"*

_____

_____

Negative Cognition (NC)

> Say, *"What words best go with the picture that express your negative belief about yourself now?"*

_____

_____

Positive Cognition (PC)

Say, *"When you bring up that picture or* _____ (the most recent time that the fear was experienced), *what would you like to believe about yourself, now?"*

_____

_____

Validity of Cognition (VoC)

Say, *"When you think of the* _____ (the most recent time that the fear was experienced or picture), *how true do those words* _____ (clinician repeats the positive cognition) *feel to you now on a scale of 1 to 7, where 1 feels completely false and 7 feels completely true?"*

1	2	3	4	5	6	7
(completely false)				(completely true)		

Sometimes, it is necessary to explain further.

Say, *"Remember, sometimes we know something with our head, but it feels differently in our gut. In this case, what is the gut-level feeling of the truth of* _____ (clinician states the positive cognition), *from 1* (completely false) *to 7* (completely true)?"

1	2	3	4	5	6	7
(completely false)				(completely true)		

Emotions

Say, **"When you bring up the picture or** _____ (the most recent time that the fear was experienced) *and those words* _____ (clinician states the negative cognition), *what emotion do you feel now?"*

_____

_____

Subjective Units of Disturbance (SUD)

Say, *"On a scale of 0 to 10, where 0 is no disturbance or neutral and 10 is the highest disturbance you can imagine, how disturbing does it feel now?"*

0	1	2	3	4	5	6	7	8	9	10
(no disturbance)										(highest disturbance)

Location of Body Sensation

Say, *"Where do you feel it* (the disturbance) *in your body?"*

_____

_____

Continue with Phases 4 through 7 for the most recent time that the fear was experienced.

Present Triggers

E. ANY ASSOCIATED PRESENT STIMULI THAT ARE TRIGGERS

Process any situations, events, or stimuli triggers that bring up the fear.

SITUATIONS, EVENTS, OR STIMULI TRIGGER LIST

_____

_____

_____

_____

_____

_____

Target or Memory

Say, *"What situation, event, or stimulus would you like to use as a target today?"*

_____

_____

Picture

Say, *"What picture represents the* _____ (state the situation, event, or stimulus) *that triggers you?"*

_____

_____

If there are many choices or if the client becomes confused, the clinician assists by asking the following:

Say, *"What picture represents the most traumatic part of the* _____ (state the situation, event, or stimulus) *that triggers you?"*

_____

_____

When a picture is unavailable, the clinician merely invites the client to do the following:

Say, *"Think of the* _____ (state the situation, event, or stimulus) *that triggers you."*

_____

_____

Negative Cognition (NC)

Say, *"What words best go with the picture that express your negative belief about yourself now?"*

_____

_____

Positive Cognition (PC)

Say, *"When you bring up that picture, the* _____ (state the situation, event, or stimulus) *that triggers you, what would you like to believe about yourself now?"*

_____

_____

Validity of Cognition (VoC)

Say, *"When you think of the* _____ (state the situation, event, stimulus, or picture that triggers you), *how true do those words* _____ (clinician repeats the positive cognition) *feel to you now on a scale of 1 to 7, where 1 feels completely false and 7 feels completely true?"*

1	2	3	4	5	6	7
(completely false)				(completely true)		

Sometimes, it is necessary to explain further.

Say, *"Remember, sometimes we know something with our head, but it feels differently in our gut. In this case, what is the gut-level feeling of the truth of* _____ (clinician states the positive cognition), *from 1 (completely false) to 7 (completely true)?"*

1	2	3	4	5	6	7
(completely false)				(completely true)		

Emotions

Say, *"When you bring up the picture* (state the situation, event, or stimulus) *that triggers you and those words* _____ (clinician states the negative cognition), *what emotion do you feel now?"*

_____

_____

Subjective Units of Disturbance (SUD)

Say, *"On a scale of 0 to 10, where 0 is no disturbance or neutral and 10 is the highest disturbance you can imagine, how disturbing does it feel now?"*

0	1	2	3	4	5	6	7	8	9	10
(no disturbance)								(highest disturbance)		

Location of Body Sensation

Say, *"Where do you feel it* (the disturbance) *in your body?"*

_____

_____

Continue with Phases 4 through 7 for the situation, event, or fear that triggered the fear. Process all of the triggers, checking after the completion of each one to see if other targets need to be processed. If so, continue the processing until all are completed and then move on to the next step.

F. FEAR SYMPTOMS

If the client has symptoms of fear during the treatment session, do the following, speak soothingly to the client as the fear arises, encouraging him as follows:

Say, *"Just notice the sensations; don't force them one way or another."*

Do BLS.

Continue the set through the fear, even in the case of a full-blown panic attack; this may dissipate the disturbing emotion and reprocess the client's fear of fear. After the fear has subsided, review a self-control technique (see Step 1 at the beginning of this chapter) with the client. This can affirm the client's ability to handle any fear that might arise (Shapiro, 2001, p. 230).

Check for other physical sensations or other manifestations of fear, including hyper-ventilation, which may not have been stimulated during the processing so far.

Say, *"What are the fear symptoms concerning your* _____ (state the phobia)? *Let's process fear symptoms one by one."*

FEAR SYMPTOM LIST

_____

_____

_____

_____

_____

Target or Memory

Say, *"With which fear symptom would you like to work?"*

_____

_____

_____

Location of Body Sensation

Say, *"Where do you feel it* (the disturbance) *in your body?"*

_____

_____

Say, *"Go with that."*

Use BLS.

Work each fear symptom with BLS until there is no more disturbance. If the disturbance does not diminish, use an Affect Scan to determine if there are earlier incidents that need to be reprocessed using the Standard EMDR Protocol (see Appendix A).

Future Template

Step 3: Incorporate a Positive Template for Fear-Free Future Action (Image as Future Template: Imagining Positive Outcomes, Shapiro, 2006)

Incorporate a detailed template for a fear-free future action.

Say, *"I would like you to imagine yourself coping effectively with* _____ (state the phobic situation) *in the future, while feeling calm and relaxed* (or state another more appropriate state). *Go with that."*

Use BLS.

Say, *"What do you notice now?"*

_____

_____

Say, *"As you think of yourself coping effectively with* _____ (state the phobic situation) *in the future, while feeling calm and relaxed* (or state another more appropriate state), *how true does it feel, from 1* (completely false) *to 7* (completely true)*?"*

1   2   3   4   5   6   7
(completely false)   (completely true)

This projection should be reprocessed until it reaches a 6 or 7 on the VoC scale. It is not unusual for the score to remain at a 6 until clients have a chance to experience the fear firsthand to be sure that they are no longer afraid. It is important for clients to keep a log of any negative responses; these will be used as targets for future treatment.

Say, *"It is important for you to keep a log of any negative responses that you have over the time until we meet again as we will use them as targets for our work together next time. It is most helpful when the log entry is like a good snapshot of what happened and includes any images, thoughts, physical sensations, and feelings that occur."*

When clients return with their logs, make sure to address any negative responses that they have. It is helpful to install a positive template for every trigger—especially for claustrophobic clients.

Step 4: Arrange Contract for Action

Contract for in vivo action.

Say, *"Now we are ready for you to contract with me to experience* _____ (name the fear or phobia)."*
Say, *"How will you proceed with this?"*

_____

_____

Say, *"Let's write it down so that we both are clear on our agreement for you to experience your phobia of* _____ (state phobia)."*

_____

_____

_____

_____

_____

_____

Step 5: Run Mental Videotape of Full Sequence and Reprocess Disturbance (Movie as Future Template or Imaginal Rehearsing, Shapiro, 2006)

Have the client close his or her eyes and run a mental videotape/movie of the time between the present session and the successful completion of the contract. Each distressing aspect of the sequence is reprocessed as it arises. The whole sequence is repeated until it is possible for him or her to view the entire videotape/movie without fear or any other negative effect.

Say, *"Before you fulfill our contract, close your eyes and imagine a movie or videotape of the time between the present session and the successful completion of _____ (state the agreed upon action). Open your eyes if there is any disturbance and then we will process this until the disturbance decreases. Before we start, do you have any questions?"*

_____

_____

_____

Say, *"Okay, go ahead and run the movie."*

If clients open their eyes, use BLS to reprocess the material and then have them continue.

Say, *"Go with that."*

When the disturbance has decreased for this disturbing moment or aspect, say the following:

Say, *"Continue the movie, again opening your eyes if there is any disturbance or until you have completed the action successfully in your mind."*

If there is more disturbance, continue to run the movie until the disturbance decreases. If it does not decrease, check for earlier incidents, blocking beliefs, anxieties, or fears that have been triggered and then process them with the Standard EMDR Protocol.

If there is no disturbance, move on to Step 6.

Step 6: Complete Reprocessing of Targets Revealed Between Sessions—Reevaluation

Instruct client to keep a log including TICES (Trigger, Image, Cognition, Emotion, Sensation) so that any targets revealed in between sessions can be reprocessed.

Say, *"The processing we have done today may continue after the session. You may or may not notice new insights, thoughts, memories, or dreams. If so, just notice what you are experiencing—take a snapshot of it in a log—what you are seeing, feeling, thinking, and the trigger on the TICES grid (Trigger, Image, Cognition, Emotion, Sensation, and SUDs). Use the Safe Place exercise to rid yourself of any disturbance. Remember to use a relaxation technique daily. We can work on this new material next time. If you feel it is necessary, call me."*

Work with any other undifferentiated material that comes up during the week.

Protocol for Excessive Grief

Scripted by Marilyn Luber
(Francine Shapiro, 2001)

Excessive Grief Script Notes

This protocol is to be used when there is a high level of suffering, self-denigration, and lack of remediation over time concerning the loss of a loved one. EMDR does not eliminate healthy appropriate emotions, including grief. It allows clients to mourn with a greater sense of inner peace. The protocol is similar to the Standard EMDR Protocol for trauma.

The goal of this work is to have your client accept the loss and think back on aspects of life with the loved one with a wide range of feelings, including an appreciation for the positive experiences they shared. Francine Shapiro often brings up the issue: *How long does one have to grieve?* She asks us to not place our limitations on our clients as this would be antithetical to the notion of the ecological validity of the client's self-healing process. For example, a woman who believed that the death of her infant son was her fault despite her doing everything she could to prevent it, worked with EMDR soon after his death. "I can feel him in my heart. I am grateful for the time we had together. He's in a better place." Her work with EMDR did not take away her grieving but allowed her to accept the loss and to have a full range of feelings about her son.

The following is a summary of the Excessive Grief Protocol (Shapiro, 2001, p. 232). When there is excessive grief, target the following:

Past Memories

1. Actual events, including the loved one's suffering or death
2. Intrusive images
3. Nightmare images

Present Triggers

4. Present triggers
5. Issues of personal responsibility, mortality, or previous unresolved losses

Future Template

6. Create a future template

Excessive Grief Protocol Script

Past Memories

Step 1: Process Actual Events, Including the Loved One's Suffering or Death

Say, *"What are the moments or events that stand out concerning your loved one's death?"*

_____

_____

_____

_____

_____

Reprocess the event using the Standard EMDR Protocol.

Incident

Say, *"The memory that we will start with today is* _____ (state the target of the loved one's suffering or death)."

_____

_____

Say, *"What happens when you think of* _____ (state the target of the loved one's suffering or death)?"

_____

_____

Or say, *"When you think of* _____ (state the target of the loved one's suffering or death), *what do you get?"*

_____

_____

_____

Picture

Say, *"What picture represents the entire* _____ (state the target of the loved one's suffering or death)?"

_____

_____

Say, *"What picture represents the most traumatic part of the* _____ (state the target of the loved one's suffering or death)?"

_____

_____

Negative Cognition (NC)

Say, *"What words best go with the picture that express your negative belief about yourself now?"*

_____

_____

Positive Cognition (PC)

Say, *"When you bring up that picture or _____ (state the target of the loved one's suffering or death), what would you like to believe about yourself now?"*

_____

_____

Validity of Cognition (VoC)

Say, *"When you think of the _____ (state the target of the loved one's suffering or death, or picture), how true do those words _____ (clinician repeats the positive cognition) feel to you now on a scale of 1 to 7, where 1 feels completely false and 7 feels completely true?"*

1	2	3	4	5	6	7
(completely false)				(completely true)		

Sometimes, it is necessary to explain further.

Say, *"Remember, sometimes we know something with our head, but it feels differently in our gut. In this case, what is the gut-level feeling of the truth of _____ (clinician states the positive cognition), from 1 (completely false) to 7 (completely true)?"*

1	2	3	4	5	6	7
(completely false)				(completely true)		

Emotions

Say, *"When you bring up the picture _____ (state the target of the loved one's suffering or death) and those words _____ (clinician states the negative cognition), what emotion do you feel now?"*

_____

_____

Subjective Units of Disturbance (SUD)

Say, *"On a scale of 0 to 10, where 0 is no disturbance or neutral and 10 is the highest disturbance you can imagine, how disturbing does it feel now?"*

0	1	2	3	4	5	6	7	8	9	10
(no disturbance)							(highest disturbance)			

Location of Body Sensation

Say, *"Where do you feel it* (the disturbance) *in your body?"*

_____

_____

Continue with Phases 4 through 7 for each incident.

Step 2: Process Any Intrusive Images That Are Occurring

Say, *"Are there any intrusive images that you are experiencing?"*

_____

_____

_____

_____

_____

Reprocess any intrusive images using the EMDR Standard Protocol.

Incident

Say, *"The intrusive image that we will start with today is _____* (select the intrusive incident to be targeted).*"*

_____

_____

_____

Say, *"What happens when you think of the intrusive image?"*

_____

_____

_____

Or say, *"When you think of the intrusive image, what do you get?"*

_____

_____

_____

Picture

Say, *"What picture represents the entire intrusive image?"*

_____

_____

Say, *"What picture represents the most traumatic part of the intrusive image?"*

_____

_____

Negative Cognition (NC)

Say, *"What words best go with the picture that express your negative belief about yourself now?"*

_____

_____

Positive Cognition (PC)

Say, *"When you bring up that picture or intrusive image, what would you like to believe about yourself now?"*

_____

_____

Validity of Cognition (VoC)

Say, *"When you think of the intrusive image* (or picture), *how true do those words* _____ (clinician repeats the positive cognition) *feel to you now on a scale of 1 to 7, where 1 feels completely false and 7 feels completely true?"*

1	2	3	4	5	6	7
(completely false)				(completely true)		

Sometimes, it is necessary to explain further.

Say, *"Remember, sometimes we know something with our head, but it feels differently in our gut. In this case, what is the gut-level feeling of the truth of* _____ (clinician states the positive cognition), *from 1* (completely false) *to 7* (completely true)*?"*

1	2	3	4	5	6	7
(completely false)				(completely true)		

Emotions

Say, *"When you bring up the picture* (or intrusive image) *and those words* _____ (clinician states the negative cognition), *what emotion do you feel now?"*

_____

_____

Subjective Units of Disturbance (SUD)

Say, *"On a scale of 0 to 10, where 0 is no disturbance or neutral and 10 is the highest disturbance you can imagine, how disturbing does it feel now?"*

0	1	2	3	4	5	6	7	8	9	10
(no disturbance)							(highest disturbance)			

Location of Body Sensation

Say, *"Where do you feel it* (the disturbance) *in your body?"*

_____

_____

Continue with Phases 4 through 7 for each incident. Process all of the intrusive images, checking after the completion of each one to see if other targets need to be processed. If so, continue the processing until all are completed and then move on to the next step.

Step 3: Process the Nightmare Images

Say, *"Are you having any nightmares concerning your loved one? What are the images that are coming up from your nightmares?"*

_____

_____

_____

_____

_____

Process the nightmares concerning the loved one with the Standard EMDR Protocol.

Incident

Say, *"The nightmare that we will start with today is _____ (select the nightmare to be targeted)."*

_____

_____

_____

Say, *"What happens when you think of the nightmare?"*

_____

_____

_____

Or say, *"When you think of the nightmare, what do you get?"*

_____

_____

_____

Picture

Say, *"What picture represents the entire nightmare?"*

_____

_____

Say, *"What picture represents the most traumatic part of the nightmare?"*

_____

_____

Negative Cognition (NC)

Say, *"What words best go with the nightmare that express your negative belief about yourself now?"*

_____

_____

Positive Cognition (PC)

Say, *"When you bring up that picture or nightmare, what would you like to believe about yourself now?"*

_____

_____

Validity of Cognition (VoC)

Say, *"When you think of the nightmare* (or picture), *how true do those words* _____ (clinician repeats the positive cognition) *feel to you now on a scale of 1 to 7, where 1 feels completely false and 7 feels completely true?"*

1	2	3	4	5	6	7
(completely false)				(completely true)		

Sometimes, it is necessary to explain further.

Say, *"Remember, sometimes we know something with our head, but it feels differently in our gut. In this case, what is the gut-level feeling of the truth of* _____ (clinician states the positive cognition), *from 1* (completely false) *to 7* (completely true)?"

1	2	3	4	5	6	7
(completely false)				(completely true)		

Emotions

Say, *"When you bring up the picture* (nightmare) *and those words* _____ (clinician states the negative cognition), *what emotion do you feel now?"*

_____

_____

Subjective Units of Disturbance (SUD)

Say, *"On a scale of 0 to 10, where 0 is no disturbance or neutral and 10 is the highest disturbance you can imagine, how disturbing does it feel now?"*

0	1	2	3	4	5	6	7	8	9	10
(no disturbance)							(highest disturbance)			

Location of Body Sensation

Say, *"Where do you feel it* (the disturbance) *in your body?"*

_____

_____

Continue with Phases 4 through 7 for each incident. Process all of the nightmares, checking after the completion of each one to see if other targets need to be processed. If so, continue the processing until all are completed and then move on to the next step.

Present Triggers

Step 4: Process Any Stimuli or Triggers Associated with the Grief Experience

Say, *"What situations, events, or stimuli trigger your grief? Let's process these situations, events, or stimuli triggers one by one."*

Situations, Events, or Stimuli of Grief Trigger List

_____

_____

_____

_____

_____

Incident

Say, *"The situation, event, or stimulus that triggers you that we will start with today is* _____ (select the next trigger to be targeted).*"*

_____

_____

Say, *"What happens when you think of the* _____ (state the situation, event, or stimulus) *that triggers you?"*

_____

_____

Or say, *"When you think of* _____ (state the situation, event, or stimulus) *that triggers you, what do you get?"*

_____

_____

_____

Picture

Say, *"What picture represents the entire* _____ (state the situation, event, or stimulus) *that triggers you?"*

_____

_____

Say, *"What picture represents the most traumatic part of the* _____ (state the situation, event, or stimulus) *that triggers you?"*

_____

_____

Negative Cognition (NC)

Say, *"What words best go with the picture that express your negative belief about yourself now?"*

_____

_____

Positive Cognition (PC)

Say, *"When you bring up that picture or* _____ (state the situation, event, or stimulus) *that triggers you, what would you like to believe about yourself now?"*

_____

_____

Validity of Cognition (VoC)

Say, *"When you think of the* _____ (state the situation, event, or stimulus) *that triggers you* (or picture), *how true do those words* _____ (clinician repeats the positive cognition) *feel to you now on a scale of 1 to 7, where 1 feels completely false and 7 feels completely true?"*

1   2   3   4   5   6   7
(completely false)   (completely true)

Sometimes, it is necessary to explain further.

Say, *"Remember, sometimes we know something with our head, but it feels differently in our gut. In this case, what is the gut-level feeling of the truth of* _____ (clinician states the positive cognition), *from 1* (completely false) *to 7* (completely true)?"

1   2   3   4   5   6   7
(completely false)   (completely true)

Emotions

Say, *"When you bring up the picture or* _____ (state the situation, event, or stimulus) *that triggers you and those words* _____ (clinician states the negative cognition), *what emotion do you feel now?"*

_____

_____

Subjective Units of Disturbance (SUD)

Say, *"On a scale of 0 to 10, where 0 is no disturbance or neutral and 10 is the highest disturbance you can imagine, how disturbing does it feel now?"*

0	1	2	3	4	5	6	7	8	9	10
(no disturbance)										(highest disturbance)

Location of Body Sensation

Say, *"Where do you feel it* (the disturbance) *in your body?"*

_____

_____

Continue with Phases 4 through 7 for each incident. Process all of the present triggers, checking after the completion of each one to see if other targets need to be processed. If so, continue the processing until all are completed and then move on to the next step.

Step 5: Address Issues of Personal Responsibility, Mortality, or Previous Unresolved Losses

Personal responsibility and safety issues may arise after the intense sadness and emotional pain are processed. Jot them down as your client is processing them and make sure to be respectful as he reveals this hidden part of his suffering. Look for earlier experiences of unresolved emotional loss(es). Make sure to question the client's thoughts about personal injury or the mortality of other family members. Using the Float-Back Technique and/or the Affect Scan can be helpful here.

Say, *"Are there any other issues where you felt responsible for saying or doing something negative or unkind to your loved one?"*

_____

_____

_____

_____

Say, *"Are there any other issues that you have concerning your personal safety or the personal safety of others?"*

_____

_____

_____

Say, *"Are there earlier losses that have come up since the loss of your loved one?"*

_____

_____

_____

_____

_____

Say, *"Are you concerned about anything happening to other family members or friends in your life since your loss or before?"*

_____

_____

_____

_____

_____

Reprocess these issues using the Standard EMDR Protocol.

Incident

Say, *"The issue that we will start with today is _____* (select the next issue to be targeted).*"*

_____

_____

_____

Say, *"What happens when you think of _____* (state the issue)*?"*

_____

_____

_____

Or say, *"When you think of _____* (state the issue), *what do you get?"*

_____

_____

_____

Picture

Say, *"What picture represents the entire _____* (state the issue)*?"*

_____

_____

Say, *"What picture represents the most traumatic part of _____* (state the issue)*?"*

_____

_____

Negative Cognition (NC)

Say, *"What words best go with the picture that express your negative belief about yourself now?"*

_____

_____

Positive Cognition (PC)

Say, *"When you bring up that picture or _____ (state the issue), what would you like to believe about yourself, now?"*

_____

_____

Validity of Cognition (VoC)

Say, *"When you think of the _____ (state the issue, or picture), how true do those words _____ (clinician repeats the positive cognition) feel to you now on a scale of 1 to 7, where 1 feels completely false and 7 feels completely true?"*

  1   2   3   4   5   6   7
(completely false)   (completely true)

Sometimes, it is necessary to explain further.

Say, *"Remember, sometimes we know something with our head, but it feels differently in our gut. In this case, what is the gut-level feeling of the truth of _____ (clinician states the positive cognition), from 1 (completely false) to 7 (completely true)?"*

  1   2   3   4   5   6   7
(completely false)   (completely true)

Emotions

Say, *"When you bring up the picture _____ (state the issue), and those words _____ (clinician states the negative cognition), what emotion do you feel now?"*

_____

_____

Subjective Units of Disturbance (SUD)

Say, *"On a scale of 0 to 10, where 0 is no disturbance or neutral and 10 is the highest disturbance you can imagine, how disturbing does it feel now?"*

  0   1   2   3   4   5   6   7   8   9   10
(no disturbance)   (highest disturbance)

Location of Body Sensation

Say, *"Where do you feel it (the disturbance) in your body?"*

_____

_____

Process all of the relevant issues concerning personal responsibility, mortality, or previous unresolved losses, checking after the completion of each one to see if other targets need to be processed. If so, continue the processing until all are completed. Again, remember that the goal of this work is to have your client accept the loss and think back on aspects of life with the loved one with a wide range of feelings, including an appreciation for the positive experiences they shared and how to hold those positive feelings and move forward into the future.

Future Template

Create a Future Template

Note that in the summary for the Protocol for Excessive Grief (Shapiro, 2001, p. 225), Dr. Shapiro does not mention the use of any future templates, however, the use of the future template is implicit in all EMDR work. See Appendix C.

Illness and Somatic Disorders Protocol

Scripted by Marilyn Luber
(Francine Shapiro, 2001)

Illness and Somatic Disorders Script Notes

When the perpetrator is the client's own body, the Illness and Somatic Disorders Protocol can be used. It is important to note that this protocol addresses both psychological and physical factors related to somatic complaints. This is not a substitute for appropriate medical care but an adjunct to it. For many, addressing the psychological dimensions will cause partial or complete remission of the physical symptoms. When primarily organic processes are involved, the psychological issues may be exacerbating the physical conditions. While physical symptoms may not remit, the clinical emphasis is on improving the person's quality of life (Shapiro, 2001).

The following is a summary of the Illness and Somatic Disorders Protocol (Shapiro, 2001, p. 234).

1. Create an action plan to address real needs.

2. Identify and reprocess relevant memories, present situations, and fears of the future dealing with

   a. Personal and physical constraints

   b. Social issues

   c. Medical experiences

3. Run "videotape" of the next 1 to 5 years.

4. Use Simonton-type imagery with appropriate cognitive groundwork.

5. Identify suitable positive cognitions.

6. Link image and positive cognition.

7. Assign homework with the self-use procedure.

8. Use log and self-care procedures.

Illness and Somatic Disorders Protocol Script

Step 1: Action Plan

Create an action plan to address the real needs of the client.

> Say, *"What are the real life issues and most pressing needs that are affecting you concerning any current issues such as problems with finance, career, or relationship? Before we address the psychological aspects of your illness, let us first devise a plan of action to deal with these problems. We are doing this because realistic fears may interfere with your ability to focus on and reprocess your psychological issues."*

_____

_____

_____

_____

_____

Note: An exception to this strategy is when the primary presentation has symptoms that are very strong. In this case, the primary intrusions should be addressed before targeting the rest of the symptoms because these fears can hamper the client's ability to think logically and effectively enough to construct appropriate action plans. Also, if there is a concern about implementing the action plan, use this as a target and use EMDR to process the concerns.

> Say, *"It seems like you have some major issues that are intruding on your well-being. Let's process these first before we work on your action plan."*
>
> Or say, *"You seem to be having concerns about implementing your action plan. Let's start working with EMDR and process your concern about implementing your action plan."*

_____

_____

_____

Incident

> Say, *"What happens when you think of _____ (state concern about implementing action plan)?"*

_____

_____

_____

> Or say, *"When you think of _____ (state concern about implementing action plan), what do you get?"*

_____

_____

_____

Picture

Say, *"What picture represents the entire* _____ (state concern about implementing action plan)*?"*

_____

_____

Say, *"What picture represents the most traumatic part of* _____ (state concern about implementing action plan)*?"*

_____

_____

Negative Cognition (NC)

Say, *"What words best go with the picture that express your negative belief about yourself now?"*

_____

_____

Positive Cognition (PC)

Say, *"When you bring up that picture or* _____ (state concern about implementing action plan), *what would you like to believe about yourself now?"*

_____

_____

Validity of Cognition (VoC)

Say, *"When you think of the* _____ (state concern about implementing action plan, or picture), *how true do those words* _____ (clinician repeats the positive cognition) *feel to you now on a scale of 1 to 7, where 1 feels completely false and 7 feels completely true?"*

1	2	3	4	5	6	7
(completely false)				(completely true)		

Sometimes, it is necessary to explain further.

Say, *"Remember, sometimes we know something with our head, but it feels differently in our gut. In this case, what is the gut-level feeling of the truth of* _____ (clinician state the positive cognition), *from 1 (completely false) to 7 (completely true)?"*

1	2	3	4	5	6	7
(completely false)				(completely true)		

Emotions

Say, *"When you bring up the picture or* _____ (state concern about implementing action plan) *and those words* _____ (clinician states the negative cognition), *what emotion do you feel now?"*

_____

_____

Subjective Units of Disturbance (SUD)

Say, *"On a scale of 0 to 10, where 0 is no disturbance or neutral and 10 is the highest disturbance you can imagine, how disturbing does it feel now?"*

0	1	2	3	4	5	6	7	8	9	10

(no disturbance)   (highest disturbance)

Location of Body Sensation

Say, *"Where do you feel it* (the disturbance) *in your body?"*

_____

_____

Use Phases 4 through 7 with each incident. When the intrusive symptoms have been addressed and the action plan has been formulated, make sure to check if the client has any dysfunctional fears or doubts about implementing the action plan.

Say, *"Okay. Now that we have completed the action plan do you have any fears or doubts about implementing the action plan?"*

_____

_____

If no, go to step 2.
If yes, do the following:

Say, *"What are the fears and doubts that you have about implementing your action plan?"*

List of Fears and Doubts

_____

_____

_____

_____

Incident

If there is more than one incident, ask the following:

Say, *"What is the fear or doubt you would like to target first?"*

_____

_____

Say, *"Can you think of a specific situation that occurred that would typify _____ (state the fear or doubt)?"*

_____

_____

_____

Or say, *"When was _____ (state the situation) experienced?"*

_____

_____

_____

Or say, *"Can you imagine _____ (state the situation)? When was that?"*

_____

_____

_____

Picture

Say, *"What picture represents _____ (state the situation)?"*

_____

_____

Negative Cognition (NC)

Say, *"What words best go with the picture that express your negative belief about yourself now?"*

_____

_____

Positive Cognition (PC)

Say, *"When you bring up that picture or _____ (state the situation), what would you like to believe about yourself, now?"*

_____

_____

Validity of Cognition (VoC)

Say, *"When you think of _____ (state the situation, or picture), how true do those words _____ (clinician repeats the positive cognition) feel to you now on a scale of 1 to 7, where 1 feels completely false and 7 feels completely true?"*

1   2   3   4   5   6   7
(completely false)   (completely true)

Sometimes, it is necessary to explain further.

Say, *"Remember, sometimes we know something with our head, but it feels differently in our gut. In this case, what is the gut-level feeling of the truth of _____ (clinician state the positive cognition), from 1 (completely false) to 7 (completely true)?"*

1   2   3   4   5   6   7
(completely false)   (completely true)

Emotions

Say, *"When you bring up the picture* _____ (or state the fear or doubt) *and those words* _____ (clinician states the negative cognition), *what emotion do you feel now?"*

_____

_____

Subjective Units of Disturbance (SUD)

Say, *"On a scale of 0 to 10, where 0 is no disturbance or neutral and 10 is the highest disturbance you can imagine, how disturbing does it feel now?"*

0	1	2	3	4	5	6	7	8	9	10
(no disturbance)										(highest disturbance)

Location of Body Sensation

Say, *"Where do you feel it* (the disturbance) *in your body?"*

_____

_____

Work with Phases 4 through 7 in the Standard EMDR Protocol.

Process as many fears and doubts as needed so that the action plan can be implemented. Then check after you have addressed each fear or doubt to see if there are any that remain. Continue to process until all concerns are reprocessed and whatever other issues that need to be addressed are resolved.

Step 2: Identify and Reprocess Past, Present, and Future Relevant Issues

Identify and reprocess relevant memories, present situations, and fears of the future dealing with the following issues:

1. Personal or physical constraints
2. Social and family issues
3. Medical experiences

Say, *"Let's identify the relevant past memories, present situations, and fears of the future that you have concerning your own personal and physical constraints because of your illness, social issues that are relevant, and any past, present, or future medical concerns."*

Past Memories

Say, *"When you think of your illness, are there any concerns about situations that have occurred with family, friends, or socially?"*

_____

_____

_____

Say, *"How have your family and friends responded or not responded to you since your illness began?"*

_____

_____

_____

_____

Say, *"What has the effect been on you?"*

_____

_____

_____

_____

Say, *"Have there been medical experiences that have occurred that come to mind concerning anything that has happened to you during this current illness or any past illnesses or experiences with medical personnel or hospitals?"*

_____

_____

_____

If not addressed, ask about the following:

Say, *"What happened when you were first diagnosed with your problem?"*

_____

_____

_____

Say, *"What personal or physical constraints have occurred because of your illness or problem?"*

_____

_____

_____

Say, *"What are your feelings about your illness?"*

_____

_____

_____

_____

Say, *"How have you managed or not managed your emotions about this illness?"*

_____

_____

_____

_____

Say, *"Are you able to speak up for yourself concerning your needs with family, friends, and medical personnel?"*

_____

_____

_____

_____

Process these past issues first, unless, again, pressing issues arise.

Incident

Say, *"Which incident of the _____ (state the issue) would you like to work on?"*

_____

_____

_____

Say, *"What happens when you think of _____ (state the issue)?"*

_____

_____

_____

Or say, *"When you think of _____ (state the issue), what do you get?"*

_____

_____

_____

Picture

Say, *"What picture represents the entire _____ (state the issue)?"*

_____

_____

Say, **"What picture represents the most traumatic part of the _____ (state the issue)?"*

_____

_____

Negative Cognition (NC)

Say, *"What words best go with the picture that express your negative belief about yourself now?"*

_____

_____

Positive Cognition (PC)

Say, "When you bring up that picture or _____ (state the issue), what would you like to believe about yourself now?"

_____

_____

Validity of Cognition (VoC)

Say, "When you think of _____ (state the issue, or picture), how true do those words _____ (clinician repeats the positive cognition) feel to you now on a scale of 1 to 7, where 1 feels completely false and 7 feels completely true?"

1   2   3   4   5   6   7
(completely false)   (completely true)

Sometimes, it is necessary to explain further.

Say, "Remember, sometimes we know something with our head, but it feels differently in our gut. In this case, what is the gut-level feeling of the truth of _____ (clinician state the positive cognition), from 1 (completely false) to 7 (completely true)?"

1   2   3   4   5   6   7
(completely false)   (completely true)

Emotions

Say, "When you bring up the picture _____ (state the issue) and those words _____ (clinician states the negative cognition), what emotion do you feel now?"

_____

_____

Subjective Units of Disturbance (SUD)

Say, "On a scale of 0 to 10, where 0 is no disturbance or neutral and 10 is the highest disturbance you can imagine, how disturbing does it feel now?"

0   1   2   3   4   5   6   7   8   9   10
(no disturbance)   (highest disturbance)

Location of Body Sensation

Say, "Where do you feel it (the disturbance) in your body?"

_____

_____

Use Phases 4 through 7 for each incident. Work with the past issues, checking to see if the other targets have been processed or still need to be processed with the Standard EMDR Protocol. Continue to process the past issues until they are no longer an issue.

Present Situations

Check to see what the current situations are that have to do with personal or physical constraints, social issues, or medical experiences.

If in need of physical assistance, ask the following:

Say, *"How are you handling having to ask for help or being dependent on others to help you?"*

_____

_____

_____

_____

Say, *"How are family and friends doing with you and your illness currently?"*

_____

_____

_____

If there are difficulties, ask the following:

Say, *"How are you doing with the way* _____ (state who is having the problem) *is handling this?"*

_____

_____

_____

Say, *"What are you thinking and feeling about how you are handling the situation?"*

_____

_____

_____

Say, *"How are you feeling about* _____ (state whatever medical procedure might be necessary)*?"*

_____

_____

_____

Say, *"Are there current personal or physical issues that are of concern for you now?"*

_____

_____

_____

It is important to address the issue of secondary gain that can arise in situations of illness and somatic disorders.

Say, *"Does your illness allow you to get the nurturing that you have needed but would not have received without your illness?"*

_____

_____

_____

Say, *"Are you able to be clear about your needs with people, especially concerning what you want them to do or not do? Tell me about your experience(s)."*

_____

_____

_____

Say, *"Does your illness allow you to avoid difficult situations that otherwise you would have to participate in? If so, what would it or they be?"*

_____

_____

_____

Note: Remember the importance of cognitive interweaves that may be relevant to your client that have to do with safety, responsibility, or choice.

Incident

Say, *"The issue that we will start with today is* _____ (select the next incident to be targeted).*"*

_____

_____

_____

Say, *"Can you think of a specific situation that occurred that would typify* _____ (state the incident)*?"*

_____

_____

_____

Or say, *"When was* _____ (state the incident) *experienced?"*

_____

_____

_____

Or say, *"Can you imagine* _____ (state the incident)*? When was that?"*

_____

_____

_____

Say, *"What happens when you think of* _____ (state the incident)*?"*

_____

_____

_____

Or say, "When you think of _____ (state the incident), *what do you get?"*

_____

_____

_____

Picture

Say, *"What picture represents the entire* _____ (state the incident)*?"*

_____

_____

Say, *"What picture represents the most traumatic part of* _____ (state the incident)*?"*

_____

_____

Negative Cognition (NC)

Say, *"What words best go with the picture that express your negative belief about yourself now?"*

_____

_____

Positive Cognition (PC)

Say, *"When you bring up that picture or* _____ (state the incident), *what would you like to believe about yourself now?"*

_____

_____

Validity of Cognition (VoC)

Say, *"When you think of the* _____ (state the incident, or picture), *how true do those words* _____ (clinician repeats the positive cognition) *feel to you now on a scale of 1 to 7, where 1 feels completely false and 7 feels completely true?"*

1   2   3   4   5   6   7
(completely false)   (completely true)

Sometimes, it is necessary to explain further.

Say, *"Remember, sometimes we know something with our head, but it feels differently in our gut. In this case, what is the gut-level feeling of the truth of* _____ (clinician states the positive cognition), *from 1 (completely false) to 7 (completely true)?"*

1   2   3   4   5   6   7
(completely false)   (completely true)

Emotions

> Say, *"When you bring up the picture _____ (state the incident)
> and those words _____ (clinician states the negative cognition),
> what emotion do you feel now?"*

_____

_____

Subjective Units of Disturbance (SUD)

> Say, *"On a scale of 0 to 10, where 0 is no disturbance or neutral and 10 is the
> highest disturbance you can imagine, how disturbing does it feel now?"*

> 0   1   2   3   4   5   6   7   8   9   10
> (no disturbance)   (highest disturbance)

Location of Body Sensation

> Say, *"Where do you feel it* (the disturbance) *in your body?"*

_____

_____

Continue with Phases 4 through 7 for each incident. Process all of the relevant
issues, checking after the completion of each one to see if other targets need to be
processed. If so, continue the processing until all are completed and then move on
to the next step.

Future Issues

Check to see what future situations have to do with personal or physical constraints, social issues, or medical experiences for the client.

> Say, *"What are your concerns for the future when it comes to family
> and friends?"*

_____

_____

_____

_____

> Say, *"What about other social issues?"*

_____

_____

_____

_____

> Say, *"Are there particular medical issues that you are concerned about?"*

_____

_____

_____

_____

Say, *"Any concerns about personal or physical constraints in the future?"*

_____

_____

_____

_____

Work with the issues above using the Standard EMDR Protocol.

Incident

Say, *"With which future issue would you like to start?"*

_____

_____

Say, *"Can you think of a specific situation that occurred that would typify _____ (state the issue)?"*

_____

_____

_____

Or say, *"When was _____ (state the issue) experienced?"*

_____

_____

_____

Or say, *"Can you imagine _____ (state the issue)? When was that?"*

_____

_____

_____

Say, *"What happens when you think of _____ (state the issue)?"*

_____

_____

_____

Or say, *"When you think of _____ (state the issue), what do you get?"*

_____

_____

_____

Picture

Say, *"What picture represents the entire _____ (state the issue)?"*

_____

_____

Say, *"What picture represents the most traumatic part of* _____ (state the issue)*?"*

_____

_____

Negative Cognition (NC)

Say, *"What words best go with the picture that express your negative belief about yourself now?"*

_____

_____

Positive Cognition (PC)

Say, *"When you bring up that picture or* _____ (state the issue), *what would you like to believe about yourself now?"*

_____

_____

Validity of Cognition (VoC)

Say, *"When you think of* _____ (state the issue, or picture), *how true do those words* _____ (clinician repeats the positive cognition) *feel to you now on a scale of 1 to 7, where 1 feels completely false and 7 feels completely true?"*

1	2	3	4	5	6	7
(completely false)				(completely true)		

Sometimes, it is necessary to explain further.

Say, *"Remember, sometimes we know something with our head, but it feels differently in our gut. In this case, what is the gut-level feeling of the truth of* _____ (clinician states the positive cognition), *from 1 (completely false) to 7 (completely true)?"*

1	2	3	4	5	6	7
(completely false)				(completely true)		

Emotions

Say, *"When you bring up the picture* (or state the issue) *and those words* _____ (clinician states the negative cognition), *what emotion do you feel now?"*

_____

_____

Subjective Units of Disturbance (SUD)

Say, *"On a scale of 0 to 10, where 0 is no disturbance or neutral and 10 is the highest disturbance you can imagine, how disturbing does it feel now?"*

0	1	2	3	4	5	6	7	8	9	10
(no disturbance)							(highest disturbance)			

Location of Body Sensation

Say, *"Where do you feel it* (the disturbance) *in your body?"*

_____

_____

Remember to do Phases 4 through 7 of the Standard EMDR Protocol for each of the above issues, checking to see, after the completion of each target, if the other targets are still an issue or need to be processed. Continue until all are neutral.

After processing and completing the above issues, check with the client concerning several important issues concerning his future and how the client is thinking about himself.

Say, *"Who am I without* _____ (state disease)*?"*

_____

_____

_____

_____

_____

Or say, *"What do I have to change or confront?"*

_____

_____

Or say, *"Do I want to live?"*

_____

_____

_____

_____

_____

Use the Standard EMDR Protocol to target each of the above answers as needed.

Incident

Say, *"With which concern would you like to begin?"*

_____

_____

_____

Say, *"What happens when you think of* _____ (state the issue)*?"*

_____

_____

_____

Or say, *"When you think of* _____ (state the issue), *what do you get?"*

_____

_____

_____

Picture

Say, *"What picture represents the entire _____ (state the issue)?"*

_____

_____

Say, *"What picture represents the most traumatic part of _____ (state the issue)?"*

_____

_____

Negative Cognition (NC)

Say, *"What words best go with the picture that express your negative belief about yourself now?"*

_____

_____

Positive Cognition (PC)

Say, *"When you bring up that picture or _____ (state the issue), what would you like to believe about yourself, now?"*

_____

_____

Validity of Cognition (VoC)

Say, *"When you think of _____ (state the issue, or picture), how true do those words _____ (clinician repeats the positive cognition) feel to you now on a scale of 1 to 7, where 1 feels completely false and 7 feels completely true?"*

1   2   3   4   5   6   7
(completely false)   (completely true)

Sometimes, it is necessary to explain further.

Say, *"Remember, sometimes we know something with our head, but it feels differently in our gut. In this case, what is the gut-level feeling of the truth of _____ (clinician states the positive cognition), from 1 (completely false) to 7 (completely true)?"*

1   2   3   4   5   6   7
(completely false)   (completely true)

Emotions

Say, *"When you bring up the picture or _____ (state the issue) and those words _____ (clinician states the negative cognition), what emotion do you feel now?"*

_____

_____

Subjective Units of Disturbance (SUD)

Say, *"On a scale of 0 to 10, where 0 is no disturbance or neutral and 10 is the highest disturbance you can imagine, how disturbing does it feel now?"*

0	1	2	3	4	5	6	7	8	9	10
(no disturbance)									(highest disturbance)	

Location of Body Sensation

Say, *"Where do you feel it* (the disturbance) *in your body?"*

_____

_____

Step 3: "Videotape" of the Next 1 to 5 Years (Future Template)

Run a videotape of the next 1 to 5 years.

Say, *"I would like you to envision yourself in the healthy state that you would like to be in the next 1 to 5 years of your life. How would that feel?"*

_____

_____

The future template can also be used to target specific events such as before, during, or after surgery, getting chemotherapy or any other types of specialized treatments, and so forth.

Or say, *"I would like you to envision yourself* _____ (state the specific situation) *in the* _____ (describe the state the client would embody during this situation). *How would that feel?"*

Say, *"What would you be seeing and hearing as you experience this healthy state?"*

_____

_____

Say, *"Okay, now what are the positive words you would like to say about this healthy state?"*

_____

_____

Next, ask the client to move from imagining this one scene or snapshot to imagining a movie about coping in the future, with a beginning, middle, and end. Encourage him to imagine coping effectively in the face of specific challenges, triggers, or snafus. Make some suggestions to help inoculate him for future problems.

Say, *"This time, I'd like you to close your eyes and play a movie, imagining yourself coping effectively in this healthy state where* _____ (name the qualities above) *in the future. With the new positive belief* _____ (state positive belief) *and your new sense of* _____ (strength, clarity, confidence, calm), *imagine stepping into the future. Imagine yourself coping with ANY challenges that come your way. Make sure that this movie has a beginning, a middle, and an end. Notice what you are seeing, thinking, feeling, and experiencing in your body. Let me know if you hit any blocks. If you do, just open your eyes and let me know. If you don't hit any blocks, let me know when you have viewed the whole movie."*

_____

_____

If the client hits blocks, address as above with bilateral stimulation (BLS), interweaves, new skills, information, resources, direct questions, Affect Scan, Float-Back, and so forth.

If the client is able to play the movie from start to finish with a sense of confidence and satisfaction, ask the client to play the movie one more time from beginning to end and introduce BLS. In a sense, you are installing this movie as a future template.

Say, *"Okay, play the movie one more time from beginning to end. Go with that."*

Use BLS.

If the client must accept death from the illness, the clinician should use EMDR to target his ability to reconcile with his family and friends, put his estate in order, and cope with the fears of death itself. It is helpful to play an imagined videotape for this purpose as well. EMDR has also been used in the hospital to assist clients who are suffering from intractable pain to let go of the guilt they feel about wanting to die and be released from the pain.

Step 4: Bolstering the Immune System With Imagery

There are many ways to bolster the immune system in order to facilitate the healing process, however, death may be inevitable for some clients. Therefore, it is important to couch the material in a way that invites a possible healing but also concentrates on the client's quality of life. The client must be made to understand that he is not responsible for the disease because his susceptibility to stressors that inhibit the immune system may be genetic, and the early modeling that encouraged some types of reactions and any psychological characteristics foisted on him long before he had any choice in the matter.

If this is an issue for the client, you can say the following:

Say, *"Even though you think that you might be responsible for ____ (state the disease), the fact is that we know that your susceptibility to stressors that inhibit the immune system may be genetic. Also, the way you learned to respond when you were very young was foisted on you way before you had a choice in this matter. The fact is you are not responsible for this illness."*

Use Simonton-type imagery (Simonton & Creighton, 1982) with appropriate cognitive groundwork as they have found that patients' attitude and mental imagery contributed to their survival rate. They suggested helping patients to formulate a mental image of the immune system as a powerful entity capable in some way of defeating the weak, as in working with cancer cells. When working with cancer, assure the client that cancer cells are the weakest in the system and that is why chemotherapy and radiation therapy work. It is important to gear the imagery to the client's psychological makeup and personal belief. A destructive, warlike force may be appropriate for some, whereas an image of the Heart of Mary or other spiritual icon sending in a healing light would be a better choice for others.

Say, *"Today we are going to use imagery to help support your immune system. Can you think of an image that would be effective for you? Some people choose a destructive, warlike force destroying the cells while others choose a spiritual person like Mary sending in a healing light. What type of imagery would work best for you?"*

_____

_____

The use of imagery can be helpful with other illnesses. It is helpful to understand the nature of the disease process of the client and use appropriate imagery.

Step 5: Identify Suitable Positive Cognitions

Identify suitable PCs.

Next say, *"Now, please think of a positive statement that goes with the image. What might that be? Some people might use a phrase like 'My immune system heals me.' What statement do you think will work for you?"*

_____

_____

Step 6: Link Image and Positive Cognition

Say. *"Now, please hold the imagery of the _____ (state what the image is) and the positive statement _____ (state the PC) and please follow my fingers* (or any other BLS you use).*"*

Then say, *"Now please close your eyes and imagine _____ (state what the imagery is). Whenever you get stuck, open your eyes and we will use the BLS."*

Continue to work with the imagery and positive cognition in the office until your client can easily access both. It is helpful for the client to pair the imagery and PC with a daily activity as in the client who would rehearse the imagery every time he urinated, thus reinforcing his PC, *My immune system heals me* with the thought that the cancer cells were being washed out of his system. That is, he simultaneously used the imagery with eye movements, and the thought, *It will take away all the poison.*

Say, *"It is helpful to continue to use your image and positive statement by pairing _____ (state the image) and your positive statement _____ (state the PC) with a daily activity."*

Come up with your own relevant to the client example or use the following:

Say, *"There is an example of a client who would rehearse the imagery every time he urinated, thus reinforcing his PC, 'My immune system heals me' with the thought that the cancer cells were being washed out of his system. That is, he simultaneously used the imagery with eye movements, and the thought, 'It will take away all the poison.' Do you have a daily activity with which you can pair your image and positive statement?"*

_____

_____

_____

Step 7: Assign Homework With the Self-Use Procedure

Say, *"Please use this positive imagery and statement with the BLS during the time in between our sessions at least three times a day and any of the other self-care or pain management techniques that are helpful. For the positive imagery and statement, you may use eye movement by choosing two points on the wall or on the back of a chair or you may prefer to tap your knees or your upper arms (demonstrate). Choose the dual attention with which you are most comfortable. Please remember to use this positive imagery and statement with the dual attention as this is the way to be most effective."*

Step 8: Log and Self-Care Procedures

It is helpful to use log and self-care procedures.

Instruct the client to keep a log including TICES (Trigger, Image, Cognition, Emotion, Sensation) so that any targets revealed in between sessions can be reprocessed.

Say, *"The processing we have done today may continue after the session. You may or may not notice new insights, thoughts, memories, or dreams. Take special care to note any doubts, resistance, pertinent memories, or current upset that may arise during your use of dual attention with your positive imagery and statement. If so, just notice what you are experiencing and take a snapshot of it in a log—what you are seeing, feeling, thinking, and the trigger on the TICES grid (Trigger, Image, Cognition, Emotion, Sensation and SUD). Use the safe place exercise to rid yourself of any disturbance. Remember to use your positive imagery and statement with dual attention at least three times a day. We can work on this new material next time. If you feel it is necessary, call me."*

Other Helpful Modalities or Resources

EMDR treatment may be considered essentially complete when clients are able to envision themselves as healthy and free of their disease and a Body Scan reveals no negative sensations.

Although the image of good health is strengthened by EMDR, it must, of course, be done with realistic goals.

Relaxation and Pain Control Techniques

Teach relaxation and pain control techniques. Here are several you might use but there are many others.

The Light Stream Technique

The Light Stream Technique is very useful with acute pain.

Say, *"I would like you to scan your whole body now and to tell me where you notice any unpleasant body sensations or tensions."*

_____

_____

Say, *"I'd like you to imagine that those sensations were energy. If the energy had a _____ (state each of the attributes below), what would it be?"*

Shape: _____

Size: _____

Color: _____

Temperature: _____

Texture: _____

Sound: _____

Say, *"What color does your body need today to heal?"*

_____

_____

Say, *"Imagine that this favorite colored light is coming in through the top of your head and directing itself at the shape in your body. Let's pretend that the source of this light is the infinite cosmos so the more you use, the more you have available. <u>Allow the soothing, healing light to come in more and more, and direct itself at the shape. As it does so, let the light resonate and vibrate in and around it, more and more. And as it does, what happens to the shape?"</u>*

_____

_____

If the client gives feedback that it is changing in any way, continue repeating the underlined portion and asking for feedback, until the shape is completely gone. This usually correlates with the disappearance of the upsetting feeling.

Say, *"Continue to allow the light to flow into your head, neck, and shoulders. Let it flow into your chest and down your arms and out your fingertips. Let the soothing, healing light flow through your torso into your legs and out through your feet. Let the light flow into every part of your body. Then, imagine saying to yourself the positive words you most need to hear right now."*

Then say, *"Then, as I count upward from one to five, I'd like you to bring yourself back here in the room, and as you do, I would like you to bring your whole and complete self here. (Pause) So, bringing your whole and complete self back in the room now, one, two (rising intonation), three, four, and five."*

Eye Movements for Pain Management

Eye movement sets have been reported to be useful for pain management. The following is a list of suggested strategies for the self-directed use of eye movements and other forms of dual stimulation.

Two Objects

Say, *"Hold the head straight, look forward, and then move the eyes to the extreme right and observe a distant object. The same movement is then made to the extreme left. Then the eyes are moved back and forth between two objects."*

Points on Wall or Room

Say, *"Look alternately at one side of the room* (or a point on the wall) *and then another."*

Index Fingers

Say, *"Sit with one hand, palm down, on each thigh* (with legs parted) *and raise one index finger at a time while the eyes move back and forth between them."*

Hand Movement

Say, *"Move a lifted hand back and forth across the line of vision."*

Moving Focal Point by Machine

Say, *"By far the easiest way to maintain the eye movements or other form of stimulation is to use an externally generated moving focal point. Some individuals have hung a pendulum from the ceiling or used a light bar. A light bar with variable speed and direction has been designed and tested and is now available for personal use* (Neurotek, www.neurotekcorp.com). *Audio and tactile aids are available from Neurotek and a variety of other sources."*

Imagination

Say, *"You can imagine me moving my fingers across your visual field, as this is what we do during our sessions."*

Supportive Group Therapy

Clients have found that group therapy is very supportive. You can check with the American Cancer Association for groups in your area and local hospitals concerning issues related to cancer. Many illnesses and disorders have their own associations that can be very helpful to the client and the client's friends and family.

Complementary Medicine

Alternative health care approaches such as massage or nutrition are used to promote a sense of self-nurturing and to mobilize psychological resources and a great sense of control is very helpful.

PART VI

EMDR and Early Intervention Procedures for Man-Made and Natural Catastrophes

The sad fact is that on a moment-to-moment basis one of our own fellow human beings is the victim of a man-made or natural catastrophe. Whether it is the result of abuse, torture, war, murder, atrocities by another person or people, the effects of natural disasters such as earthquakes, hurricanes, tornadoes, floods, mine collapses, catastrophic illnesses, and so forth, devastating trauma impacts us, our family, our friends, and cohabitants in our world on a regular basis. As the years go by, the number of these incidents seem to increase. To sit with a survivor of any of these terrible and terrifying events is to know the absolute helplessness as one bears witness to the total suffering of another human being. Many of us in the mental health profession have experienced the sheer frustration of trying to relieve and, ultimately, transform the negative affects, sensations, and beliefs associated with these situations to no avail.

There have been many attempts to shift the effects of these difficult experiences over the millennia: prayer, meditation, hypnosis, imaging work, exposure techniques, and so forth. Many of these modalities have been helpful to those who use them by taking the edge off the experience(s) or even by helping clients make a miraculous or total recovery.

In 1987, Francine Shapiro made an observation that proved to be the inspiration for a whole new way of working with clients who present with trauma. By noticing that her repetitive disturbing thoughts disappeared while she was moving her eyes in a saccadic pattern, her observation enabled her to open herself to a range of new possibilities. Intrigued by her finding, Dr. Shapiro (1989a) tested it out on a number of volunteers and clients. She wanted to find out how this natural occurring phenomenon could be used for therapeutic purposes. Dr. Shapiro's eventual procedure—first called Eye Movement Desensitization (EMD)—was based on observing hundreds of treatment sessions. She created a multifaceted way of targeting the memory of the trauma including the visual, auditory, affective, and sensation elements of the experience. Over the years, as it became clear that during recent trauma, clients were more apt to remember only fragments and pieces of the memory, ways to work with recent trauma were developed.

The material that follows in Parts VI and VII are the creations of skilled clinicians faced with the catastrophic physical, emotional, mental, affective, and spiritual responses of their clients to man-made or natural disasters. Using the basic tenets of the EMDR methodology, these gifted mental health practitioners fashioned their work to meet the challenges of their clients and the situations with which they were presented. Judith Guedalia, Frances Yoeli, and Gary Quinn address how to work with the newly traumatized who appear in a hospital setting. David Blore addresses the particular needs of clients who have experienced underground trauma and includes a specialized protocol to deal with those who do not want to talk about what happened to them.

Elan Shapiro and Brurit Laub, in the Recent Traumatic Episode Protocol, provide a new conceptualization of how to think about the developmental changes that occur in the client's perceptual response to the trauma over time and then suggest new protocols to address these different changes. Their chapter contains a more lengthy introduction to help readers follow their evolutionary way of thinking.

Each of these protocols represents hundreds of hours of experience and dedication by these men and women to transform their clients' suffering so that they could heal and return to as normal a day-to-day existence as possible.

EMDR for Mining and Related Trauma: The Underground Trauma Protocol

David Blore

David Blore has now been providing EMDR to traumatized miners since 1993. As with other specialized client groups, the Single Trauma (STP) and Recent Trauma Protocol (RTP) have required modifications. The author has collated the modifications made, and presented them here as the Underground Trauma Protocol (UTP). The UTP is intended to provide a rapid and effective method of conducting EMDR with traumatized miners and other similar, very specific, client groups.

The Underground Trauma Protocol Script Notes

The principal use of the UTP is for traumatized miners of coal, gold, nickel, gems, and so forth. It has also been used with the following populations: traumatized tunnelers (e.g., excavators of tunnels in both war and peace); those traumatized in rail accidents in tunnels (e.g., fire in Channel Tunnel, Kings Cross tube fire); those traumatized in underground leisure pursuits (e.g., exploration of caves, pot holing); those traumatized by being trapped (e.g., in collapsed buildings as in Turkish earthquakes); and those traumatized during 9/11 in New York and the 7/7 bombings in London.

There are three golden rules to follow when working with traumatized miners.

1. If possible visit a coal mine and check out the underground environment for yourself—there's nothing better for getting an idea of working conditions and increasing your standing amongst the miners themselves, as well as picking up some of the jargon.
2. *Always* remember the underground environment is *totally different* to a trauma on the surface. The environment can be *so* different it is difficult to believe you are on planet Earth!

3. *Never* underestimate the significance of *heat* in relation to traumatic memories of the underground environment.

David Blore recommends that the treatment of this client group only be undertaken by fully trained EMDR clinicians who have experience with modifying protocols and existing clinical experience of using cognitive interweave. In addition to Shapiro's instructions (Shapiro, 2001), it is important to cover the following points for miners.

Important information to ask for during history taking is to be clear how much of the underground environment was involved in the incident. "Integrity" of the underground environment refers to the whole underground environment, not just the immediate site of the incident in question. It is important to remember that the underground environment is not like the surface; it is a world in miniature. If the integrity of the underground environment is affected, in essence, the whole underground world is affected.

Checking whether safety procedures were followed in the United Kingdom can be gleaned after investigations via Her Majesty's Mines Inspectorate. In the United Kingdom, Her Majesty's Mines Inspectorate comes under the Health and Safety Executive (HSE): www.hse.gov.uk then do search for Her Majesty's Mines Inspectorate. Other countries have equivalent systems. A good place to start is the U.S. Department of Labor Web site: www.msha.gov. This covers mining safety organizations in 17 countries.

During the Assessment Phase, use the Standard Trauma Protocol (STP) for all memories, *except for those below ground*. Through the author's experience, an efficient order of tackling targets is the following: heat, darkness, and then disorientation. This is probably because they are related to fear (thus negative affect), which in turn relates to survival.

For underground memories, target the "hottest" or most affect-laden first or use the Recent Trauma Protocol, starting with the memories below ground. For underground memories, target the memories of the actual event in the following order: associated heat, associated darkness, and associated disorientation. For the miner, "hottest" means the most affect-laden and "cool" is the equivalent of relaxed or chilled out. In fact, SUDs can become SUTs (Subjective Units of Temperature Scale), if necessary.

Say, *"On a scale of 0 to 10 where 0 is cool or cold and 10 is the hottest you can imagine. . . ."*

Some useful process material can be gleaned from Blore (1997). Bear in mind that images specifically relating to damage to the integrity of the underground environment are frequently associated with a tactile sense of heat. These memories can be very intense and distressing to recall and can challenge the strongest machismo. Emotions are a foreign commodity to most miners and these memories feature in virtually all underground memory abreactions. All *other* abreactions generally relate to subsequent above ground events such as attending colleagues' cremations, for example, of which there can be many.

Since miners are medically checked regularly, they are not going to be physically weak, but their pretrauma beliefs are likely to be inaccurate. It is very common for miners to have given no thought whatsoever—prior to an accident—to the potential for disaster (e.g., when there is a mile of rock above you). On the other hand, most miners can expect injuries at some time in their working life, but generally not to the extent that they will realize their invulnerability belief exists or needs to be challenged. Miners are known for having no cognitions; so it does help to be mindful of these points when it comes to treating them.

Related to the previous comments is the issue of the client identifying memories that clash with perceived machismo. One way around this is to initially label memories A, B, C, and so on. Although this may smack of covert avoidance to the cognitive-behavioral among us, EMDR is the only psychotherapy that the author knows of that can be conducted blind to even the therapist (See chapter 25, the "Blind to Therapist Protocol"). The author considers that it is a means to an end. If images can be readily and rapidly treated this way, there is no reason why later on some judicious cognitive therapy cannot be added to the EMDR to challenge belief structures. Shapiro frequently tells us that EMDR is not a stand-alone treatment and that it should be part of an overall therapeutic program.

The Underground Trauma Protocol Script

Phase 1: Client History

When working with clients presenting with underground trauma, there are important types of information that are crucial to creating effective case conceptualization and treatment.

1. Say, *"During the traumatic event was there damage to the integrity of the underground environment? For instance, did the traumatic event damage a significant part of the underground environment such as a roof collapse or affect a component of the working environment that could affect the entire environment as in damage to ventilation or airflow?"*

_____

_____

_____

If the answer is yes, the following are the types of events to look for:

1. Roof collapse or cave-in
2. Gas blowout (fractured pocket of gas under high compression)
3. Oil inrush (fractured pocket of oil under high compression)
4. Explosion, fire, or major disruption to airflow
5. Major equipment failures
6. Some "tripping-out" incidents (e.g., failure in situ of winding gear)

If one of the above occurred, proceed to Question 3.

In complex traumas—at a colliery—it is helpful to obtain a sketch of the underground layout and identify the direction of airflow prior to the traumatic event. Then, estimate how long the client had been underground and, if possible, how much fluid the client consumed during the time underground.

If the answer is no, it is likely that the trauma involved a very local incident, possibly even a single coal miner in a specific situation, then ask the following:

2. Say, *"During the traumatic event if there was no damage to the integrity of the underground environment, what happened?"*

_____

_____

_____

_____

These are the types of events that can occur:

1. Fatal accident (client in immediate proximity of fatal event)
2. Serious injury to colleague
3. First aid responsibilities to colleague (successful or otherwise)
4. Serious injury to self
5. Dehydration (Another factor unique to the underground environment—geothermal and equipment underground, depth of mining level and thus adequate fluid intake—ongoing during heavy manual work thus the possibility of dehydration is an ever-present threat. Dehydration can alter memory

quality and become a small trauma all on its own. Also dehydration relates to heat and heat [see later] communicates trauma around the underground environment).

6. Witness to extreme anxiety in another miner (including panic attacks underground)

7. Other personal incidents (unless widespread such as in "tripping-out")

Now ask the following questions, tailored to the specific event just identified:

3. Say, *"How, specifically, did you become aware of the traumatic event?"*

_____

_____

Note: Heat, or sudden rise in environmental temperature underground is thus a "language of trauma" and on a potential treatment target in itself. Clinical experience seems to suggest that the heat sensation relates to increasing ambient temperature brought about by disruption to underground airflow management. This means that a major accident can, and is, communicated around the underground environment by means of methods other than direct verbal communication. In addition, increase in heat can increase the risk of dehydration, which can also bring about distortions to memories. Consequently miners who were underground at the time of the accident, yet who were neither in the direct vicinity of the accident nor were involved in the rescue, can easily have traumatic memories characterized by a sensation of heat. It is possible to assess to what extent this was a problem at the time by reviewing underground site plans that usually contain information about airflow.

4. Say, *"Was there an increase in environmental temperature?"*

_____

_____

5. Say, *"What were the reactions of your colleagues?"*

_____

_____

Note: Memories of smells can be particularly resistant memories and seem to play a large part in reactivating traumatic memories at a later date. Large quantities of disinfectant can be used (even pumped through airflow systems) to mask smells of decomposition—rescue working conditions are already hampered by rapid decomposition because of increased temperatures and humidity. Unfortunately, what helps to facilitate rescue working conditions at the time ends up being part of the traumatic memory repertoire that requires treatment. More problematic still are the actual images themselves that can easily seem to produce evidence that the client didn't cope.

6. Say, *"Were there any changes in smells?"*

_____

_____

Note: Disruption to airflow throughout the underground tunnels during a major traumatic event very quickly communicates the trauma around the underground tunnels in some instances several miles underground.

7. Say, *"Were there any changes in airflow?"*

_____

_____

8. Say, *"Were there any other changes that you noticed?"*

_____

_____

9. Say, *"What other things did you notice that were not from what others told you?"*

_____

_____

Note: Communications themselves are traumatic and damage to the underground environment may mean that low-tech methods of communications (word of mouth) predominate until communications can be restored. In the meanwhile, "Chinese whispers" can result in unintentional secondary traumas.

10. Say, *"Were there things that people told you that bothered you and that you cannot get out of your mind?"*

_____

_____

11. Say, *"At the time, what was your perception of what happened?"*

_____

_____

Note: A perennial problem underground is dust. Coal dust mixed with air is a highly explosive "cocktail." The problem is kept under control in coal mines by mixing the coal dust and air with stone dust. However, this can't be controlled during a major incident such as a roof collapse. The amount of dust is vast and tends to obscure vision of the disaster site. The degree of lack of visibility thus indicates proximity to the primary site of the disaster.

12. Say, *"Was it that you did not see what happened through a loss of visibility or are you unable to recall what happened?"*

_____

_____

13. Say, *"What were you doing at the time?"*

_____

_____

14. Say, *"What had been your work instructions?"*

_____

_____

15. Say, *"Who gave you those instructions?"*

_____

_____

Note: Perhaps "location" should be "distance from the shaft" as the farther from the shaft, the longer underground the traumatized miner is likely to be. Remaining effectively trapped underground—even if not physically injured—can greatly intensify the trauma. It therefore follows that the farther from the shaft a traumatized miner is, the more dehydrated he is likely to be. Clearly the question on losing track of time and disorientation will assist the history taking.

16. Say, *"Where were you underground?"*

_____

_____

Note: United Kingdom rules on the wearing of equipment including watches and carrying cigarette lighters (obviously) underground are very strictly enforced—loss of time is easy with no access to daylight either and is even worse during emotionally charged situations such as mines rescue work.

17. Say, *"At any POINT, did you lose track of time or were you disoriented?"*

_____

_____

18. Say, *"Do you have any images associated with 'heat'?"*
    See earlier explanation about the important role of heat in mining disaster memories.

_____

_____

Note: Coal miners are an extremely close-knit community much more so than virtually all other occupational groups with the possible exception of the armed forces. Often dads and sons may work together—thus emotional ties form a critical mass to the trauma itself.

19. Say, *"Did you know the individual(s) involved personally?"*

_____

_____

Note: Under normal circumstances, underground miners often work in small teams. They rely upon each other, but small incidents may cause serious injuries to others. If memories are associated with guilt, it may well be because the individual miner feels personally responsible for his colleagues' injuries. During mine rescue work where time is of the essence, corners can be cut in practice for the sake of the rescue. In either case, Her Majesty's Mines Inspectorate will hold an inquiry and interview each person involved—this can also be a traumatic experience. Knowing whether relevant procedures were or were not followed will help identify all manner of secondary and subsequent issues, even secondary gain.

20. Say, *"Were there specific safety procedures being followed?"*

_____

_____

21. Say, *"How long were you underground?"*

_____

_____

22. Say, *"Approximately how much fluid did you consume during the time underground?"*

_____

_____

Note: Miners worldwide have a reputation for alcohol consumption. The author has encountered miners who consume well over 200 + units (a unit is defined as 10 millilitres/8 grams of ethanol) per week. They have built an enormous tolerance to alcohol. It is unrealistic in many cases to ask them to cut down on alcohol consumption prior to EMDR. However, this subject should be addressed as alcohol comes as a very natural method of blotting out traumatic memories.

23. Say, *"What is the approximate minimum number of drinks you consume in an average working week?"*

_____

_____

24. Say, *"What is the approximate maximum number of drinks you consume in an average working week?"*

_____

_____

25. Say, *"How frequently do you drink the maximum?"*

_____

_____

Note: Also, miners may hugely underestimate other coping strategies such as smoking. They can't smoke underground so asking how much is smoked will not help. Ask if they chew tobacco or take snuff or both while working. This may be important, as there is anecdotal evidence that snuff can also mask smells.

26. Say, *"Do you chew tobacco while working? If so, in what quantity?"*

_____

_____

27. Say, *"Do you take snuff while working? If so, in what quantity?"*

_____

_____

Ask any other questions deemed appropriate here that are important for the therapist's history taking.

Phase 2: Preparation

Forming a Bond With the Client

If at all possible, familiarize yourself with the basics of mining jargon. Just as languages vary worldwide, so does jargon. If you don't understand a term, ask. This is important to your clients' faith in your ability to understand who they are and what they have been through.

Alcohol should not be consumed on the day of the EMDR session—this author once had a miner who had convinced me he had not drunk any alcohol that day and who subsequently lost his balance while tracking eye movements and fell off the seat (fortunately without injury)!

Creating a Safe Place

Safe places involving images relating to fishing, the family, open air, sunlight, gardening, and holidays were the most popular amongst a group of 20+ miners treated. One miner picked being a mile underground at a colliery with a better safety record as his safe place image, but this had to be replaced!

The Safe Place for Miners Script

Image

Say, *"I'd like you to think about some place you have been or imagine being that feels very safe or calm. Perhaps being on holiday somewhere or doing something relaxing such as gardening or fishing."* (Pause) *"What might you be doing?"*

_____

_____

Emotions and Sensations

Say, *"As you think of that safe* (or calm) *place or activity, notice what you see, hear, and feel right now."* (Pause) *"What do you notice?"*

_____

_____

Enhancement

Say, *"Focus on your safe* (or calm) *place or activity, its sights, sounds, smells, and body sensations. Tell me more about what you are noticing."*

_____

_____

Bilateral Stimulation (BLS)

Say, *"Bring up the image of that place or activity. Concentrate on where you feel the pleasant sensations in your body and allow yourself to enjoy them. Now concentrate on those sensations and follow my fingers* (or whatever BLS you use)."

Use four to six sets.

Say, *"How do you feel now?"*

_____

_____

Repeat several times if the process has enhanced the client's positive feelings and sensations.
If positive, say the following:

Say, *"Focus on that."*

Repeat BLS.

Say, *"What do you notice now?"*

_____

_____

Cue Word

Note: An interesting choice of cue word that cropped up from time to time was "cool" or even "cold"—especially given the importance of "heat" in the traumatic memories described earlier.

Say, *"Is there a word or phrase that represents your safe* (or calm) *place or activity?"*

_____

_____

Then say, *"Think of _____* (cue word) *and notice the positive feelings you have when you think of that word. Now concentrate on those sensations and the cue word and follow _____* (state BLS using).*"*

Use short sets (four to six) of BLS with any positive responses.

Say, *"How do you feel now?"*

_____

_____

Repeat several times. Enhance positive feelings with BLS several times.

Self-Cuing

Say, *"Now I'd like you to say that word _____* (cue word) *and notice how you feel."*

_____

_____

Cuing With Disturbance

Say, *"Now imagine a minor annoyance and how it feels."*
(Pause)

_____

_____

Say, *"Now bring up your safe* (or calm) *place or activity* _____ *and notice any shifts in your body."*

Do BLS.

Guide the client through the process until he is able to experience the positive emotions and sensations. Repeat as often as necessary.

Self-Cuing With Disturbance

Say, *"Now I'd like you to think of another mildly annoying incident and bring up your safe* (or calm) *place or activity by yourself, again, especially noticing any changes in your body when you have gone to your safe* (or calm) *place."*

Practice

Say, *"I'd like you to practice using your safe place or activity, between now and our next session, any time you feel a little annoyed. Keep track of how things go and we'll talk about it next time we meet."*

Past Memories

Phase 3: Assessment

Above Ground Trauma Targets. Use the Standard Trauma Protocol (STP) for all memories, *except for those below ground* (see below). For above ground trauma related to underground events, tackle targets according to the following order: heat, darkness, and then disorientation.

Say, *"Let's list the issues we are going to tackle according to how hot they are. For instance on a scale from 0 to 10 where 0 = Cold memories or no sense of heat; 10 = Hottest memories of all."*

0   1   2   3   4   5   6   7   8   9   10
(cold memories or no sense of heat)   (hottest memories)

"Let's start with the hottest problem and then all those that follow."

_____

_____

_____

_____

_____

_____

Incident

When a picture is unavailable, Shapiro advises the clinician to have the client "think of the incident." An alternative, and one that in the past this author has used instead of locating any picture is the following:

Say, *"Think of anything you remember about the accident that is hot* (failing this, substitute hot with dark or disorientated)."

_____

_____

Note: See Phase 1 above, relating to memories associated with heat.

Picture

Say, *"What image represents the worst part of the memory or incident?"*

_____

_____

Negative Cognition (NC)

Mining still has a huge machismo problem and it can hamper rapid treatment if the client feels he must identify perceived failings such as admission of certain negative cognitions. The following have been the negative cognitions most encountered clinically:

"I am useless."
"I am worthless."
"I am weak."
"I'm a waste of space."
"I can't cope."
"I let my colleagues down."

Say, *"What words go best with the picture that express your negative belief about yourself now?"*

_____

_____

Positive Cognition (PC)

Say, *"When you bring up that picture or incident, what would you like to believe about yourself now?"*

_____

_____

Validity of Cognition (VoC)

Say, *"When you think of the incident* (or picture), *how true do those words _____* (clinician repeats the positive cognition) *feel to you now on a scale of 1 to 7, where 1 feels completely false and 7 feels completely true?"*

1	2	3	4	5	6	7
(completely false)				(completely true)		

Emotions

Say, *"When you bring up the picture* (or incident) *and those words _____* (clinician states the negative cognition), *what emotion do you feel now?"*

_____

_____

Subjective Units of Disturbance (SUD)

Adapting the SUD Scale to the Miner Population

There is no reason to stick with "distress" as the posting to your SUD scales. Others may be more appropriate, try any of these suggestions:

    0 = Cold memories or no sense of heat; 10 = Hottest memories of all
    0 = Light memories (e.g., daylight); 10 = Very dark memories (i.e.,
    zero visibility)
    0 = Normal size or oriented content; 10 = Very large or completely
    disorientated content

Say, *"On a scale of 0 to 10, where 0 is _____* (state scale using: no disturbance, cold memories, no sense of heat, light memories as in daylight, normal size, or oriented content) *or neutral and 10 is the _____*(state scale using: highest disturbance, hottest memory of all, very dark memories with zero visibility, very large, or completely disorientated content) *that you can imagine. How _____* (disturbing, hot, dark, large, or disorientated) *does it feel to you now?"*

    0   1   2   3   4   5   6   7   8   9   10
    (no disturbance)   (highest disturbance)

Location of Body Sensation

Say, *"Where do you feel it* (the disturbance) *in your body?"*

_____

_____

After this list is processed, using Phases 4–7, go on to the next list if it is necessary.

Say, *"Let's list the issues we are going to tackle according to how dark they are. For instance on a scale from 0 to 10 (0 = Light memories [e.g., daylight]; 10 = Very dark memories [i.e., zero visibility])."*

    0   1   2   3   4   5   6   7   8   9   10
    (light memories)   (very dark memories)

"Let's start with the darkest problem and then all those that follow."

_____

_____

_____

_____

_____

_____

After this list is processed, using Phases 4–7, go on to the next list if it is necessary.

Say, *"Let's list the issues we are going to tackle according to how disorientated they feel. For instance on a scale from 0 to 10 where 0 = Normal size or oriented content (10 = Very large or completely disorientated content).*

0   1   2   3   4   5   6   7   8   9   10
(normal size or oriented) (very large or completely disorientated content)

"Let's start with the most disorientated problem and then all those that follow."

Use Phases 4–7 of the Standard EMDR Protocol to process this list completely.

_____

_____

_____

_____

_____

Underground Trauma Memory Targets. For underground memories, target the "hottest" or most affect-laden first or use the Recent Trauma Protocol (see chapter 20 in this volume), starting with the memories below ground. When targeting the actual event, use the following order: associated heat, associated darkness, and associated disorientation. See above for scripts.

Phase 4: Desensitization

Present Triggers

Use the Standard EMDR Protocol format for the past memories and any present triggers. The latter can include many current problems including news broadcasts, changes in circumstances relating to any injury, changes in income, loss of contact with colleagues, issues relating to being trapped, the post-incident inquiry, or merely uncertainty about the future and so on.

Future Template

As regards to the future template, it is useful to know the miner's intentions. Is he returning to work underground, working as redeployed to surface work, or leaving mining altogether? It is likely that a single image will be insufficient if the miner is returning to work underground because the process of returning is complicated so installing the future template as multiple images in the form of a video can be useful.

If the miner is returning to surface working or leaving mining altogether, use the standard future template with a single image of coping or readjusting.

If the miner is returning to underground work in the mine, do the following:

Say, *"Which of the following elements of your return to work underground create anxiety when you think of them now?"*

- *Sight of the headstocks to the colliery* (The headstock is the visible—sometimes from several miles—metal structure usually with a single, large cable winding-wheel showing at the top.)
- *Clothing and equipment*

- *Top of shaft* (sometimes called the tally room)
- *Descending or ascending in the cage* (also called the chair—the term for the lift in the shaft)
- *The shaft bottom*
- *Underground transport* (underground trains are sometimes referred to as Paddys)
- *Coal face itself or other working location*
- *Other aspects of working underground particularly any awareness of increases in temperature*

Identify each component and desensitize as per normal as follows:

Say, *"I would like you to imagine yourself coping effectively with _____ (insert item from list above) in the future. With the positive belief _____ and your new sense of _____ (i.e., strength, clarity, confidence, calm), imagine stepping into this scene.*
Notice what you see and how you are handling the situation.
Notice what you are thinking, feeling, and experiencing in your body.
Are there any blocks, anxieties, or fears that arise as you think about this future scene?"

_____

_____

_____

_____

If yes, say the following:

Say, *"Then focus on these blocks and follow my fingers (or any other BLS)."*

If the blocks do not resolve quickly, evaluate if the client needs any new information, resources, or skills to be able to comfortably visualize the future coping scene. Introduce needed information or skills.

Say, *"What would you need to feel confident in handling the situation?"*
Or say, *"What is missing from your handling of this situation?"*

_____

_____

If the block still does not resolve and the client is unable to visualize the future scene with confidence and clarity, use direct questions, the Affect Scan, or the Float-Back Technique to identify old targets related to blocks, anxieties, or fears. Use the EMDR Standard Protocol to address these targets before proceeding with the template. (See Worksheets in the Appendix.)

When there are no apparent blocks and the client is able to visualize the future scene with confidence and clarity as in the following:

Say, *"Please focus on the image, the positive belief, and the sensations associated with this future scene and follow my fingers (or any other BLS)."*

Do several sets until the future template is sufficiently strengthened.

Then say, *"Close your eyes and keep in mind the experience that you will have in the future. Then bring your attention to the different parts of your body, starting with your head and working downward. Any place you find any tension, tightness, or unusual sensation, tell me."*

_____

_____

If any sensation is reported, do BLS.

If it is a positive or comfortable sensation, do BLS to strengthen the positive feelings.

If a sensation of discomfort is reported, reprocess until the discomfort subsides. Check the VoC.

Say, *"When you think of the incident* (or picture) *how true do those words _____* (clinician repeats the positive cognition) *feel to you now on a scale of 1 to 7, where 1 feels completely false and 7 feels completely true?"*

1   2   3   4   5   6   7
(completely false)   (completely true)

Movie as a Future Template

Next, ask the client to move from imagining one scene or snapshot to imagining a movie about coping in the future, with a beginning, middle, and end. Encourage him to imagine coping effectively in the face of specific challenges or triggers. Make some suggestions to help inoculate him for future problems.

Say, *"This time, I'd like you to close your eyes and play a movie, imagining yourself coping effectively with _____* (state where client will be) *in the future. With the new positive belief _____* (state positive belief) *and your new sense of _____* (strength, clarity, confidence, calm), *imagine stepping into the future. Imagine yourself coping with ANY challenges that come your way. Make sure that this movie has a beginning, a middle, and an end. Notice what you are seeing, thinking, feeling, and experiencing in your body. Let me know if you hit any blocks. If you do, just open your eyes and let me know. If you don't hit any blocks, let me know when you have viewed the whole movie."*

_____

_____

If the client hits blocks, address as above with BLS, interweaves, new skills, information, resources, direct questions, Affect Scan, or Float-Back, and so forth.

If the client is able to play the movie from start to finish with a sense of confidence and satisfaction, ask the client to play the movie one more time from beginning to end and introduce BLS. In a sense, you are installing this movie as a future template.

Say, "*Okay, play the movie one more time from beginning to end. Go with that.*"

Phase 5: Installation

Say, "*How does _____ (repeat the PC) sound?*"

_____

_____

Say, "*Do the words _____ (repeat the PC) still fit, or is there another positive statement that feels better?*"

_____

_____

If the client accepts the original positive cognition, the clinician should ask for a VoC rating to see if it has improved.

Say, "*As you think of the incident, how do the words feel, from 1 (completely false) to 7 (completely true)?*"

  1   2   3   4   5   6   7
(completely false)   (completely true)

Say, "*Think of the event, and hold it together with the words _____ (repeat the PC).*"

Do a long set of BLS to see if there is more processing to be done.

Phase 6: Body Scan

Say, "*Close your eyes and keep in mind the original memory and the positive cognition. Then bring your attention to the different parts of your body, starting with your head and working downward. Any place you find any tension, tightness, or unusual sensation, tell me.*"

_____

_____

Phase 7: Closure

Say, "*Things may come up or they may not. If they do, great. Write it down, and it can be a target for next time. If you get any new memories, dreams, or situations that disturb you, just take a good snapshot. It isn't necessary to give a lot of detail. Just put down enough to remind you so we can target it next time. The same thing goes for any positive dreams or situations. If negative feelings do come up, try not to make them significant. Remember, it's still just the old stuff. Just write it down for next time. Then use the tape or the Safe Place exercise to let as much of the disturbance go as possible. Even if nothing comes up, make sure to use the tape every day and give me a call if you need to.*"

Phase 8: Reevaluation

It is important to pay attention to the following questions when the client returns after doing EMDR work.

> Say, *"When you think of whatever is left of the problem that we worked on last time, how disturbing is it now on a scale of 0 to 10, where 0 is no disturbance or neutral and 10 is the highest disturbance you can imagine, how disturbing does it feel now?"*

> 0   1   2   3   4   5   6   7   8   9   10
> (no disturbance)   (highest disturbance)

> Say, *"Have you noticed any other material associated with the original memory since the last session?"*

_____

_____

_____

> Say, *"Have all the necessary targets been reprocessed so that you can feel at peace with the past, empowered in the present, and able to make choices for the future?"*

_____

_____

_____

> Say, *"Has the work that we have done with EMDR helped you be more adaptive in your day-to-day life?"*

_____

_____

_____

The author welcomes feedback on its use. Free help is available if using this protocol via e-mail: help@davidblore.co.uk

EMDR "Blind to Therapist Protocol"

David Blore and Manda Holmshaw

EMDR "Blind to Therapist Protocol" Script Notes

The "Blind to Therapist Protocol" (B2T) is, essentially, that. It allows a client to go through the Standard EMDR Protocol, without revealing the content of the problem. This protocol is often used in conjunction with any client group in which divulging information might be uncomfortable to the individual prior to the use of EMDR. It has been used to treat train engineers, airplane pilots, ship captains, police officers, prison guards, doctors, nurses, paramedics, and firemen—workers characterized by the need to make life-and-death decisions for which they are personally responsible. In other words, those who have memories associated with not being in control at precisely the time when they are responsible for being in control. Another client group that can often have difficulties with divulging information is child abuse survivors where the client fears overwhelming or disgusting the therapist with the nature of the material to be treated. In such instances the protocol is very successful and can be a useful addition to the therapist's repertoire. It helps build the therapeutic relationship by demonstrating to the client that the therapist has trust in them. Once the client has seen how the therapist copes with material being raised, the Standard EMDR Protocol would be used.

EMDR "Blind to Therapist Protocol" Script

Phase 1: Client History

This phase is unchanged. It is likely at this stage that the therapist will become aware of the client's reticence at describing detail relating to their problem.

Phase 2: Preparation

This phase is unchanged, except for when the client does not want to reveal the content of the problem in detail.

Suggested text to include:

> Say, *"Normal treatment requires the client to describe, in detail, images and memories that are upsetting. However, it is possible to conduct EMDR without describing the image or memory content.*
>
> *Although you are not describing the image or memory content, treatment will not suffer as a result and you will still be in control throughout treatment. There is no need to tell me about the content of your images, memories, any changes that occur, your evaluation of your memories, or your evaluation of your actions. Remember, treatment will not suffer as a result. Anything you do tell me is entirely confidential anyway and will not be fed back to the company or organization (or state whomever the client might be concerned about knowing their problem)."*

Past Memories

Phase 3: Assessment

Notice the change in the beginning part of the Assessment to accommodate the client's need to NOT disclose the content of the problem.

> Say, *"Please focus on the image or memory you do NOT wish to describe. Do you have it?"*

_____

_____

> Say, *"Now, if you would, choose a cue word that either <u>reminds</u> you of that image or memory without using a word that might give an easy clue about the image content, such as 'failure,' 'out of control,' and so forth.*
>
> *Neutral elements of the image work best such as '27,' 'lamp post,' 'nearby,' or a word that represents the <u>present, qualitative</u> nature of that image or memory such as 'It's in my face,' 'Only yesterday,' 'Huge,' all work well. What cue word works for you?"*
>
> Cue word: _____

Note: Make no attempt to identify either a negative or a positive cognition as this could give away the content of the image and because it will immediately tap into the negative cognition that the client may find too uncomfortable to acknowledge at this stage. Because there is no attempt to develop a positive cognition at this stage either, there can be no rating the validity of the positive cognition. However, experience shows that some clients while not wishing to discuss a negative cognition *may* nevertheless have sufficient confidence to identify a positive cognition spontaneously. If this happens, it is likely to be along the lines of the client saying: "I would prefer to think I was in control."

PC: _____

If this spontaneous PC occurs don't try developing it, for instance, by getting the wording exactly correct because the client may feel more vulnerable at a crucial point in which she had felt *just* sufficient confidence. Instead acknowledge the PC and rate the VoC.

> Say, *"When you think of the image you have identified by the cue word _____ (state the cue word), how true do your words* (the PC) *feel to you now?"*

If there is no spontaneous PC, do not try to identify one. Only rate the PC if it emerges in Phase 3. If it emerges later, for example in Phase 4, it may well be misleading to rate the PC part way through the processing.

Now proceed as follows:

> Say, *"Now, focus on the image you have identified by the cue word _____ (state the cue word)."*

Emotions

> Say, *"When you bring up the picture* (or incident) *and those words _____ (clinician states the negative cognition), what emotion do you feel now?"*

_____

_____

Subjective Units of Disturbance (SUD)

> Say, *"On a scale of 0 to 10, where 0 is no disturbance or neutral and 10 is the highest disturbance you can imagine, how disturbing does it feel now?"*

> 0   1   2   3   4   5   6   7   8   9   10
> (no disturbance)   (highest disturbance)

Location of Body Sensation

> Say, *"Where do you feel it* (the disturbance) *in your body?"*

_____

_____

Provide coaching about what constitutes "processing." Give examples because just saying processing equals change is not sufficient.

> Say, *"I cannot assess the amount of processing you are doing so I need you to be briefed so as to know* <u>*what the experience of change*</u> *is."*

Keep the coaching simple.

> Say, *"During processing, images can change in many different ways. They can move away or seem to get smaller. The images can go out of*

focus like viewing the image behind frosted glass or there may be more or less detail. You might see totally new images or different images may come to mind for example."

Phase 4: Desensitization

Commence desensitization with the undisclosed target plus associated emotion plus emotion's bodily location. Here again, ignore cognitions.

> Say, *"I would like you to bring up _____ (cue word), and notice your emotions and where you feel it or them in your body _____ (state BLS you are using)."*

_____

_____

If a PC is revealed in Phase 4, encourage the client to verbalize it *at that point* and explain that this will be returned to in the next phase. Install the PC in Phase 5 as per normal.

If a PC is revealed, it is important not to make any attempt to identify the negative equivalent. (Be wary of your own nonverbal body language at this point!) Use the VoC, only when, and if, the PC is revealed.

> Say, *"Notice those positive words _____ (state the PC). We will use them a little later in the processing."*

Validity of Cognition (VoC)

> Say, *"When you think of the incident* (or picture), *how true do those words ____* (clinician repeats the positive cognition) *feel to you now on a scale of 1 to 7, where 1 feels completely false and 7 feels completely true?"*

> 1   2   3   4   5   6   7
> (completely false)   (completely true)

Returning to target: Bring the client back to the undisclosed image or memory (by using the cue word) plus emotion and take SUDs as normal.

> Say, *"Please return to whatever is left of ____ (state cue word) and on a scale of 0 to 10, where 0 is no disturbance or neutral and 10 is the highest disturbance that you can imagine, how disturbing does it feel to you now?"*

> 0   1   2   3   4   5   6   7   8   9   10
> (no disturbance)   (highest disturbance)

Other Past Events

Make use of the Float-Back Technique to identify any other targets (such as training, instruction, education, apprenticeship) associated with the same emotion or bodily sensation.

> Say, *"Are there earlier times in your life when you have had these same emotions or bodily sensations?"*

_____

_____

If so, use the same template as above for each target.

Say, *"Please focus on the image or memory you do NOT wish to describe. Do you have it?"*

_____

_____

Say, *"Now, if you would, choose a cue word that either* <u>reminds</u> *you of that image or memory without using a word that might give an easy clue about the image content, such as 'failure,' 'control,' for example. Neutral elements of the image work best such as '27,' 'lamp post,' 'nearby,' or a word(s) that represent the* <u>present, qualitative</u> *nature of that image or memory such as 'It's in my face,' 'Only yesterday,' 'Huge,' all work well."*

Cue word: _____

Make *no attempt* to identify either a negative or a positive cognition as this could give away the content of the image and because it will immediately tap into the negative cognition that the client may find too uncomfortable to acknowledge at this stage.

Now proceed as follows:

Say, *"Now, focus on the image you have identified by the cue word* _____ (state the cue word).*"*

Emotions

Say, *"When you bring up the picture* (or incident) *and those words* _____ (clinician states the negative cognition), *what emotion do you feel now?"*

_____

_____

Subjective Units of Disturbance (SUD)

Say, *"On a scale of 0 to 10, where 0 is no disturbance or neutral and 10 is the highest disturbance you can imagine, how disturbing does it feel now?"*

0	1	2	3	4	5	6	7	8	9	10
(no disturbance)								(highest disturbance)		

Location of Body Sensation

Say, *"Where do you feel it* (the disturbance) *in your body?"*

_____

_____

Looping

Since you cannot use the cognitive interweave, if basic strategies do not overcome looping, use visual interweaves. The Two Image Strategy works very well. Morphing is another strategy.

The Two Image Strategy

Say, *"Place the 'stuck' image at arm's length on the left. Then, select a 'coping' version of the same image at arm's length on the right."*

Use BLS.

Say, *"Now, go with that."*
Say, *"Did you notice a change?"* or *"What do you get now?"*

_____

_____

Morphing

Say, *"Stretch the image from the stuck one to an image that looks funny, or one that can easily 'be controlled.'"*

Use BLS.

Say, *"Now, go with that."*
Say, *"Did you notice a change?"* or *"What do you get now?"*

_____

_____

Current Triggers

Experience suggests that current triggers are not a problem with the occupational groups mentioned earlier, but might be with sexual abuse victims. Occasionally, current triggers may need to be handled carefully, especially if they involve a strong sense of smell. Use the Standard EMDR Protocol if memories have been disclosed. If the client still does not wish to disclose an image of a current trigger, merely substitute the opening statement.

Say, *"I would like you to bring up _____ (cue word), and notice your emotions and where you feel it or them in your body _____ (state BLS you are using)."*

Then continue as per Phase 4 from above.

Future Template

Experience suggests there are unlikely to be problems with identifying and disclosing targets relating to a future template even when talking about the worst-case scenario. Since the adaptive information processing (AIP) model predicts that information flows toward an adaptive conclusion, it is possible that by the time the client is focusing on the future template, there is far less chance of blocks to disclosing material.

Phase 5: Installation

Install any revealed PCs.

Say, *"Think about whatever is left of the original incident (or say cue word) and any positive words that you came up with _____ (state PC)."*

"On a scale of 1 to 7, where 1 feels completely false and 7 feels completely true, how true do they feel <u>now</u>?"

1	2	3	4	5	6	7
(completely false)				(completely true)		

Say, *"Think of ____ (state cue word or image if it has now been revealed) and hold it together with the words ____ (repeat the PC)."*

Do sets of BLS to fully install the PC (VoC = 7).
Alternatively, merely do usual bilateral stimulation with just the undisclosed target.

Say, *"Think of _____ (state cue word) and any positive words that now come to mind that seem linked to it."*

Phase 6: Body Scan

Say, *"Close your eyes and keep in mind the original memory and the positive cognition. Then bring your attention to the different parts of your body, starting with your head and working downward. Any place you find any tension, tightness, or unusual sensation, tell me."*

_____

_____

Phase 7: Closure

Say, *"Things may come up or they may not. If they do, great. Write it down, and it can be a target for next time. If you get any new memories, dreams, or situations that disturb you, just take a good snapshot. It isn't necessary to give a lot of detail. Just put down enough to remind you so we can target it next time. The same thing goes for any positive dreams or situations. If negative feelings do come up, try not to make them significant. Remember, it's still just the old stuff. Just write it down for next time. Then use the tape or the Safe Place exercise to let as much of the disturbance go as possible. Even if nothing comes up, make sure to use the tape every day and give me a call if you need to."*

Phase 8: Reevaluation

Review the previous session using cue words, unless the client has disclosed the image or memory content already. Be aware that sometimes clients will end one session still having not disclosed the image or memory content, but will disclose the content during Phase 8. If material is disclosed, be prepared to extend the time allocated to Phase 8 to accommodate any explanations the client feels they must make. Alter the wording below according to whether the image or memory content has been disclosed.

Say, *"When you think of whatever is left of (cue word or disclosed target image) that we worked on last time, how disturbing is it now on a scale of 0 to 10, where 0 is no disturbance or neutral and 10 is the highest disturbance you can imagine, how disturbing does it feel now?"*

0	1	2	3	4	5	6	7	8	9	10
(no disturbance)								(highest disturbance)		

Say, *"Have you noticed any other material associated with* _____ (cue word or disclosed target image) *in the original memory since the last session?"*

_____

_____

_____

Say, *"Have all the necessary targets been reprocessed so that you can feel at peace with the past, empowered in the present, and able to make choices for the future?"*

_____

_____

_____

Say, *"Has the work that we have done with EMDR helped you be more adaptive in your day-to-day life?"*

_____

_____

Use the answers to these questions to determine what steps to take next.
Free help is available if using this protocol via e-mail: help@davidblore.co.uk

EMDR Emergency Room and Wards Protocol (EMDR-ER)

Judith S. B. Guedalia
and Frances R. Yoeli

The EMDR-Emergency Room and Wards Protocol (EMDR-ER©) was developed by Dr. Judith Guedalia, after being present at more than 26 Mass Casualty Events (MCEs). She and the other members of Shaare Zedek Medical Center's Trauma Team attended to more than 38% of the 1,623 patients injured in Jerusalem terror attacks during the "Second Intifada." The Second Intifada spanned nearly 4 years, lasting from November 2000 until September 2004.

EMDR Emergency Room and Wards Protocol (EMDR-ER) Script

Phase 1: History Taking

Screening

The EMDR-ER Protocol is used with patients who do not seem able to move on to the ambulatory staging area (i.e., are still on gurneys, frozen on a chair, or on a hospital bed), and who display difficulty in being able to reassume normal appropriate affect, physical, psychological, or behavioral functions at an adequate level given the situation.

Since patients are usually in the emergency room (ER) for many, many hours (5 to 8 hours), there are numerous opportunities to assess the patient's ability to communicate by various means, including just being nearby, standing or sitting next to the patient—whether the patient is on a chair, gurney, bed, and so forth, or doing a more formal type of assessment. Once the patient reaches a basic level of safety, the therapist then can begin communicating safety phrases to the patient. The criteria for the patient reaching a basic level of safety are the following: shows a basic level of physical relatedness, can focus eyes, can respond to questions, looks around the gurney or chair, shows interest at some level of the surroundings, breathing cadence slows down to normal.

When the patient shows the basic level of safety, the therapist can nod, hold the patient's hand, breathe in the same cadence as the patient. At this point of the patient's recovery, it is not necessary to respond to questions asked by the patient with verbal answers. This is because verbal areas of the brain may have shut down and the acutely stressed patient many not hear answers but can sense presence and holding. Very often patients in this situation have not been able to relate to language as evidenced by repeating the same questions despite the answers given. Often, they are in a dissociative-like state that is more of a biological response to acute stress. This state need not be labelled or medicated immediately.

The next step is for the therapist to begin to say short, comforting, and grounding phrases such as the following:

> *"You are alive";*
> *"You are safe now";*
> *"You are in the hospital;"*
> *"I am here for you."*

When this level of trust and safety is achieved, the work begins to move forward. Installing a sense of safety, trust, and the realization that they are among the living, is facilitated by the presence of a trained EMDR clinician. Once the sense of immediate safety is established, the introduction of the EMDR-ER protocol is possible and recommended. This protocol can be used with good results even with patients who speak a different language than the therapist; however, an interpreter might be helpful.

When the patient is showing dissociative responses to the trauma such as: hysterical paralysis or a fugue-like state, do not attempt any EMDR. Also, EMDR is not used in the ER with patients who seem to have below borderline intelligence as assessed by clinically administered (bedside) tests such as the Mini Mental State Examination (MMSE). The needs of these patients are different. Repetition in a quiet environment—without a lot of stimulation of the ER—may be better for them. EMDR may be too stimulating for them.

Receiving permission to engage the patient, in some form of bilateral stimulation (BLS), is frequently not possible during the initial stages of hospitalization. When a patient cannot provide permission—and BLS might still be appropriate—only a physician or nurse is allowed to touch the patient. Once the clinician has received an okay to touch the patient from the patient himself, BLS in the form of tapping is possible.

Phase 2: Preparation

Safe Contact—With Dual Attention Elements

The patients are generally prone on a gurney (possibly compounding the drawing of attention inward to their recent trauma). With medical permission, check if the patient can be raised or somewhat raised to a sitting position and then say the following:

Say, *"Hello, my name is _____ (state name)."*
Then say, *"You are in the hospital now and you are safe. Is it okay for me to touch you here?"*

_____

_____

If the client nods his head, it is taken as an agreement that permits touch. If the patient does not agree, go into the cognitive explanation before conducting bilateral stimulation with touch.

Point to where you will touch the patient.

With those who cannot respond verbally at this time, either touch in two places, or stand in their line of vision as well as touching them. This draws their attention outward to the safe present; this is the ER type of "Dual Attention" that keeps the patient in the *present* and provides a reality check to the fact that they are now *safe*. The external attention created by the touch, the calm tone of voice, and the safe presence of the therapist in the patient's line of vision is particularly important for the hyper-aroused patient who requires grounding.

Introduce the EMDR-ER Protocol or Intervention With a Cognitive Neuropsychological Lesson

Say, *"When we experience trauma, our brain takes in many sounds, feelings, images, smells, and even tastes, all at the same time. This avalanche of sensations coupled with the very real fear of dying, gets encoded or locked in our brain. The area of the brain that is generally activated in such situations is called the Limbic System. This is the area that stores and processes emotion in our brain. This area experiences memories and is not generally seen as accessible by speech."*

We use this further explanation to encourage the patient's recovery and cooperation.

Say, *"This is especially true soon after the event has occurred* (this seems to be a neuropsychological reality). *Initially trauma is a cortical experience in the Limbic System, specifically the hippocampus. The hippocampus is an area of the brain that looks like a seahorse. It is responsible for episodic memory and spatial navigation. Unlike motor memory such as remembering how to ride a bicycle or swim or factual memory such as recalling dates of historical events, episodic memory involves day-to-day, short-term memories—what we did yesterday, or whom we met last week. It is the area that scientists now understand to be affected in traumatic experiences. What seems to occur is very visceral* (internal in the brain) *and is not neuropsychologically available for verbal encoding. The senses such as feeling, seeing, smelling, hearing, and taste are the modalities by which information is received, processed, and encoded by the brain. Research has shown* (and our clinical experience has found) *that before these images, smells, sounds, and so forth get stored, it is beneficial to talk and give words to these sensory inputs so as to allow them to be available for verbal access in the future."*

This may be very complicated and wordy for the ER patient. But the presence of the therapist's voice and the explanation well understood or not, tends to foster a sense of calm and safety. In general, we begin this after the patient is somewhat stabilized. Also, it gives family members something to hang onto once we begin. They may be afraid of responses that we understand to be normal for Acute Stress Disorder (ASD) patients. Also, some aspects of the cognitive intervention may be understood and begin to help the patient formulate a frame of reference and then build on it in a logical scaffolding sort of way.

Phase 3: Assessment

It is important for the therapist to be there with acceptance and the safety of her physical presence. This seems to act as an affirmation of the patient's existence. The clinician's presence creates a dual attention; the therapist assists the patient to move from an internal focus to an external focus as he is now safe and becomes more aware of that safety in the present with the therapist. You might whisper, again to reinforce the reality of the situation.

Say, *"You are alive," "You are safe now,"* or *"You did get away from there."*

LISTEN TO THE PATIENT'S NARRATIVE OR STORY OF THE EVENT

Attend to body language during the recitation of the story. Note, if there is agitation in the patient's vocabulary, specific to individual or cultural background as it punctuates the narrative, for example, "Time stopped," "I can't move (speak or hear)," "I am dead," and use this to reflect or suggest negative cognitions (NCs) "I am helpless," "I am out of control," "I am going to die (am dying)." Take notes without interrupting or asking for clarifications.

Say, *"Please tell me what happened."*

_____

_____

_____

_____

_____

_____

_____

_____

Target, Memory, or Image of the Actual Traumatic Event

Say, *"Please allow yourself to focus on an image, picture, or sound of the event."*

_____

_____

_____

_____

Image

Say, *"What do you see now?"*

_____

_____

_____

_____

Positive Cognition (PC)

The NC and PC are reversed in order to further affirm, enforce, enhance, and embed the issues of safety, control, and recovery. It is TOO early for the patient to say, "I am in control" or that "I will be ok," safe and alive are the most positive we can get.

Say, *"When you bring up that image, can you now feel that you are alive and safe?"*

_____

_____

Note: Some humor may be appropriate here.

Say, *"I am alive and speaking to you, which proves to me that you are also alive."*

Clinical experience has demonstrated that when patients respond with a smile, it is diagnostic of available resources. They may not truly believe that they *are* alive.

Validity of Cognition (VoC)

Say, *"When you think of the incident* (or picture), *how true do those words _____* (clinician repeats the positive cognition) *feel to you now on a scale of 1 to 7, where 1 feels completely false and 7 feels completely true?"*

1	2	3	4	5	6	7
(completely false)				(completely true)		

Negative Cognition (NC)

Say, *"What words go best with that picture and expresses your negative thinking and belief about yourself now?"*

_____

_____

_____

Emotions

Say, *"When you bring up that picture or incident and those words _____* (repeat the NC), *what emotion(s) do you feel now?"*

_____

_____

_____

Note: Connect the patient's words to the emotion in order to narrow the distance between the words and feelings or the cognitive and the visceral. Don't be afraid to show your own emotions—by crying or sighing—as it can help the patient emote and expresses your own genuineness and empathy.

Subjective Units of Disturbance (SUD)

Say, *"On a scale of 0 to 10, where 0 is no disturbance or neutral and 10 is the highest disturbance you can imagine, how disturbing does it feel now?"*

0	1	2	3	4	5	6	7	8	9	10
(no disturbance)							(highest disturbance)			

Note: This question can evoke an abreaction and therefore it is not necessary to insist on a SUD at this point.

Location of Body Sensation

Say, *"Where do you feel it in your body?"*

_____

_____

Note: This question can be problematic when the patients are physically injured. In such cases, this question should not be asked.

Phase 4: Desensitization

Ask the patient to repeat the narrative and pay close attention to what the patient is saying and to your notes from previous visits to this patient. Be aware of what can be used from the narrative as a metaphor that can distance them from the scene such as video, reversed binoculars, television, or other nonreminders of the situation that brought him to the ER. Be attuned to the use of words in the past tense, "I saw," "The sounds were," "He was," and so forth, as opposed to using the present tense.

Say, *"Please tell me again what happened. Sometimes, it is helpful to think about it as if it were on television or that you are looking at it with reversed binoculars* (or any other relevant metaphors).*"*

_____

_____

_____

_____

_____

As time in the ER goes on, and the patients are off the gurneys and onto chairs, it is sometimes feasible to do bilateral stimulation (BLS). However, there is usually no private space that is quiet or secluded enough to comfortably carry this out. Subtle tapping on hands, shoulders, or knees may be more suitable as active cooperation is not required here.

Say, *"I am going to touch you gently on your* _____ (hands, shoulders, knees—wherever is appropriate or accessible); *this may help you to feel more comfortable."*

In a Mass Casualty Event (MCE), there is generally a low patient-to-staff ratio (more injured than available staff members). This may be particularly true of the psychology and social-work staff members, as each patient may bring twice as many family members in need of assistance and guidance. With this fact in mind, the therapist keeps going around and coming back to each patient. Using notes to keep track of what time the therapist was last with the client is helpful, as well as the specifics and sequence of the patient's narrative. During some MCEs, there may be tens of patients per therapist.

The therapist continues to return to the patient and restarts the processing. The time lapses tend to reduce or dilute the emotion of the narrative (a form of titration) and this reinforces the processing. When the therapist leaves to move on to someone else, she gives him homework, such as breathing exercises, if this is not physically painful. It is important to keep reinforcing that the patient is in the hospital and is in a safe place now.

> Say, *"Please tell me again what happened. Sometimes, it is helpful to think about it as if it were on television or that you are looking at it with reversed binoculars* (or any other relevant metaphor).*"*

> _____

> _____

> _____

> _____

> _____

> Say, *"Okay. I want to tell you that you are safe now. You are in the hospital and you are safe here with us. I will be back soon. While I am gone, please focus on something that you can see right here and then count your breaths—each inhale and each exhale—in your mind with your mouth closed. If there is another breathing exercise you like to do, go ahead and do that."*

This tends to keep the patient (and family member) busy and less focused on his traumatic experience literally externalizing his energies.

Each time the therapist returns to the specific patient, she refocuses the patient by being in his line of vision or touching him on his arm or other noninjured area. The therapist speaks softly if his eyes are closed. Generally, the patient does NOT want to close his eyes, as the images that he sees then are so horrific, he prefers to leave his eyes open. The therapist might suggest that he close his eyes once assuring him that she is standing near, thereby reinforcing the safe place.

> Say, *"If it is helpful, you might want to close your eyes now knowing that I am right here with you and you are safe now in the hospital."*

Phase 5: Installation

The therapist uses her notes from the last time she saw the patient as a scaffold to build a richer, more complete story. Generally the therapist might emphasize or reframe any reference to acts of kindness or positive experiences the patient referred to in his narrative. Repeat the narrative again, interweaving new information and the positive experience, checking the patient's physical and emotional state while using BLS if possible.

Help incorporate sequences such as time and place concepts into a narrative.

> *"What time did you leave the house, office, or school?"*
> *"What happened next . . . ?"*
> *"Where were you standing, sitting, or walking?"*
> Say, *"_____ (repeat the narrative building in a more complete story)."*

As the therapist repeats the story, it is important to utilize the patient's own words, where possible. The idea is to amplify the points made and help him understand the sequence of his narrative so that he has a cohesive experience of what happened to him and gains a sense of control, self-determination, power, and a sense that it is "worth it" to continue living notwithstanding what has just happened and that he will be released from the safe hospital space. The narrative that is created will be the one that will (hopefully) be crystallized for future reference. This process may take hours! Continue repeating the narrative above as needed.

Emotions

Say, *"When you bring up that picture or incident, and those words* _____ *(repeat the NC), what emotion(s) do you feel now?"*

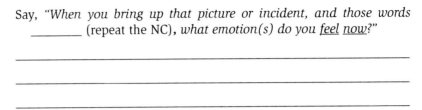

Note: Connect his words to the emotion in order to narrow the distance between the words and feelings or the cognitive and the visceral. Again, don't be afraid to show your own emotions—by crying or sighing—as it can help the patient emote and expresses your own genuineness and empathy.

Subjective Units of Disturbance (SUD)

Say, *"On a scale of 0 to 10, where 0 is no disturbance or neutral and 10 is the highest disturbance you can imagine, how disturbing does it feel now?"*

0   1   2   3   4   5   6   7   8   9   10
(no disturbance)   (highest disturbance)

Note: This question can evoke an abreaction and therefore it is not necessary to insist on a SUD at this point.

Location of Body Sensation

Say, *"Where do you feel it in your body?"*

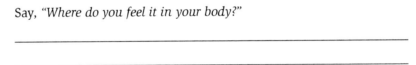

Note: This question can be problematic when the patients are physically injured. In such cases, this question should not be asked.

Do this until the patient has reprocessed the event and demonstrated that he is "speech-full," that is, the patient is able to give at least some words to verbalize the sensory experiences, or a coherent account with generally appropriate affect.

Reduction of Observable SUD

The goal is to get the patient up and out of the gurney, chair, bed, and the ER, on their way home through the exit processes. This means that the therapist probably will not get the target to go down to a SUD of 0; however, the patient's physical movement off of the existing ER place (gurney, bed, or chair) is viewed as a decrease in the SUD.

Phase 6: Body Scan

In the ER, when using the EMDR-ER Intervention/Protocol, attention to the body is directed at checking differences and changes in the patient's emotional tone such as in the following: stopping uncontrollable crying, more control of emotional reactions, and the decrease of physical signs such as uncontrollable shaking, perspiring, and perseverative verbalizations.

As the process goes on, rather than specifically asking the patient for a Body Scan, which, with the physically injured, tends to have another connotation (the patient may give a more medical symptom review rather than a measure of tensions still affecting the body), the therapist watches for changes in body language such as slower cadence of speech and fuller breathing. Also, other more verbal signs of change may be the following: a richness fills out the narrative, and the patient begins worrying about specifics such as "Where is my wallet?" "How will I get home?" "My passport or ID is missing." Another good sign (of return to normal rather than hyperarousal and in-trauma functioning) is when the patient starts to say "I'm hungry."

The Body Scan is more appropriate at the final discharge staging area, when the primary purpose is to check for residual, unprocessed information that is thought to be stored as sensory or body memories, and may require further processing so as to further reduce tension and lead into closure at a future time. This information should be relayed to the patient and his family as part of the cognitive discharge process (immediately before or after the medical discharge process—see below).

Phase 7: Closure

Final Feedback

Final feedback occurs when the patient repeats the narrative in the presence of the internist or physician and in the presence of a social worker, psychologist, or psychiatrist. This takes place during the final medical check that ascertains that the patient has had all the tests: x-rays, blood tests, medical specialist evaluations, and so forth, which were initially ordered in the ER. The patient's delivery of the narrative is assessed and when it is deemed cohesive and affect appropriate, the patient is released from the trauma (MCE) process.

Say, *"Please tell us about what happened to you."*

_____

_____

_____

Normalization

The patient receives a prepared handout with information concerning the normal responses that may occur to someone after being present during, for example, an explosion that may cause ringing ears, acute stress, sleep disruptions, and nightmares, and the telephone numbers to call for further treatment (outpatient clinic). This, then, is the final medical exam and the patient is seen by a social worker, psychiatrist, or psychologist before being discharged.

Say, *"Here is a handout that tells you about what to expect after an event such as what happened to you. It also gives you the telephone numbers that you can call for further help or treatment. You may still have a day or two of disrupted sleep, you might find yourself startling more often, or you may have other signs of stress. I want you to know that this is normal in light of the terrible experience that you have been through. If you find that these symptoms are lasting longer than a few days and do not seem to be subsiding, be sure to ask for further help by calling someone who is listed on this sheet. If for some reason you cannot find your sheet, you can always telephone us or come back here and someone here can give you the information that you need. Do you have any questions?"*

_____

_____

Social Services Consultation and Release

This can be tailored to your circumstances. In this situation, the social worker verifies that there is a home to go to, and that the person is not a tourist who will be alone in a hotel, and that there is someone to pick up the individual from the ER. The patient is then given an official release form from the hospital, along with the phone number of Bituach Leumi (Israeli National Insurance), and the code number of this specific MCE for future reference (all of this is printed out and handed to the patient).

Say, *"Where will you go when you leave here?"*

_____

_____

Say, *"Do you have someone to pick you up now?"*

_____

_____

Say, *"Here is your official release from the hospital _____ (and any other information that needs to be given)."*

Phase 8: Reevaluation

This phase can be tailored to your needs. In this situation, patients are generally required to come back for follow-up of their medical conditions within a day or two; others who are not as physically injured are told to get in contact with their family physician and Bituach Leumi if they don't live near the hospital and can call our Post-MCE/Trauma/Acute Stress Psycho-Social Department. Within a few days the national insurance arranges a phone call by an assigned social worker who will become the case manager for this patient. As a result of research and clinical experience throughout Israel, patients are eligible for group therapy or other services as deemed necessary by the agency in charge of the MCE/Terror victims once the event has been classified as such.

The Recent-Traumatic Episode Protocol (R-TEP): An Integrative Protocol for Early EMDR Intervention (EEI)

Elan Shapiro and Brurit Laub

Early EMDR Intervention (EEI)

The question of how early to intervene with EMDR in the face of natural and man-made disasters has been an important part of the dialogue of those working in this field. As a result of the human beings suffering in the wake of these catastrophes, a number of ideas have ensued and new ways to work with the pain and anguish explored. Whereas the majority of people who experience a significant trauma will recover spontaneously, there is often prolonged suffering and about one-third may be left with enduring distressing clinical or subclinical symptoms of posttraumatic stress disorder (PTSD) and other psychiatric disorders (NICE, 2005).

Early EMDR intervention, before consolidation of the memory has taken place, may influence adaptive integration (e.g., process sticking points), promote positive coping (especially if this is not occurring spontaneously), and contribute to the development of resilience. Therefore, early EMDR intervention should be considered following a significant trauma. How and when to intervene with EEI most effectively and whether it can thereby reduce the incidence of PTSD and other disorders that can follow trauma are among the challenges that need to be studied empirically.

Informed by the work of Francine Shapiro, Roger Solomon, and all of the friends and colleagues in the field who have contributed to the evolution of their thinking and practice and following clinical and empirical experience with early EMDR intervention in the wake of the 2006 Lebanon war, the authors have observed that the existing EEI protocols appear to focus on certain aspects or parts of the traumatic episode along an approximate time line continuum following a trauma, in accordance with the *Diagnostic and Statistical Manual of Mental Disorders* (*DSM-IV*) (APA, 2000). They concluded that the unfinished processing of recent traumatic events may require a broader focus than existing early EMDR intervention (EEI) protocols provided.

251

Looking at the existing protocols, Shapiro and Laub (2008a, 2008b) suggest that the earliest interventions (e.g., emergency room protocols) that use elements of EMDR such as Bi-Lateral Stimulation (BLS) are primarily used for calming and stabilization for Acute Stress Response (ASR). The EMD Protocol is most effectively used for processing intrusive sensory phenomena. The Recent Event (RE) protocol is used for processing an unconsolidated discrete event and the Standard EMDR Protocol is used to process memories that are already consolidated in a theme cluster. However, they suggest that the original traumatic incident and its aftermath may be conceived more like an ongoing *trauma continuum* while the experiences have not yet been consolidated. They propose a new protocol called the Recent-Traumatic Episode Protocol (R-TEP), which incorporates and extends the existing EEI protocols by providing a new comprehensive, integrative protocol. The R-TEP thus bridges the gaps left by previous protocols and facilitates a transition from the EMD and RE protocols to the Standard EMDR Protocol.

The R-TEP takes the wisdom of the Standard EMDR Protocol (Shapiro, 1995, 2001), and applies it in adapted form for recent events to provide a comprehensive approach to Early EMDR Intervention. It is a protocol that utilizes both the EMD and EMDR protocols together with some elements of the Recent Event Protocol within a newly conceived extended time perspective, termed here the "Traumatic Episode." The Traumatic Episode (or T-Episode) comprises multiple targets of disturbing images, events, or other experiences, in the trauma continuum from the original incident until the present, including disturbing thoughts about the future, which need to be processed.

New theoretical conceptualizations of the process of memory consolidation, relating to Francine Shapiro's Adaptive Information Processing (AIP) model (Shapiro, 1995, 2001), guided the development of the R-TEP. It is suggested that the stages of this process proceed hierarchically according to part/whole relations aiming toward adaptive integration (see Figure 27.1). This process is of a broadening focus from the intrusive image or sensory data, to the event, to the episode that includes many events, to the theme, and to the identity that is comprised of clusters of themes. When a part (such as intrusive sensory image, etc.) is stuck, the AIP is disrupted and cannot move toward the next whole, and thus fails to reach integration. Information

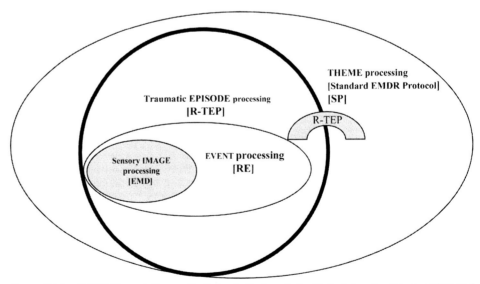

Figure 27.1   R-TEP (Recent-Traumatic Episode Protocol). Part/whole levels of processing and a bridge from episode to theme in early EMDR interventions (EEI) (Shapiro & Laub, 2008a).

is transmitted at increasing levels of complexity, from the perceptual (sensory), to the experiential (somatic and emotional), and to the meaning (cognitive) levels, perhaps matching the evolution of the brain. The AIP system moves toward integration via the associative interconnections between negative and positive stored memories. Perhaps this dialectical movement (Laub, 2001; Laub & Weiner, 2007) is the primary vehicle by which part/whole components of information are processed in an adaptive way.

The R-TEP employs an adapted 8-phase structure, with some modifications for application to early EMDR intervention. These modifications are based on the fragmented nature of the memory, on the need for containment and safety, and the wider T-Episode time frame. The T-Episode is conceived as a continuum from the original incident to present disturbance and anticipated future concerns.

Main Issues in Early EMDR Intervention (EEI)

Clinical experience indicates that EMDR can be beneficial for alleviating excessive distress and complications in the weeks and months following critical events. However, there seems to be uncertainty and inconsistency among many clinicians about which protocols to use for Early EMDR Intervention and how and when to use them. It is noted that there is little in the literature relating to studies with special EEI protocols and no published controlled empirical studies to inform us here. Consequently, there is a need for a comprehensive model and set of guidelines in the EMDR practitioner's toolbox to assist in approaching the prospect of EEI with more confidence and to generate research.

There are three main issues to consider when working with EEI.

1. *Memory:* In recent trauma the nature of the memory is fragmented and not consolidated; it requires a different protocol.
2. *Therapeutic Situation:* The nature of the situation for client and therapist is that there is an atmosphere of emergency or urgency that often results in high arousal or distress and sometimes avoidance; this requires a special attention to containment and safety.
3. *Therapy Contract:* The nature of the therapy contract may be unclear, and as a result professional and ethical standards may be compromised; this requires good practice guidelines.

The Recent-Traumatic Episode Protocol

Main Features of R-TEP

The Recent-Traumatic Episode Protocol has a number of important features.

1. Comprehensive approach to EEI: The 8 Phases.
2. Integrative approach to EEI: This approach incorporates EMD, RE, and EMDR Protocols.
3. The Traumatic-Episode (T-Episode): This is a newly conceived trauma continuum time frame.
4. The Google-Search (G-Search): This is a mechanism for identifying multiple targets of disturbance within the T-Episode.
5. "Telescopic Processing": Expanding focus of regulation of chains of associations.
6. Special attention to containment and safety.
7. Maintaining standards of good practice.
8. Theoretical underpinning.

Adapted 8 Phases of the R-TEP

This novel application of the 8-phase framework for EEI provides a structure that fosters safety and maintains professional standards of good practice even in recent event situations where they risk being compromised. The 8 phases follow the Standard EMDR Protocol, but they are divided into three groupings to emphasize the specific features of the R-TEP:

A. Episode history taking and preparation (usually neglected in EEI)

    1. Phase 1: History
       To assess readiness for EEI

    2. Phase 2: Preparation
       To attend to safety and containment

B. Episode Micro Level (identify and process unconsolidated targets)

    1. Micro level Phases 3, 4, 5, (no 6), 7:

    2. To identify multitargets with G-search and to process within the T-Episode with telescopic processing.

       a. T-Episode narrative plus Bi-Lateral Stimuli (BLS)
          To tell the story of the traumatic episode out loud with BLS

       b. "Episode Google search"
          To identify targets of disturbance relating the to the T-Episode from the original incident until today, including all the related events

       c. "Telescopic Processing"
          To expand focus in the following sequence

          i. Begins with the EMD Protocol: no chains of association

          ii. Expands to the T-episode focused EMDr: limited chains of association

          iii. Expands further, if necessary, to the Standard EMDR: unlimited chains of association

C. Episode Macro Level—the T-Episode is related to as a whole

    1. Check Episode SUD

    2. Macro Level Phase 5: Installation of episode PC

    3. Macro Level Phase 6: Episode Body Scan

    4. Phase 7: Closure of the Episode

    5. Phase 8: Follow-up

The Google Search (G-Search)

The Google Search (G-Search) is a metaphor for a mechanism to identify multiple targets of disturbance within the T-Episode. It identifies targets nonsequentially, perhaps in the way the person's brain has stored the memories. The targets identified from the entire episode can usually be processed over several sessions. When there are no more targets identified at this micro level (within the T-Episode), go to the macro level (the entire T-Episode, which includes the Episode PC and Installation, Body Scan, and Closure; this is usually quite a short procedure) within the entire episode.

The Standard EMDR Protocol has a 3-pronged perspective of past, present, and future, in which a few discrete episodic memories can represent past, present, and future aspects of the current disturbance. Recent traumatic events have tended to be approached as 1-pronged, when they focus mainly on processing the (past) original incident. The R-TEP protocol proposes a 3-pronged perspective with EEI as well. The (recent) past traumatic incident influences our sense of safety and control in the present as well as our future expectations. Therefore, concerns about the future arising during the G-Search may also be important targets for processing.

Special Attention to Containment and Safety

In addition to the containment and safety provided by the adapted 8 phase framework, there are some other measures.

T-Episode Narrative

During Phases 1 and 2, the client is deliberately not asked to recount the details of the trauma yet, except in general terms, so as to avoid triggering abreaction and possible retraumatization before containment and safety measures are in place and treatment processing can begin. The T-Episode narrative is carried out adding BLS during the telling of the story with an optional distancing technique. This appears to increase the sense of safety because of the presumed grounding and de-arousal effects of the BLS.

Telescopic Processing

The possibility of regulating chains of associations can provide boundaries for focused contained processing. Identified targets are processed with a strategy of a widening focus, beginning with the narrow focused EMD protocol (going back to target after each set). If the SUD is not reducing after several sets, the focus can be expanded to permit associations related to the Current Traumatic Episode, which is called the EMDr protocol (R. Kiessling, 2008, personal communication). If the SUD is still not reducing or processing gets stuck, the focus expands further (with consent) to permit all associations as in the Standard EMDR Protocol processing using Telescoping Processing; this step is optional (see Figure 27.2).

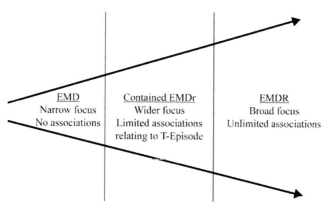

Brief R-TEP "Telescopic Processing"
•Expanding from EMD to EMDr to EMDR

EMD	Contained EMDr	EMDR
Narrow focus	Wider focus	Broad focus
No associations	Limited associations relating to T-Episode	Unlimited associations

Figure 27.2   Brief R-TEP "Telescopic Processing." Expanding from EMD to EMDr to EMDR.

Guidelines for Maintaining Standards of Good Practice

It is important to maintain standards of good practice. However, during the unusual circumstances of EEI, there are a number of risks that should be noted to ensure optimal EMDR therapy practice.

1. *Premature Intervention*. There is potential conflict with the EMDR self-healing ethos such as concerns about premature intervention and pathologizing normal responses to abnormal situations (the meta communication of the presence of mental health professionals implying that something is wrong with them).
2. *Prior History*. The way in which the clinician intervenes in EEI needs to be considered. In general, the clinician will encounter normal people who have been exposed to abnormal situations. However some of them will have previous histories of pathology, dysfunction, or trauma. Specifically, care should be taken to avoid common pitfalls such as: excessive shortcuts in Phases 1 (insufficient history, intake, ego strength assessment) and 2 (insufficient rapport and preparation), as well as opening other clinical issues when this is not part of the therapy contract (in EMDR you know where you start but not where you may go).
3. *Traumatic Episode*. When possible, give priority to focusing on the traumatic episode and its concomitants, and only go into other clinical issues that arise if this is not sufficient to promote adaptive processing. While we need to be flexible in these circumstances, we also need to bear in mind our professional boundaries and standards when working with recent trauma.
4. *Timing of Intervention*. The question of when to intervene is still an open question and there are various opinions. Pragmatic answers include: Shalev's (2007) recommendation that when there are still ASD symptoms about 1 month after the incident clinicians should intervene and Bisson's (2006) view to focus on high risk individuals with more symptoms 1 to 3 months after the incident. Solomon (2008) advocates a longitudinal assessment of functioning or needs, and Shapiro and Laub (2008a) suggest intervening when there is excessive suffering and persistent disturbing symptoms, especially intrusive sensory images and sleep disturbance, or where high risk is assessed, even a shorter time after the traumatic event.

The R-TEP, therefore, embodies a set of guidelines, with built-in safeguards for checking one's work and maintaining standards of good practice in line with the Standard EMDR Protocol.

The Recent-Traumatic Episode Protocol (R-TEP)

Phase 1: Client History

Obtain as much client history and information as possible in the circumstances to screen for previous pathology and to estimate Severity, Motivation, and Strengths (SMS) ratings on a 5-point scale: 1 = low to 5 = high in order to decide whether it is appropriate to proceed with EMDR processing with the client at this time. Minimum strengths and motivation ratings of 3 are advocated to proceed when the severity is high. Administer the Impact of Events Scale (IES-R) when possible, to obtain a baseline measure prior to intervention as part of the assessment and again postintervention to assess effectiveness.

A summary of SMS ratings based on all information obtained and clinical impression is listed.

S = Severity	(low) 1	2	3	4	5 (high)
M = Motivation	(low) 1	2	3	4	5 (high)
S = Strengths	(low) 1	2	3	4	5 (high)

Phase 2: Preparation

In early EMDR intervention, clients are likely to be easily flooded with states of high arousal and distress. Therefore, Phase 2 preparation is particularly important for establishing sufficient safety and containment to enable EMDR processing.

In all cases, start with stabilization and resource exercises for calming and enhancing control such as: The 4 Elements, Safe Place, and Resource Connection. (See scripts for resources in Part III of this book.) Write down the exercises or scripts used for each of these.

During Phases 1 and 2, the client is deliberately not asked to recount the details of the trauma yet, except in general terms, so as to avoid triggering abreaction and possible retraumatization before containment and safety measures are in place and treatment processing can begin.

Micro Episode Level

Micro Level Phases 3, 4, 5, and 7: Episode Processing (Multi-Target Processing at the Micro Level)

These phases include assessment and processing of multiple targets identified from the original traumatic event, the experiences after it, and its changing meaning.

The goal of episode processing is to integrate the disturbing images and other sensory data, events, or other experiences within the traumatic episode, from the original incident until today including disturbing thoughts about the future, so that processing can proceed.

1. Episode Narrative With Bi-Lateral Stimulation (BLS)

In the Episode Narrative, the client tells the story of the traumatic episode out loud with BLS. This helps to ground and contain affect while the client begins the processing. This is the first time that the client speaks about the details of the trauma. Using a distancing metaphor, such as a TV screen, gives additional containment if needed.

2. Episode "Google Search" (or G-Search) With BLS (Episode Micro Level)

Note: For clients who may not understand the Google Search metaphor, then just say Scan.

3. Telescopic Processing

The possibility of regulating associations can provide boundaries for focused contained processing from a narrow to broad focus, from EMD, to EMDr, to EMDR.

Episode Narrative and Initial Google Search Script

In the Episode narrative, the client tells the story of the traumatic incident out loud with EMDR.

Say, *"Do you feel* (relatively) *comfortable and safe here now in this room?"*

_____

_____

If the answer is no, then more preparation and stabilization is needed first.

Say, *"I am going to ask you to view the whole T-Episode, beginning a few minutes before it started until today. Feel your feet on the ground, the safety of this room, and tell the story out loud."*

If this is too close for the client, suggest the following:

Say, *"I am going to ask you to view the whole T-Episode, beginning a few minutes before it started until today. Feel your feet on the ground, the safety of this room and tell the story out loud and watch the whole episode as on TV. Imagine that you are watching the episode on a screen with a remote control that can make the screen smaller, farther away, lower the volume, or even pause it."*

Use continuous BLS during the Episode narrative.

_____

_____

_____

_____

_____

_____

_____

_____

_____

_____

Say, *"Now, without talking out loud this time, return to scan the whole episode, like a Google Search in the computer, for anything that is disturbing, in no particular order. Just notice what comes up as you search the whole episode from the original event until today and stop at what is disturbing you."*

Use continuous BLS during the G-Search.

_____

_____

Target and process each point of disturbance (event, part of event, experience, etc.). For Phase 3, use as much of the Standard EMDR Protocol assessment as appropriate such as NC, PC, VoC, Emotion, SUD, Body Sensation. Then, using Telescopic Processing, begin with EMD, if necessary expand to EMDr, and, if still necessary, expand to EMDR.

EMD Protocol for R-TEP Script (Adapted From the EMD Protocol, Shapiro, 1995)

Phase 3: Assessment

Target

Say, *"Describe the disturbance."*

_____

_____

_____

_____

Negative Cognition (NC)

Say, *"What negative words go with that _____ (state the target) or about yourself now?"*

_____

_____

If there is high arousal or difficulty in rapidly finding an NC, suggest a suitable NC. Clients usually speak about physical survival categories of safety or control in these types of situations such as "I'm in danger," "I am helpless," "It shouldn't happen."

Positive Cognition (PC)

Say, *"When you bring up that _____ (state target), how would you like to think about it, or about yourself?"*

_____

_____

If it is difficult to find a PC while the level of disturbance is high, offer a tentative PC that is appropriate to the NC.

Say, *"Would you like to believe that 'It happened and it's over,' 'I survived,' 'I am safe now from THAT event,' 'I can cope'? Is that what you would like to believe or is there something else you prefer?"*

_____

_____

Validity of Cognition (VoC)

You can skip the VoC if it is not appropriate to ask at this stage.

Say, *"On a scale of 1 to 7, where 1 is completely false and 7 is completely true, how true do these words <u>feel</u> to you <u>now</u>?"*

1	2	3	4	5	6	7
(completely false)				(completely true)		

Emotions

Say, "*When you bring up that _____* (state target) *and those words _____* (state the negative cognition), *what emotion do you feel now?*"

_____

_____

Subjective Units of Disturbance (SUD)

Say, "*On a scale of 0 to 10, where 0 is no disturbance or neutral and 10 is the highest disturbance you can imagine, how disturbing does the image feel to you now?*"

```
0     1     2     3     4     5     6     7     8     9     10
(no disturbance)                              (highest disturbance)
```

Location of Body Sensation

Say, "*Where do you feel it in your body?*"

_____

_____

Phase 4: Desensitization

Unlike the Standard EMDR Protocol, you repeatedly go back to target and check SUD levels. Continue processing with several more sets of Bi-Lateral Stimulation (BLS). Longer sets are recommended such as 45 seconds. If this appears to be too much for the client, try shorter sets, such as 15 seconds. Go back to target (the original image or target) after each set until the target is no longer disturbing. This means that the SUD level is reduced to ecological validity, or when it can be viewed relatively calmly.

Say, "*I'd like you to bring up that _____* (state target), *those negative words _____* (state the negative cognition), *and notice where you are feeling it in your body. Go with that.*"

1. Do a set of BLS for 15 to 45 seconds. After the set, say the following:

Say, "*Take a deep breath. What do you get now?*"

_____

_____

_____

Say, "*On a scale of 0 to 10, where 0 is no disturbance or neutral and 10 is the highest disturbance you can imagine, how disturbing does it feel now?*"

```
0     1     2     3     4     5     6     7     8     9     10
(no disturbance)                              (highest disturbance)
```

2. Do another long set of BLS for 15 to 45 seconds.

Say, "*Take a deep breath. What do you get now?*"

_____

_____

Say, *"On a scale of 0 to 10, where 0 is no disturbance or neutral and 10 is the highest disturbance you can imagine, how disturbing does it feel now?"*

0	1	2	3	4	5	6	7	8	9	10

(no disturbance)   (highest disturbance)

3. Do another long set of BLS for 15 to 45 seconds.

Say, *"Take a deep breath. What do you get now?"*

_____

_____

Say, *"On a scale of 0 to 10, where 0 is no disturbance or neutral and 10 is the highest disturbance you can imagine, how disturbing does it feel now?"*

0	1	2	3	4	5	6	7	8	9	10

(no disturbance)   (highest disturbance)

4. Do another long set of BLS for 15 to 45 seconds.

Say, *"Take a deep breath. What do you get now?"*

_____

_____

Say, *"On a scale of 0 to 10, where 0 is no disturbance or neutral and 10 is the highest disturbance you can imagine, how disturbing does it feel now?"*

0	1	2	3	4	5	6	7	8	9	10

(no disturbance)   (highest disturbance)

Continue until SUD level reduces to ecological validity or when the original target can be viewed relatively calmly. Then proceed to installation.

Note: If the SUD level is not reducing after about four or five sets, proceed without interrupting the flow (and without a new assessment), with a transition to the EMDr protocol (directly below), which simply permits associations relevant to the current traumatic episode.

EMDr Protocol for R-TEP Script

EMDr is T-Episode focused processing.

1. If the association is about the T-Episode, say the following:

Say, *"Go with that."*

Continue with BLS and chains of associations as long as the association is related to the episode.

2. If the association is not about the T-Episode:

Say, *"Go back to the original disturbing _____ (state the target), what do you get now?"*

_____

_____

_____

Say, *"On a scale of 0 to 10, where 0 is no disturbance or neutral and 10 is the highest disturbance you can imagine, how disturbing does it feel now?"*

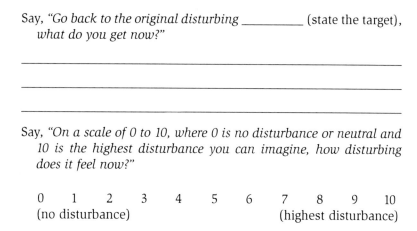

```
0    1    2    3    4    5    6    7    8    9    10
(no disturbance)                    (highest disturbance)
```

Continue the processing in this way until the SUD level drops to an ecological level or target can be viewed calmly. Then proceed to the Installation Phase (see the Standard EMDR Protocol Script below).

Choice Point: If the SUD level still is not reducing or processing gets stuck, then, using your clinical judgment and with the client's consent, continue in a natural way (and with no new assessment) with a transition to the Standard EMDR Protocol simply by allowing full chains of association as is customary in this protocol.

Standard EMDR Protocol Script (Adapted From the Standard EMDR Protocol for R-TEP, Shapiro, 2001)

Following, the Standard EMDR Protocol, continue processing chains of associations with no regulation as long as change occurs. As you are continuing from the EMDr protocol, there is no need in getting the elements of the Assessment Phase again. Continue processing until the SUD drops to an ecological level or the target can be viewed calmly. Then proceed to the Installation Phase.

When associations arise that are beyond the Trauma Episode focus, move on to the Standard EMDR Protocol and say the following:

Say, *"Is it okay to continue with this _____ (refer to the new association)?"*

If the SUD level still remains relatively high or processing is stuck, treat it as an "unfinished" target, without doing installation and proceed to a new G-Search.

Say, *"Now, without talking out loud this time, return to scan the whole episode, like a Google Search in the computer, for anything that is disturbing, in no particular order. Just notice what comes up as you search the whole episode from the original event until today and stop at what is disturbing you."*

Use continuous BLS during the G-Search.

_____

_____

Target and process each point of disturbance (event, part of event, experience, etc.). According to the therapist's clinical judgment, use as much of the Standard EMDR Protocol assessment as appropriate such as NC, PC, VoC, Emotion, SUD, Body Sensation.

Negative Cognition (NC)

Say, *"What negative words go with that _____ (state target) or about yourself now?"*

_____

_____

If there is high arousal or difficulty in rapidly finding an NC, suggest a suitable NC. Clients usually speak about physical survival categories of safety or control in these types of situations such as "I'm in danger," "I am helpless," "It shouldn't happen."

Positive Cognition (PC)

Say, *"When you bring up that _____ (state target), how would you like to think about it, or about yourself?"*

_____

_____

If it is difficult to find a PC while the level of disturbance is high, offer a tentative PC that is appropriate to the NC.

Say, *"Would you like to believe that 'It happened and it's over,' 'I survived,' 'I am safe now from THAT event,' 'I can cope'? Is that what you would like to believe or is there something else you prefer?"*

_____

_____

Validity of Cognition (VoC)

You can skip the VoC if it is not appropriate to ask at this stage.

Say, *"On a scale of 1 to 7, where 1 is completely false and 7 is completely true, how true do these words feel to you now?"*

1	2	3	4	5	6	7
(completely false)				(completely true)		

Emotions

Say, *"When you bring up that _____ (state target) and those words _____ (state the negative cognition), what emotion do you feel now?"*

_____

_____

Subjective Units of Disturbance (SUD)

Say, *"On a scale of 0 to 10, where 0 is no disturbance or neutral and 10 is the highest disturbance you can imagine, how disturbing does the image feel to you now?"*

0   1   2   3   4   5   6   7   8   9   10
(no disturbance)   (highest disturbance)

Location of Body Sensation

Say, *"Where do you feel it in your body?"*

_____

_____

Continue processing until the SUD = 0 or an ecological resolution and the VoC = 7 or an ecological resolution.

Phase 5: Installation

During assessment, a tentative PC was offered. An opportunity is given to find a more suitable PC now that the SUD has reduced.

Say, *"How does _____ (repeat the PC) sound?"*

_____

_____

Say, *"Do the words _____ (state the PC) still fit, or is there another positive statement that you feel would be more suitable?"*

_____

_____

If the client accepts the original positive cognition, the clinician should ask for a VoC rating to see if it has improved.

Validity of Cognition (VoC)

Say, *"As you think of the original target and those words _____ (repeat the selected PC), how true do they feel, from 1 (completely false) to 7 (completely true?)?"*

1   2   3   4   5   6   7
(completely false)   (completely true)

Say, *"Go with that."*

Do BLS. Then say the following:

Say, *"Think of the _____ (state the target) and hold it together with the words _____ (repeat the PC). How true do they feel, from 1 (completely false) to 7 (completely true?)?"*

1   2   3   4   5   6   7
(completely false)   (completely true)

Continue installation as long as the VoC strengthens and material is becoming more adaptive.

Note: There is no Phase 6: Body Scan at this Micro Level as this is just one target of many. The Phase 6 processing is not finished until the G-Search reveals no more targets of disturbance.

Continue with the Episode G-Search as before to check if there are any other targets of disturbance left and process similarly with Telescopic Processing.

Say, *"Now, again, without talking out loud, return to scan the whole episode, like a Google Search on the computer, for anything else that is disturbing you, in no particular order. Just notice what comes up as you search the whole episode from the original event until today and stop at what is still disturbing you and we will use it as a target for EMDR processing."*

Use continuous BLS during the G-Search.

_____

_____

_____

Process any additional identified targets using Telescopic Processing; start with EMD, if necessary, expand to EMDr, and, if still necessary, expand to EMDR. Repeat until there are no more targets. There are usually several targets that may require several sessions.

Future Targets

Concerns about the future such as "What if it happens again?" a disrupted sense of personal safety, and challenges to the client's basic assumptions may arise during the G-Search. These future targets are processed in the same way as other targets. This may be helpful for strengthening resilience.

Since the T-Episode is comprised of several targets, the G-Search can be used over several sessions.

Ensure a strong closure at the end of each session.

Macro Episode Level

Checking the Episode-SUD (E-SUD) (Macro Episode Level)

When no more targets emerge with G-Search, check the SUD for the entire T-Episode.

Say, *"When you think of the entire episode now, how disturbing is it to you on a scale of 0 to 10, where 0 is no disturbance or neutral and*

10 is the highest disturbance you can imagine. How disturbing does it feel now?"

0	1	2	3	4	5	6	7	8	9	10

(no disturbance)   (highest disturbance)

When the SUD is ecological, proceed to installation of the Episode PC.

Completion of the Episode (Macro Episode Level)

Goal of Episode Processing: To integrate the entire traumatic episode within a positive theme cluster, completing the transition from external physical survival to internal adaptive identity theme.

Phase 5: Installation of Episode of Positive Cognition (E-PC) (Macro Episode Level)

Obtain a PC for the *entire* episode.

Say, *"When you think about the original incident and all that has happened since the entire episode, how would you like to think about it now? What have you learned from it?"*

_____

_____

_____

Obtain a PC for the *entire* episode.
Check the VoC.

Say, *"As you think of the entire episode again, how do the words _____ (state the E-PC) feel, from 1 (completely false) to 7 (completely true)?"*

1	2	3	4	5	6	7

(completely false)   (completely true)

Say, *"Hold them together, the entire episode and these words ____ (repeat the E-PC)."*

Install with sets of BLS and check the VoC.

Say, *"As you think of the entire episode again, how do the words _____ (state the E-PC) feel, from 1 (completely false) to 7 (completely true)?"*

1	2	3	4	5	6	7

(completely false)   (completely true)

Continue installation until it no longer changes and VoC is 6 or 7.
If the VoC is less than 7, say the following:

Say, *"What prevents this from being a 7?"*

_____

_____

Do BLS.

Say, *"Go with that."*

Phase 6: Episode-Body Scan (Macro Episode Level)

Say, *"When you think of the entire episode and your positive cognition _____ (state E-PC), notice any body sensations. Go with that."*

_____

_____

Use sets of BLS as in the Standard EMDR Protocol.

Phase 7: Closure of the Episode

The protocol may take several sessions so ensure a strong closure (return to Safe/Calm Place, Resource Connection, or 4 Elements exercise).

_____

_____

Phase 8: Reevaluation

Obtain feedback from previous work and check the Episode SUD Level.

Say, *"On a scale of 0 to 10, where 0 is no disturbance or neutral and 10 is the highest disturbance you can imagine, how disturbing does the <u>entire episode</u> feel now?"*

0   1   2   3   4   5   6   7   8   9   10
(no disturbance)   (highest disturbance)

If SUD does not = 0 or does not seem ecological, use G-Search to identify any residual targets that may require additional processing.

Say, *"Now, again, without talking out loud, return to scan the whole episode, like a Google Search on the computer, for anything else that is disturbing you, in no particular order. Just notice what comes up as you search the whole episode from the original event until today and stop at what is still disturbing you and we will use it as a target for EMDR processing."*

Use continuous BLS during the G-Search.
If ecological, confirm appropriateness of Episode-PC.

Say, *"How does _____ (repeat the PC) sound?"*

_____

_____

Say, *"Do the words _____ (state the E-PC) still fit, or is there another positive statement that is more appropriate for you now?"*

_____

_____

If the client accepts the original positive cognition, the clinician should ask for a VoC rating to see if it has improved.

Say, *"When you think of the entire episode, how true do those words _____ (clinician repeats the E-PC) feel to you now on a scale of 1 to 7, where 1 feels completely false and 7 feels completely true?"*

1   2   3   4   5   6   7
(completely false)   (completely true)

Say, *"Think of the entire episode and hold it together with the words _____ (repeat the E-PC)."*

Do a long set of BLS to see if there is more processing to be done. Administer the Impact of Events Scale-R again.

Comments about the process:

_____

_____

_____

_____

Emergency Response Procedure

Gary Quinn

Emergency Response Procedure Script Notes

The Emergency Response Procedure (ERP) was initially developed to help victims within hours of a terrorist attack, but can be applied in the immediate aftermath of any trauma. Patients may present with "silent terror," shaking and inability to speak, or if they are verbal, often they are in a highly agitated state. The procedure has been used in the emergency room and during hospitalization. It is also appropriate for immediate intervention at the scene of critical incidents such as car accidents, earthquakes, natural or man-made disasters, and in ambulances. While taking an initial history, prior to the Preparation Phase of EMDR, ERP can be put into effect if patients suddenly abreact.

This procedure presumes familiarity with the Standard EMDR Protocol of which it is an adaptation. Clinicians highly experienced in dealing with patients immediately after a traumatic event—who are not familiar with EMDR—will still benefit from this report.

Note: This procedure has not received official sanctioning from the EMDR Institute and has not been validated by research. This procedure can only be considered after all medical needs have been evaluated or treated.

Emergency Response Procedure Script

Phase 1: History Taking

If patients cannot communicate, information about the incident is reported to the clinician by the ambulance or hospital staff. A more complete history regarding the immediate trauma can be done after the patient becomes verbal, once the ERP has been effective at establishing a present orientation (that they are safe from the recent dangerous event).

If the patient is verbal, history taking is focused on the immediate trauma.

Say, *"What happened to you? Please tell me what happened starting just before the incident occurred until now?"*

_____

_____

_____

_____

_____

_____

_____

_____

_____

_____

Phase 2: Preparation

Initial Preparation

During the patient's uncontrollable shaking or feeling overwhelmed, it is essential to normalize this behavior.

Say, *"Your current shaking, rapid heartbeat, and breathing ____ (or whatever signs they are showing) is the body's normal healthy way of dealing with a dangerous situation."*

Preparation

Give a brief explanation describing EMDR.

Say, *"I will be using a procedure based on the natural state of dreaming when your eyes move rapidly back and forth. This can help you learn new things and be calm. It will also help you come back to the present. I am going to ask you to follow my fingers with your eyes, or with your permission, I am going to tap on your hands. If you would like me to stop just raise your hand. Would that be okay with you?"*

_____

_____

If the patient does not respond add the following:

Say, *"I understand that you are extremely preoccupied with this event you have been through and are not talking now. I will assume you agree to do this procedure unless you say no or shake your head no."*

If there is any possibility of neck injury, do not ask them to shake their heads.

Phase 3: Assessment

In the Standard EMDR Protocol, the Assessment Phase allows patients to fully access their memory of the event on all levels. In the highly agitated state of Acute

Stress Reaction (ASR), patients are very much in their internal world, already actively accessing the memory fully, on the sensory, emotional, and body levels. Therefore, the formal Assessment Phase of EMDR is not necessary and the informal assessment proceeds as follows:

- The assumed initial negative cognition (NC): "I am in danger."
- The assumed initial positive cognition (PC): "I am safe now from that event."
- The term *from that event* is added to give truth to the PC, allowing for ongoing danger (e.g., war, terrorism, natural disaster).
- Emotion is assumed to be high fear or terror.
- Subjective Units of Disturbance (SUD) is assumed to be at or close to 10 where 0 is no disturbance and 10 is the worst disturbance imaginable.
- Body Sensation: The therapist observes the body sensations such as muscle tension, catatonia, shaking uncontrollably, breathing rapidly, and so forth.

Phase 4: Desensitization

The bilateral stimulation (BLS) used during the Desensitization Phase of ERP is based on the EMDR concept of utilizing dual attention. Patients are accessing the past event as if it is happening now (first attention) and this is the cause of their distress. The patients, in their current reality of being in the emergency room (ER), are now safe (second attention) from the recent traumatic event. The way to use dual attention is by repeating the following:

> Say, *"You are in the ER and safe now from that past event. That is over."*

Patients are directed to focus on the here and now of being safe in the hospital (or wherever they currently are) outside of their shaking bodies and away from the flashbacks of the incident.

> Say, *"You are in the hospital* (or wherever they are) *now and are safe from that past event. That is over."*

Although flashbacks of the incident keep patients in the past, BLS (such as eye movements or hand tapping), together with the therapist's voice, bring them back to the present and the current reality of safety by seeing, hearing, and feeling the therapist during this intervention.

Begin BLS. At first, there can be a reexperiencing of trauma followed by calming and the ability to communicate.

> Say, *"I am going to ask you to follow my fingers with your eyes or, with your permission, I am going to tap on your hands."*

Begin BLS.

> Say, *"You are in the emergency room* (or wherever they are) *and you are safe. That event is over out there. You are safe here in the emergency room. Focus on being in the hospital and safe, notice my standing with you, listen to my voice, and feel my hands tapping on yours."*

Do BLS. Repeat the above statements several times, approximately every 5 to 10 sets. BLS can be given in short or long sets as is done during abreaction in EMDR.

Stopping points can be when the patients appear to relax somewhat or start to be verbal. Otherwise, a traditional set of 24 can be used.

Say, *"Take a breath. Let it go. What are you noticing?"*

_____

_____

If patients do not verbally respond, say the following:

Say, *"Just notice what is happening,"* while doing more BLS and repeating the statement, *"You are safe now from that event that is over and you are in the hospital."*

Continue this until you see their bodies calming and they are able to tell you what they are noticing.

Say, *"Take a breath. Let it go. What are you noticing?"*

_____

_____

For those patients who present in a state of silent terror and are nonverbal, being able to communicate and recognizing current safety can be seen as a stopping place. An assumed completed SUD would be approximately 3 to 5 out of 10 as inferred from their body language.

Patients who were initially verbal will be able to verbalize their recognition of current safety and will demonstrate body language reflecting this. Most patients will still have a degree of agitation. This can be seen as ecological for their current state.

The goals of ERP are to allow patients to recognize that they are safe now from the recent trauma. Becoming verbal and demonstrating body language that suggests a calmer state are the major goals in ERP.

Note: Sound BLS is not usually utilized because of the fatigue factor of snapping fingers unless a sound device is available.

Phase 5: Installation

Formal EMDR installation is not done. Instead, assess the patient's awareness of current safety.

Say, *"Where are you now?"*

_____

_____

When patients state they are oriented to being currently safe in the ER (or wherever they are), then say the following:

Say, *"Are you able to recognize that you are currently safe and that the dangerous event is over?"*

_____

_____

Once they can say they are safe and recognize that the event is over, you are ready to proceed to closure.

For those who wish to continue to talk about the traumatic incident, the following is recommended.

Narrative of Event

At this point, it is possible for patients to give a narrative of what they experienced. Do not push for details. This narrative is therapeutic. This can be helpful as it is using left-brain processing to establish the proper sense of past, present, and future.

> Say, *"Please tell me what happened from just prior to the start of the event until now. Feel free to tell me just what you are comfortable relating."*

_____

_____

_____

_____

_____

_____

At times, this narrative reveals another cognition that is an additional source of stress. The use of the narrative of the event often requires a fresh assessment. Patients may still remain distressed because another negative cognition is active, such as a false sense of responsibility as in survival guilt. Common negative cognitions are "I should have done something," or, "I did something wrong" (by not warning others or not saving other victims).

In this case, the EMD Protocol (Shapiro, 1989a, 2004) may be utilized if time permits. This may be not possible during mass trauma as many people are in need of immediate treatment.

If patients have not been able to calm down using ERP, other standard non-EMDR types of treatment such as medication can be utilized.

Phase 6: Body Scan

Body Scan is not formally done but the ability to verbalize, cessation of shaking, and noticeable calming of the body, will indicate an ability to move to closure. It can be seen as normal for many people to be agitated up to 2 to 3 days following a traumatic incident.

Phase 7: Closure

Closure is done with the following statement:

> Say, *"It is common to have a reaction to what has happened to you. You might have flashbacks of what happened, difficulty sleeping, and a number of emotions such as distress, fear, or anger. You may notice that you are much more jumpy and startle more easily by loud sounds or anything that reminds you of what happened. If you find these symptoms lasting longer than 2 to 3 days and not subsiding, this is not unusual but we can help you to handle these reactions so that you will be calmer. Here are some numbers to call _____*

(give contact information), *if you would like more assistance. Do you have any questions?"*

According to the protocols of the emergency room, patients are given a final medical exam before being released. In addition they are given a fact sheet describing the common physiological and emotional symptoms occurring within the first 48 to 72 hours of involvement in a traumatic incident. Examples may include flashbacks, difficulty sleeping, and increased sensitivity to loud noises. Also listed are unusually strong reactions such as increased anger and withdrawal. It is mentioned that most patients will usually experience steady improvement over the following month. Referral numbers are listed should further psychological treatment be desired.

Phase 8: Reevaluation

The nature of emergency treatment does not easily lend itself to follow-up and reevaluation is not usually standard. Whenever possible, it is preferable to contact patients by phone within the week to assess their situation and give support.

Acknowledgment

I would like to acknowledge Debby Zucker who has utilized ERP during her work with patients in ambulances.

PART VII

EMDR and Early Interventions for Groups

At a recent conference on EMDR, my colleague, Gary Quinn, expressed a wish to meet the creators of the EMDR Integrative Group Protocol (IGTP). As luck would have it, I happened to know where they were and I introduced Gary to Luci Artigas and Ignacio Jarero, two of the four originators of the IGTP. The reason Gary wanted to meet them was to thank them for the tremendous contributions that they have made to the world of trauma treatment and he went on to tell them several stories about the uses of the IGTP in four different countries.

The first began in a country that had suffered from a devastating earthquake. A colleague of Gary's had gone there to help and used the IGTP. In the first city, he worked with 1,200 children who had lost both of their parents and he was amazed that—despite his not knowing the local dialects—he began to see in the children's drawings the changes in their perceptions concerning this devastating natural disaster. He also noted that their demeanors changed and their spirits rose. This colleague traveled to a number of cities working in the same manner and with the same results.

A group had gathered around us as Gary continued talking to Luci and Nacho and there was not a dry eye in the group.

Gary went on to tell them of his own experience in Israel after one of the recent wars that had children and their families sequestered in bomb shelters. As Gary used IGTP, he began to see the transformation of the children's experience, again, through their drawings. What started as terrible pictures of death and destruction, as the process progressed, turned into drawings that began to show grass and then people going about their daily living. At one point, when they were beginning to exit the shelter, the bombing began anew and a little girl began to cry. Gary reminded her of the Butterfly Hug (a method for self-bilateral stimulation created by Luci), she began to do it, and immediately felt better. This was repeated with the same results in the other shelters that Gary and his colleagues worked.

In 2007, Gary went to the EMDR-European conference in Paris. There, he saw the work that a Palestinian colleague had done treating children with IGTP. Although there seemed to be a certain political influence in the first pictures, the children progressed in the same positive way—and appeared almost identical—to the pictures of the Israeli children. This was the same type of result that occurred when the IGTP was used with children in Thailand after the tsunami. Gary was astounded. At that moment, he felt transformed by the profound understanding of the universal nature of all peoples—no matter their culture or their political views—and how this extraordinary treatment has tapped into the common innate ability to heal.

The numbers of traumatized individuals in this world of ours is staggering. The need for treatment to help large groups of people get back to baseline functioning as rapidly as possible is essential. The chapters in this section on EMDR and Early Intervention for Groups mainly grew out of the early use of the EMDR Integrative Group Protocol created in the aftermath of Hurricane Pauline. This hurricane, in 1997, devastated the western coast of Mexico. The members of AMAMECRISIS came up with the IGTP when they were overwhelmed by the enormous need for mental health services. The flap of these butterfly wings (the Butterfly Hug is an important component of the IGTP) have been heard around the world.

Aiton Birnbaum has contributed a unique group protocol (that can also be used with individuals) in the form of a written workbook. The workbook allows for early intervention and for active involvement on the part of the participants through the use of writing. For those clients who process best through visual modalities, the workbook is ideal. It also allows group members to proceed at their own pace and have a record of their work. This chapter also includes a more comprehensive format as it includes an accompanying workbook for clients that follows the script for therapists. Aiton's work follows in the spirit of Luci and Nacho's work to bring this to as many people as possible.

In a statement to Luci Artigas and Ignacio Jarero, on the occasion of receiving the Francine Shapiro Award from the EMDR Ibero-America in 2007, Francine Shapiro said the following about the IGTP:

> And if others will follow in their footsteps, and conduct the randomized research needed to solidify the work in the eyes of the world, to have it declared "empirically validated" by the large international organizations such as UNICEF, then thousands and thousands more will be healed in the coming years. So as you applaud the work of these wonderful people, please see what a difference can be made through a dedication to relieve suffering.

The call by Francine Shapiro to enlist the assistance of mental health practitioners to aid those who were suffering and follow in the footsteps of our Mexican colleagues has been heard. Victims of man-made and natural disasters are being treated using EMDR all over the world. Children and adults of many diverse nationalities and ethnic backgrounds have been added to the hundreds of children who were treated in Mexico. However, there is always more work to be done. The protocols in Parts VI and VII are the protocols used by clinicians to treat these issues. Use them and conduct the randomized research that will support the empirical validation needed to reach even more of the world's victims of disasters and to help them relieve their suffering. Assistance for these endeavors is available through the national and international EMDR associations, as well as the EMDR Humanitarian Assistance Programs (see Appendix C).

The EMDR Integrative Group Treatment Protocol (IGTP)

Lucina Artigas, Ignacio Jarero, Nicté Alcalá, and Teresa López Cano

The effectiveness of EMDR with trauma survivors has been widely reported (e.g., Gelinas, 2003; Ironson, Freund, Strauss, & Williams, 2002; Korn & Leeds, 2002; Lee, Gavriel, Drummond, Richards, & Greenwald, 2002; Manfield & Shapiro, 2003; Mc-Cullough, 2002; Perkins & Rouanzoin, 2002). Studies support the use of EMDR in the treatment of symptoms caused by trauma in children and adolescents (Cocco & Sharpe, 1993; Greenwald, 1994, 1998, 1999, 2000; Johnson, 1998; Lovett, 1999; Pellicer, 1993; Puffer, Greenwald, & Elrod, 1998; Russell & O'Connor, 2002; Scheck, Schaeffer, & Gillette, 1998; Shapiro, 1991; Soberman, Greenwald, & Rule, 2002; Stewart & Bramson, 2000; Taylor, 2002; Tinker & Wilson, 1999).

Studies have evaluated the usefulness of EMDR following disaster events (Fernandez, Gallinari, & Lorenzetti, 2004; Grainger, Levin, Allen-Byrd, Doctor, & Lee, 1997; Jarero, Artigas, & Hartung, 2006; Jarero, Artigas, & Montero, 2008; Konuk et al., 2006) finding that this approach could be effective in significantly reducing post-traumatic symptoms. EMDR has been reported as effective in the treatment of children following a hurricane in Hawaii (Chemtob, Nakashima, Hamada, & Carlson, 2002), with victims of the 9/11 terrorist attacks in New York City (Silver, Rogers, Knipe, & Colelli, 2005), and with victims of earthquakes in Turkey (Korkmazlar-Oral & Pamuk, 2002).

Group therapy is a well-proven form of treatment for traumatized children and adolescents (Cemalovic, 1997; Kristal-Andersson, 2000; Meichenbaum, 1994; Samec, 2001).

IGTP Script Notes

The EMDR-IGTP was developed by members of AMAMECRISIS when they were overwhelmed by the extensive need for mental health services after Hurricane Pauline ravaged the western coast of Mexico in 1997. This protocol combines the Standard EMDR Treatment Phases 1 through 8 (Shapiro, 1995, 2001) with a Group Therapy model (Artigas, Jarero, Mauer, López Cano, & Alcalá, 2000; Jarero, Artigas,

Mauer, López Cano, & Alcalá, 1999). It is hypothesized that the resulting format offers more extensive reach than individual EMDR applications and that the treatment may produce a more effective outcome than expected from traditional group therapy (Jarero et al., 2008).

Designed initially for work with children, the EMDR-IGTP has also been found suitable for group work with adults. The protocol is structured within a play therapy format and has been used with disaster victims ages 7 to 50 +. Because of its utility, it has been used in the original format in multiple settings around the world (Adúriz et al., in press; Errebo, Knipe, Forte, Karlin, & Altayli, 2008; Jarero et al., 2006, 2008), or with adaptations to meet the circumstances (Fernandez et al., 2004; Gelbach & Davis, 2007; Korkmazlar-Oral & Pamuk, 2002; Wilson, Tinker, Hofmann, Becker, & Marshall, 2000; Zaghrout-Hodali, Ferdoos, & Dodgson, 2008). "EMDR-IGTP has been found effective in several field trials and has been used for thousands of disasters survivors around the world" (Maxfield, 2008, p. 75). This protocol is also known as the Group Butterfly Hug Protocol, The EMDR Group Protocol for Children, and the Children's Group Protocol.

The protocol was designed to accomplish the following main objectives:

- Be part of a comprehensive program (continuum of care) for trauma treatment.
- Identify those who need further assistance.
- Reduce posttraumatic symptoms.
- Confront traumatic material.
- Bring to conscious awareness those aspects of the trauma that were dissociated.
- Facilitate the expression of painful emotions or shameful behaviors.
- Offer the patient support and empathy.
- Condense the different aspects of trauma into representative and more manageable images.
- Increase patient's perception of mastery over the distressing elements of the traumatic experience.
- Reprocess traumatic memories.
- Treat more clients on the same experience.
- Normalize the reactions: The clients can see that their reactions are normal since other patients are working on their memories in the same manner.

Advantages of this protocol are:

- Group treatment can be used in nonprivate settings such as under a mango tree, in shelters, open-air clinic, and so forth.
- Clients in the group do not have to verbalize information about the trauma.
- Therapy can be done on subsequent days and there is no need for homework between sessions.
- Protocol is easily taught to both new and experienced EMDR practitioners.
- Equally effective cross-culturally.
- People are treated more quickly, involving larger segments of the affected community.
- Single clinician can be assisted by paraprofessionals, teachers, or family members of the children, which allows wide application of this protocol in societies with few mental health professionals.

The EMDR Integrative Treatment Protocol Script

Phase 1: Client History

First, team members educate teachers, parents, and relatives about the course of trauma and enlist these individuals to identify affected children. Team members have to be aware of the needs of the clients within their extended family, community, and culture.

Family members can be involved in a continuum of passive-to-active roles. The family member can be asked simply to be present and to witness or to perform a function as part of the Emotional Protection Team (EPT).

> Say, *"I would like to ask the team members if they could please help the children that need assistance in writing or in understanding any thing that we will be doing today."*

Phase 2: Preparation—First Part

The professionals who work with survivors of a traumatic event, especially in the immediate aftermath of trauma, should listen actively and supportively, but not probe for details and emotional responses or push for more information than survivors are comfortable providing. Professionals must tread lightly in the wake of disaster so as not to disrupt natural social networks of healing and support. During this protocol the rest of the team forms an Emotional Protection Team (EPT) around the children in order to be aware of their emotional reactions and help them when necessary. We recommend a ratio of one team member for eight children. If you do not have enough clinicians in the team, the children's teachers and family members can help.

This phase begins with an integration exercise. At first, obtain the children's attention and establish rapport. We use a little Mexican doll called Lupita, a little drum, and a dolphin puppet, but any other materials may be used. It is helpful for the mental health professionals to use whatever techniques they prefer to capture the child's attention and establish rapport.

The aims are: (a) To familiarize the children with the space where they are going to work or play; (b) To encourage the children to approach the therapist in order to establish rapport and trust; (c) To facilitate group formation.

Lupita, the doll, introduces the drum and the dolphin to her friends. The therapist plays soft sounds on the drum and asks the children to approach as giants; when she plays loud sounds, they have to retreat as little people. The therapist may say something like the following:

> Say, *"Hi, my name is Lupita* (therapist holds the doll and shows the drum and the dolphin). *This is my drum and this is my dolphin and I want you to get to know them. As you listen to the sound of the drum, please become the largest giants you can be and come forward* (play soft sounds). *Wonderful. Now,* (play loud sounds) *become little people and move away as fast as you can."*

During this time, the team leader says whatever she needs to say according to the circumstances. As this is creative work, the leader must have knowledge of children and how to work with them empathically in a group setting.

The therapist uses the dolphin to show the children different expressions of feeling. The therapist makes the dolphin form big and small mouths, mouths that look happy, sad, bored, afraid, surprised, angry, and so forth, and the children follow the leader by imitating the expressions of the dolphin.

Say, *"Here is the dolphin and see how he makes his mouth soooo big and then soooo small. What does he look like now* (make a happy face)*?"*

_____

_____

Say, *"Can you make your face look like the dolphin's happy face? Go ahead. That is great!"*

_____

_____

Say, *"What does he look like now* (make a sad face)*?"*

_____

_____

Say, *"Can you make your face look like the dolphin's sad face? Go ahead. That is great!"*

_____

_____

Say, *"What does he look like now* (make a scary face)*?"*

_____

_____

Say, *"Can you make your face look like the dolphin's scary face? Go ahead. That is great!"*

_____

_____

Say, *"What does he look like now* (make a surprised face)*?"*

_____

_____

Say, *"Can you make your face look like the dolphin's surprised face? Go ahead. That is great!"*

_____

_____

Say, *"What does he look like now* (make an angry face)*?"*

_____

_____

Say, *"Can you make your face look like the dolphin's angry face? Go ahead. That is great!"*

_____

_____

Again, the team leader works with the group in the way that is particular to the group. The dolphin helps the children make contact with their emotions, expressing them through their bodies.

Using the doll, the team leader teaches the children the abdominal breathing technique.

> Say, *"Close your eyes, put one hand on your stomach and imagine that you have a balloon inside your stomach. Now, inhale and see how the balloon grows and moves your hand up. Now you can exhale and see how the balloon deflates and your hand goes down. Just observe."*

The Butterfly Hug

The team leader teaches the children the Butterfly Hug (BH) (Artigas et al., 2000).

> Say, *"Would you like to learn an exercise that will help you to feel better?"*

> Say, *"Please watch me and do what I am doing. Cross your arms over your chest, so that with the tip of your fingers from each hand, you can touch the area that is located under the connection between the clavicle and the shoulder. Your eyes can be closed, or partially closed, looking toward the tip of your nose. Next, you alternate the movement of your hands, like the flapping wings of a butterfly. You breathe slowly and deeply* (abdominal breathing)*, while you observe what is going through your mind and body such as thoughts, images, sounds, odors, feelings, and physical sensation without changing, pushing your thoughts away, or judging. You can pretend as though what you are observing are like clouds passing by."*

It is important to observe the children to make sure that they are able to follow. Members of the EPT can be alert and quietly go up to a child to help as needed.

> Say, *"Now, please close your eyes and use your imagination to go to a place where you feel safe or calm. What images, colors, sounds, for example, do you see in your safe place."*
> Say, *"Now please do the Butterfly Hug."*

The EPT members are spaced around the group so that they are able to hear the children's answers. Normally, the children will say their answers out loud, giving the members of the team the possibility of responding to each individual child as needed.

The goal here is to make sure that each child has found a Safe/Calm Place in their imagination.

Optional

> Say, *"Now, please take out your paper and draw the Safe/Calm Place that you imagined. When you are finished, please do the Butterfly Hug while looking at your drawing."*

The children can take the picture home to use it with the Butterfly Hug whenever they need to feel better. The Butterfly Hug is used to anchor positive affect, cognitions, and physical sensations associated with images produced by the technique of "guided imagination."

Make sure to notice the children's responses. There is no talking during the process so that the children are not taken out of their process. If a child is experiencing any difficulty, one of the EPT members can assist the child.

Trauma Work

Say, *"Please raise your hand if you have been having trouble sleeping, are scared, if you feel sad, if you still have nightmares, if you feel angry, or if you often think about and remember the natural or human-provoked disaster that you have suffered."*

The therapist goes on to say, *"It is normal for you to feel this way; you are normal boys and girls who have suffered an abnormal experience, and that is why it is normal for you to have these feelings. It is also normal to have different feelings than your friends and other children, since each person experiences and feels things differently. This is really normal."*

The aim is to validate the signs and symptoms of posttraumatic stress.

The therapist goes on and says, *"When you return home after this exercise, you can talk to the people you trust about your thoughts and feelings, as much as you want and when you feel most comfortable doing so."*

The aim is to verbalize the traumatic memories and to respond to the acute need that arises in many survivors to share their experience, while at the same time respecting their natural inclination with regard to how much, when, and to whom they talk.

Child's Reaction to Traumatic Events Scale (CRTES)

The team administers the Child's Reaction to Traumatic Events Scale (CRTES) (Jones, Fletcher, & Ribbe, 2002) here at the end of the first part of the Preparation Phase.

Say, *"Here is a scale for you to look at. Please answer the questions on it. If you have any questions, please ask one of the Emotional Protection Team Members to help you out."*

Standardized psychological assessment is used cautiously. It is helpful for team members to be concerned about the rapport with the family members and children. They need to demonstrate by their behavior that they are truly interested in the children as human beings and not as objects of scientific curiosity. This custom weakens the scientific value of data gathered, while it respects the wishes of our Latin American clients not to be stigmatized by formal testing procedures. In our experience, clients also tend to reject assistance from those they judge to be opportunists, in this case anyone who seems interested in the victim as an object of study.

Phase 2: Preparation—Second Part

Show the children the faces that measure SUDS from 0 to 10, with 0 being no disturbance, and 10 being maximum disturbance. If you do not have the original faces you can draw them on the blackboard.

Say, *"Here are faces that measure our feelings on a 0 to 10 scale, where 0 does not bother you at all and 10 bothers you the most possible."*

Note: Clinicians are welcome to use the best words and pictures possible for their population.

Familiarize the children with the scale.

Say, *"How do you feel when you get good grades? Please point to the face that describes how you feel."*

Now say, *"How do you feel when you are sick? Please point to the face that tells us how you feel."*

We have observed that the children who are not yet familiar with the numbers will sometimes say a number and point to a face that does not correspond. Thus, it is better to pick the face they point to over the number they say (one of the members of the EPT can write the correct number). The members of the EPT hand out white pieces of paper and crayons to each of the children (have extra crayons in case the children ask for more).

Say, *"Please write your name and age on the top left side of the paper (show how to do it)."*

EPT members can aid those who cannot do it.

Say, *"Now, please divide the other side of the paper in four equal parts like this. Draw a cross at the center like this and write a small letter at the top left corner of each section like this."*

The therapist shows them how to do it on the blackboard and the EPT helps.

Note: In this protocol we had to divide the sheet of paper in four, given the scarcity of the materials in the shelters, but it is acceptable to use four sheets of paper, making sure that each has the name and the age of the child and the corresponding letter, so that the sequence can be identified.

Phase 3: Assessment

The therapist says, *"Whoever remembers what happened during the event _____ (mention the event—hurricane, flooding, explosion, etc.), please raise your hands."*

The children raise their hands.

Say, *"Now, close your eyes and observe what makes you the most frightened, sad, or angry about that event _____ (mention the event) NOW."*

The therapist continues, *"Take whatever emerges from your head to your neck, to your arms, to your hands and fingers, to the crayon, and now open your eyes and draw it in square A."*

When all the children are finished, show them the faces again.

Say, *"Here are the faces again. In square A, please write the number of the face that corresponds to the feeling you get when looking at your drawing (SUDS)."*

Note: The clients may write spontaneously what they are feeling: "I am afraid," "I am in danger," "I can die" = Negative Cognition. It is not necessary to ask the children for it. Just accept what they do in their drawing. The emotional impact doesn't always appear in the first drawing; sometimes it will appear in the second or third one.

Phase 4: Desensitization

Once all of the children have done this, say the following:

> Say, *"Please put your crayons aside and do the Butterfly Hug while you are looking at your drawing."*

This lasts for approximately 60 seconds.

> Next, the therapist says, *"Now, observe how you feel and draw whatever you want in square B related to the event."*

When they finish drawing in B, the children are shown the faces again.

> Say, *"Please look at the faces again and write down the number of the face that corresponds to how you feel when you look at your drawing in square B."*

After writing down the number, say the following:

> Say, *"Please put your crayons down and look at your drawing. While you are looking at your drawing, please do the Butterfly Hug."*

This lasts for about 60 seconds.

> Next, the therapist says, *"Now, observe how you feel and draw whatever you want in square C related to the event."*

When they finish drawing C, the children are shown the faces again.

> Say, *"Please look at the faces again and write down the number of the face that corresponds to how you feel when you look at your drawing in square C."*

After writing down the number, say the following:

> Say, *"Please put your crayons down and look at your drawing. While you are looking at your drawing, please do the Butterfly Hug."*
> Next, the therapist says, *"Now, observe how you feel and draw whatever you want in square D related to the event."*

When they finish drawing in D, the children are shown the faces again.

> Say, *"Please look at the faces again and write down the number of the face that corresponds to how you feel when you look at your drawing in square D."*

After writing down the number, say the following:

> Say, *"Please put your crayons down and look at your drawing. While you are looking at your drawing, please do the Butterfly Hug."*
> Next, the therapist says, *"Look carefully at the drawing that disturbs you the most. On the back of your paper, where you wrote your name*

and age, write the number that goes with the face (SUDS) that best describes how you feel about your drawing NOW. Write that number on the upper right hand corner of the paper."

Phase 5: Future Vision (Instead of Installation)

Phase 5 (Installation) of the Standard EMDR Protocol cannot be conducted in large groups for the following reasons: Each participant may have a different SUD level because some children can't go any further; blocking beliefs; previous problems and trauma; or have different timing for processing (for some it cannot be enough to follow the four designs format) and reach an ecological level of disturbance.

We can do the Installation Phase during the individual follow-up intervention (see Phase 8). At this stage of the protocol, we work on a Future Vision to identify adaptive or nonadaptive cognitions that are helpful in the evaluation of the child at the end of the protocol. An example of a nonadaptive cognition: An 8-year-old boy had reported a SUD of 0 when he returned to the target, drew himself in the sky with his dad, God, and angels, and he wrote: "I want to die soon to be in the sky with my dad." His mom had told the 8-year-old boy that his dad (that had died in a flood) was very happy in the sky with God and the angels.

Say, *"Now draw how you see yourself in the future."*
Then say, *"Write a word, phrase, or a sentence that explains what you drew."*
Then say, *"Look at your drawing and what you wrote about it and do the Butterfly Hug."*

We believe that if the client has an adaptive cognition, the Butterfly Hug will help in their installation and if the client does not have an adaptive cognition, the BH will help in the processing to an adaptive state. The EPT monitors this and then gathers all the drawings.

Phase 6: Body Scan

The team leader teaches the children the Body Scan Technique.

The therapist says something like the following:

Say, *"Close your eyes and scan your body from your head to your feet. If you feel any disturbing or pleasant body sensations do the Butterfly Hug and report it to the person who is helping you (EPT)."*

At the end of this exercise the leader says, *"Now move your body like this* (the therapist moves all her body like a dog shaking water off after a bath, making the children laugh)."
This is a fun, play exercise to end on a positive, playful note.

Phase 7: Closure

The therapist then says, *"Go to your Safe Place using the Butterfly Hug."*

Do this for about 60 seconds.

Then say, *"Breathe deeply three times and open your eyes."*

Phase 8: Reevaluation and Follow-Up

At the end of the group intervention, the EPT identifies children needing further assistance. These children will need to be thoroughly evaluated to identify the nature and extent of their symptoms, and any co- or preexisting mental health problems. Such a determination is made by taking into consideration reports made by the child's teacher and relatives, the CRTES results, the entire sequence of pictures and SUDS ratings, Body Scan, the Future Vision drawing and cognition, and the Emotional Protection Team Report.

The team can treat those who require individual follow-up attention, using the EMDR-IGTP in small groups or on an individual basis, keeping in mind the Targeting Sequence Plan and the 3-Pronged Protocol.

The Imma EMDR Group Protocol

Brurit Laub and Esti Bar-Sade

The Imma Group Protocol is based on the Integrative Group Treatment Protocol (IGTP) by Jarero, Artigas, Alcalá, and López Cano (chapter 29), the Four Elements Exercise by Elan Shapiro (chapter 9), and the principles of group therapy work.

The Imma Group Protocol Script Notes

This protocol is designed for small groups of children from the age of 5 upward. The language can, of course, be adjusted to suit the developmental level of the group. The protocol is to be used only by EMDR-trained therapists. The therapist must have the ability to react on the spot, evaluate, and provide further treatment for clients who are overwhelmed by the traumatic material. We recommend that work with this protocol include at least two group facilitators, in addition to the leader, in order to monitor the group and help the children carry out the instructions. The younger the children, the more facilitators are needed to insure that each child feels safe and emotionally supported.

Phase 1: History Taking

As much as is possible, relevant information about the participants is obtained; this can include material from parents and teachers. The Child Report of Post-Traumatic Symptoms (CROPS) and Parent Report of Post-Traumatic Symptoms (PROPS) are measures helpful in collecting information concerning posttraumatic symptoms in children (Greenwald & Rubin 1999).

Phase 2: Preparation

Setting

There are two circles in the room. In the inner circle, the group processing and group sharing are done. In the outer circle, the individual processing occurs via the artwork. The inner circle can be set up with chairs, or alternatively, children can be seated on the floor. The children sit facing the center of the circle with their drawings on the floor in front of them. They all tap together. The outer circle is set up with tables for the individual art work. If the tables are high the children can work while standing. On the tables, there are crayons, five sheets of paper stapled together (four computer standard pages and a separate page for drawing the future picture at the end of the process). Using a whole page for each drawing is important to enable the children to express themselves emotionally and creatively. In the outer circle, where, for the most part, the individual processing through the artwork is done, the therapists and facilitators are able to observe and relate to the needs of each child.

The inner circle is where the "group container" is built. The group serves three functions: containing fear and anxiety, boosting resources and hope, and creating connectedness among the children. The individual process in the outer circle enables each child to bring up the traumatic material in his own unique way as he draws in his own space and at his own pace. The movement from the inner circle to the outer circle is a reflection of the alternating group and individual process. The transitions from the inner to the outer circle are enhancing the dialectical healing movement between the problem pole (of the traumatic memories) and the resource pole (of the group resources) (Laub & Weiner, 2007; Shapiro & Laub, 2008a, 2008b).

The Four Elements Exercise Script

Joining and Introduction

The children sit in the inner circle. The leader and the facilitators introduce themselves and ask each child to say his name and age.

> Say, *"We all have gone through some difficult events lately and this is why we are here together to share and learn how to make the difficult experience less disturbing and to strengthen each other. We will start with an exercise that will help you reduce your fear and tension."*

From the beginning of the session there is an emphasis on the group setting as a resource. Therefore, it is important to provide time for the children to share their own experiences in the group.

Each child receives an "Imma bracelet." The bracelet can be a colored elastic band or length of yarn. Instead of a bracelet one might use a sticker on a watch or a cell phone.

> Say, *"Here is an Imma bracelet for you to put on your wrist. Go ahead and do that."*
>
> Say: *"First we will learn a special activity to help you relax. We call it the Four Elements: Earth, Air, Water, and Fire. It is a good fire, and not rocket fire. It lights our imagination into a good place."*

The leader may write this on the blackboard as she explains.

> Say, *"You can put it on your wrist now and stretch it like this."*

The leader demonstrates.

> Say, *"Every time you stretch the bracelet it will remind you that you know how to relax yourself with the Four Element exercise. Notice how*

tense you feel now using the numbers from 0 to 10. Ten means very, very tense and 0 is not tense at all. What is your number today?"

If the children are too young to follow these instructions,

Say, *"Notice how tense you are. Are you very, very tense; a little bit tense; or not at all tense?"*

Earth (Grounding Equals Safety in the Present Reality)

Say, *"Now let's start with EARTH. Let's stand and shake our hands and bodies a little to let go of the tension in our muscles (shaking hands together). You may sit down and notice how your body feels, notice your feet on the ground. Stamp hard and feel how good it feels in the soles of your feet, how the ground holds and supports you. You can also feel how the chair supports you as you lean back. Let yourself enjoy that good feeling of steadiness and support that means you're here right now . . . with all of your body . . . connected to the ground."*

Air (Breath Equals Strength and Centering)

Say, *"Next is AIR and this has to do with learning to breathe deeply. Put one hand on your tummy and one hand on your chest. Now breathe deeply and notice how the hand on your tummy moves with the air that comes in. Try to bring the air higher into your chest until you can't hold the air any longer than breathe out slowly . . . slowly . . . until all the air comes out. Now we'll do that together two more times. Ready?"*

_____

_____

Say, *"Let's do it again. Breathe deeply again and notice how the hand on your tummy moves with the air that comes in. Bring the air higher into your chest until you can't hold the air any longer than breathe out slowly . . . slowly until all the air comes out. Great. Now one more time. Breathe deeply again and notice how the hand on your tummy moves with the air that comes in. Bring the air higher into your chest, until you can't hold the air any longer than breathe out slowly . . . slowly until all the air comes out."*

Water (Saliva Equals Relaxation, Control)

Dr. Escudero (2003), a Spanish physician, taught his clients to create saliva to ignore the pain when he operated without anesthesia.

Say, *"The third element is WATER. Notice the saliva in your mouth. Our mouth is like a little pool of water. When we're very frightened the pool is dry. When there's water in our little pool, that's a sign that we're relaxed and we're in control of our thoughts and our bodies. Now we'll learn how to fill our little pool with the saliva that's in our mouth. You don't have to work hard to do that. Just notice how the saliva comes by itself into your mouth. Imagine that you're eating chocolate or something else that you like to eat and feel how more and more saliva comes into your mouth. Little by little you can learn to fill the pool more and more. Try now for a few*

> *minutes. You can continue filling your pool while we proceed to the next stage."*

Fire (Firing or Lighting Up the Imagination Into a Good Place)

> Say, *"Now let's focus on the element of FIRE, which stands for firing or lighting up the imagination into a good place. Imagine yourself with someone you love, someone who makes you feel relaxed and safe. You may also imagine a place where you feel really good, where you really love to be."*

To be with someone you feel loved or protected with is a social resource connection (SRC) created by Yair Emanuel (2006).

Drawing of the Safe Place Resource

The children are invited to go to the outer circle for the drawing process.

> Say, *"Now go to the table and draw a picture of the good place or good calming person that you love to be with that you just imagined. Draw that picture on page number 1."*

The group leader and the facilitators may help the children who need it. It can be another opportunity to create a personal contact and to check if there are children who could not find safe cue words.

Name

When the children finished their drawing, they are directed to give a name to their resource picture.

> Say, *"Now think of a name or a title to your picture. This can be a one-word name or a sentence."*

_____

_____

The Butterfly Hug

The children are invited to the inner circle with their resource drawing. The leader demonstrates how to do the Butterfly Hug with slow taps. The idea here is to have a cue word that is associated with the Safe Place so if they need to use it outside the session, they can easily connect with the Safe Place by thinking of the Butterfly Hug.

> Say, *"Put the picture on the floor in front of you and look at it. Notice what you are feeling as you look at it and where you feel it in your body. Now let's do what we call the Butterfly Hug."*

The Butterfly Hug becomes an attachment cue as it is connected to the soft touch of mommy or daddy or a "good loving hug" (Bar-Sade, 2003a, 2003b, 2005a, 2005b, 2005c).

> Say, *"This is like a soft touch of mommy or daddy's hug, a good loving hug. Let's do it together now."*

The children do the Butterfly Hug together with the leader for about 10 taps.

Strengthening the Four Elements Exercise

Say, *"Look at your Imma bracelet and stretch it. Notice the tension in your body and rate it from 0 to 10, 10 being very, very strong and 0 no tension at all. Is there a difference from the number you had when you started the exercise? Did you succeed in lowering your tension even a little bit? By even one number? If so, good for you! If it didn't change, it is okay. You are now practicing how to do it."*

Trauma Processing

It is helpful to focus on the Safe Place resource and then the trauma. The idea is that having the child look at the resource whenever he wants creates a dialectical movement between the resource and the traumatic memory that facilitates the healing process.

Say, *"Look once more at the picture that you drew of something positive* (the resource). *You can look at it whenever you want to."*

Phase 3: Assessment

First Drawing—The Disturbing Picture

Say: *"Now I would like each one of you to think of a disturbing or frightening situation that happened recently. An example might be a siren or an explosion. Notice what feels most frightening or makes you feel sad or angry as you think of that disturbing situation. Notice if a picture comes into your mind that is very unpleasant to remember. What do you see? What do you hear? Perhaps the picture also brings with it a particular, unpleasant smell. Notice how you feel now in your body as you remember that picture. Now each one of you can sit at the table in the outer circle to draw whatever comes into your mind on page number 2."*

The children are invited to the outer circle for the drawing process.

Subjective Units of Disturbance (SUD)

This is to separate it from the drawing. The leader and the facilitators help the children to note the SUD while they are drawing.

Say, *"Let's look at the picture that you drew. Write on the picture how much it is disturbing you now. Ten is the highest disturbance and 0 means that it doesn't bother you at all. Put a little square around the number that you've written."*

Phase 4: Desensitization

Tapping

The differentiation of the bilateral stimulation (BLS) between the resource installation and the trauma processing enhances the healing dialectical movement between the problem pole and the resource pole. The Butterfly Hug (BH) tapping becomes an anchoring for relaxation. Tapping on the knees and following the tapping with the eyes are the types of stimulation used for trauma processing. Elan Shapiro suggests more than one kind of BLS to strengthen the dual attention mechanism; this is the reason that the children are asked to follow the tapping with their eyes. The two different anchored stimulations can be effective, especially in ongoing trauma, where there are fast transitions from safety to anxiety.

The children are invited to return to the inner circle with their first drawing.

The leader taps with the children up to 20 times. The number of taps can be changed according to the rhythm of the group and the age of the children.

> Say: *"Now we'll learn to tap on our knees. Put your picture on the floor in front of you. Put one hand on each knee and begin to tap slowly, first on one knee, then on the other. Look at your picture and move your eyes back and forth as you follow the hand that is tapping . . . until something new comes into your mind. Now we'll start."*
>
> Say, *"Now take a deep breath as we have learned . . . slowly . . . slowly. . . ."*

Second Drawing

The children are invited to go to the outer circle for the next drawing process.

> Say, *"Now go to the table and draw the picture that now comes into your mind on page number 3. When you've finished drawing, write the number between 0 and 10 that describes how disturbing that picture is to you now. Ten is the highest disturbance and 0 means that it doesn't bother you at all. Put a little square around the number that you've written."*

Tapping

The children are invited to return to the inner circle with their second drawing.

> Say, *"Put the picture on the floor in front of you. Look at it, then begin drumming slowly. Move your eyes back and forth as you follow the hand that is tapping, until something new comes into your mind."*

The leader taps about 20 times, too.

> Say, *"Now take a deep breath . . . as we learned, s-l-o-w-l-y."*

Third Drawing

The children are invited to go to the outer circle for the drawing process.

> Say, *"Now draw the new picture that comes into your mind on page number 4. When you've finished drawing, write the number between 0 and 10 that describes how disturbing that picture is to you now. Ten is the highest disturbance and 0 means that it doesn't bother you at all. Put a little square around the number that you've written."*

Tapping

The children are invited to return to the inner circle with their third drawing.

> Say, *"Put the third picture on the floor. Look at it and begin tapping slowly. Move your eyes from side to side, following the hand that is drumming until something new comes up."*

The leader taps about 20 times.

Say, *"Now take a deep breath, s-l-o-w-l-y."*

Fourth Drawing

The children are invited to go to the outer circle for the drawing process.

> Say, *"Now draw the picture that came into your mind on the fifth page. When you finish, write the number between 0 and 10 that describes how disturbing the picture feels. Ten is the highest disturbance and 0 means that it doesn't bother you at all. Put a little square around the number that you've written."*

Return to the First Picture

> Say: *"Now look again at the scary picture that you drew on page 2 and write on it how disturbing it feels to you now using the numbers 0 to 10. Put a little square around the number that you've written."*

Phase 5: Installation

Future Resource—Fire Up the Imagination

> Say, *"Close your eyes and imagine how things will look when everything is over. How would you like to see yourself in the future? Everyone can draw a picture of the imagined future on page number 6."*

For young children or those who need more direction, the leader can ask them to draw the "good" future they would like to see.

> Say, *"Close your eyes and imagine how things will look when everything is over. How would you like to see yourself in the future? Everyone can draw a picture of the good future they would like to see on page number 6."*

A Positive Sentence

> Say, *"Look at the future picture and choose a positive sentence for it, or a word, and write the sentence or word on the picture."*

The leader and the facilitators should walk around and help the children who need it.

Group Resonance

The children are invited to return to the inner circle. The group leader asks them to make a group puzzle out of the future drawings. Then they are asked to sit.

> Say, *"Each of you can put your future drawing in the center of the circle and all the drawings together will create a big sun-shaped puzzle. Then, you can sit down when you have done that."*
>
> Say, *"Now each one of you will share with us your positive word or sentence."*

This group echoing creates a collective resonance of coping.

> Say, *"Now we will all do the Butterfly Hug together, while each of you bring up the positive future drawing and the positive sentence or word relating to the future."*

In an ongoing crisis situation, the group leader may add positive sentences that strengthen coping and relative safety like the following:

> Say, *"Up until now I am coping," "Up until now I am safe," "I can keep some of the fear and let go of all the rest of it," "I know now how to calm myself," "Whatever has happened is over."*

Note: In times of ongoing crises, such as war, there is no safety, and people cannot make a generalization like "I am safe" or "I can cope." All we can ask them to do is to look at the situation from a past and present perspective. If they managed to cope up until now or if they were safe up until now, this is good enough and it is a comforting and a resourceful idea. These statements are ecologically suitable positive cognitions. It is important to remember the circumstances of an ongoing crisis and how it is essential to modify the cognitions and beliefs to a situation and time where there is great uncertainty.

Phase 6: Body Scan

Butterfly Hug

> Say, *"Now let's finish together with the Butterfly Hug while each one of you looks at your future picture. Notice how you feel in your body."*

The group leader taps about 10 times.

Phase 7: Closure

The children are reminded of their bracelet or sticker and are asked to stand one behind the other like a train and to put their hands on the shoulders of the child in front of them. They are asked for songs that bring them hope for the future and then they tap all together as they sing the songs they have suggested.

> Say, *"We are at the end of our meeting and I want to tell you that you worked very well. Remember your bracelet or your sticker, so that you can lower your tension whenever you want to with the Four Elements. We will finish with the train. Tell me what song you know that brings you hope for a good future."*

Phase 8: Reevaluation

The way that a child responds is diagnostic, so it is important to identify those who showed unusual or noncooperative responses. To follow up, the leaders would check to see if the change is stable with each one of the participants.

A Written Workbook for Individual or Group EMDR

Aiton Birnbaum

Writing in Therapy, EMDR, and Group EMDR

Early group EMDR intervention following trauma may facilitate adaptive processing of traumatic event(s) and help prevent consolidation of traumatic memories following large-scale natural or man-made disaster (e.g., Birnbaum, 2006; Fernandez, Gallinari, & Lorenzetti, 2004; Jarero, Artigas, & Hartung, 2006; Shani, 2006). Group EMDR may also be usefully applied with homogenous groups (e.g., addictions, eating disorders, anxieties; Jane Lopacka, personal communication, August 2, 2006), and where professionals are exposed to high levels of work-related stress (e.g., medical personnel, casualty notification officers; Birnbaum, 2007). Writing is a useful clinical tool in narrative therapy (White & Epston, 1990), bibliotherapy and writing therapy (e.g., Pennebaker, 1997). Written journaling to monitor behavior is commonly practiced between sessions of cognitive behavioral therapy. In EMDR, clients are instructed to keep a log between sessions. Writing during group EMDR has been employed with survivors of the East Asia Tsunami of 2004, and with Israeli civilian refugees and military casualty notification officers in the Lebanese War of 2006 (Birnbaum, 2005a, 2005b, 2007).

Benefits of the Group EMDR Workbook Protocol

- Clients can see the step-by-step instructions on paper.
- Clients actively participate by writing down their responses.
- Helps clients whose optimal learning style or mode of processing input or expressing output is via writing or drawing.
- Clients proceed at their pace, increasing effectiveness and client control.
- Clients' writing entails additional levels of information processing (L'Abate, 2004).
- Clients coping with language or communication deficits are supported by working with drawings.
- Cross-cultural barriers can be bridged through drawing.

297

- Clients who need highly structured situations benefit from the workbook framework.
- Clients can process without necessarily sharing specific content with the therapist or group.
- Therapist and client maintain a record of the process, for clinical review or research.
- Appropriate for individual or group EMDR application.
- Group allows for lower staff-to-client ratio: If one client requires individual attention, the others continue by following the workbook instructions.
- Group workbook format allows cost-effective, follow-up treatment and booster sessions for clients who have undergone individual EMDR, and do not require or cannot afford further individual therapy, but still have issues requiring processing.

Evaluation for Group EMDR

Using this approach with participants inexperienced with EMDR requires special care. In addition to standard screening for EMDR, clients must be able to work with a written workbook and relate to others in a group without intensive individual attention, or undue risk of severe abreaction that could disrupt group process. Clients currently unable to benefit from group EMDR can be assigned to individual or group preparatory treatment in which resource development and stress reduction techniques are taught and practiced, along with communication and social skills necessary for adaptive functioning in group.

Ideally, potential participants should first have one or more individual EMDR sessions. In addition to allowing for joining and formation of a therapeutic relationship, the assessment of such clients' suitability for group can then rely on their response to individual EMDR. These clients will be better able to follow written instructions and flow with the process independently, while therapists will be alert to potential trouble spots based on their previous responses.

EMDR Staff

Group EMDR intervention requires EMDR-trained and other staff sufficient to handle abreactions, sometimes referred to as the "Emotional Protection Team (EPT)" (Jarero et al., 2006). While initial work has shown that the group may actually provide a holding environment that can help prevent or contain untoward reactions, one must expect the unexpected. The group needs to feel the safety and flexibility required to allow processing. They are told that they can stop, and can get individual attention by raising their hand, and, if necessary, leave the room with a therapist to discuss any personal difficulty or problem with the workbook. Similarly, their reactions can be discussed at the end of the session, or in further individual or group sessions, as appropriate.

The Written Workbook for Individual or Group EMDR

The workbook format has participants independently work through a somewhat simplified and streamlined version of Francine Shapiro's Standard EMDR 3-Pronged Protocol (Shapiro, 2001). Written measures of subjective units of disturbance (SUD) and validity of cognition (VoC) use a continuous number line on which participants circle their response, thus increasing understanding of the scales and their reliability. Examples of negative and positive cognitions are included to help clients identify appropriate cognitions. Another option is to provide placards, a generic page of common negative and positive cognitions, or more specific lists for certain populations and problems (see for example EMDR HAP, Clinical Aids, www.emdrhap.org). Similarly, several examples of basic emotions are included in the workbook format, to help those less adept with feelings. These minor modifications of the Standard EMDR Protocol are designed to facilitate smooth group movement through the Assessment Phase, since individual clarification of cognitions and emotions would be time-consuming and could disrupt group process. Such clarification is best reserved for discussion before or after group processing. For instance, in the group discussion following a processing session it may emerge that a certain participant became stuck. Analysis of their negative cognition (NC) and positive cognition (PC) may reveal a potential problem that can be corrected with the help of the group, thus serving to educate all members.

The Written Workbook Protocol allows close adherence to the *EMDR Standard 3-Pronged Protocol* at all steps until the end of the processing phase, when constraints of the group format come more dramatically into play. For instance, since all participants process for the same specified length of time, some will complete while others will not. (It is likely that future research will find an increasing synchronicity effect in processing rhythms among EMDR group members over time.) Clients who complete processing before the time allotted can go to their safe place, or practice relaxation and connection to resources. If they are experienced with EMDR they may even continue processing of present triggers and future template, with appropriate instructions included at the end of the workbook. Other clients will not complete processing in the time allotted. The therapist alerts the group two sets before the end of processing time, to allow a final push in the processing.

Group Cognitive Interweaves

Cognitive interweaves necessary to clear potential blocks to processing are more difficult to tailor and implement in group. Therapists need to make special efforts to tune into the details of clients' processing in order to identify blocks or looping. The fact that clients write or draw a response after each set is helpful in this regard. Therapists can suggest an interweave with a whisper or, often better, with a written phrase on the worksheet. (If therapists are unsure about an appropriate interweave, they may consult with other members of the EPT.) The written interweave remains for the client to more fully absorb, and becomes part of the written record, available for reevaluation and research. If clarification is necessary, the client can temporarily go with a therapist to an adjacent room, and then return to group.

The potential power of "group cognitive interweaves" emerged spontaneously during multifamily group EMDR with tsunami survivors in Thailand (Birnbaum, 2006). The following dialogue occurred in the processing phase, while children worked on drawings of tsunami-related losses, in between sets of shoulder tapping supplied from behind by parents and grandparents (translation by organizer Dr. Su):

Therapist:	"Who are the people behind you?"
Children:	"Our family!"
Therapist:	"Why are they here with you?"
Children:	"They care about us!"
Therapist (to adults):	"Is that correct?"
Adults:	"Yes!"

Therapist (to children):   "How do you feel about them?"

Children: "We love them!"

Therapist: "So the tsunami didn't wash away the love?"

Children: "No!"

Therapist (to all):   "So even after the tsunami you have love?!"

All: *"Yes!"*

Then one youngster said, *"Even more than before!"* and the group was instructed to do bilateral stimulation (BLS) thinking about that.

This evolving dialogical group positive interweave indicates potential not only for healing trauma, but for posttraumatic growth (Tedeschi & Calhoun, 1995). The fact that it came from a group member demonstrates how a group can generate its own resources, and utilize its positive models to rise to its highest common denominator. As in EMDR generally, group EMDR simply provides a framework that facilitates such natural healing and growth.

Group cognitive interweaves also are possible during processing breaks to quickly check-in with participants. If the group is small and experienced and if time allows, they quickly share the gist of their processing up to that point and any blocks they may be experiencing. Cognitive interweaves may be suggested by therapists or group members, and a general group-level interweave based on shared issues may be offered by the group leader before participants resume individual processing. More often, the search for appropriate individual- and group-level interweaves (if needed) will await the Reevaluation Phase in the next session. The model can be set up to allow alternating sessions of processing followed by group discussion or reevaluation (yet another level of bilateral stimulation).

Importance of the Group

Participants requiring individual attention and temporarily leaving the room during group processing need to be returned to group quickly, to help prevent unnecessary disruption, inadvertent reinforcement of gratuitous abreaction or becoming stuck, and overdependence on the therapist. The group as a whole needs the EPT staff, whose goal is to keep group processing on track. *Group EMDR* is not just a number of people doing *parallel processing*—there is a level of group meta-processing going on as well. Stimuli that disrupt group cohesion will negatively affect group-level processes, and may compromise individual work as well. The more participants experience the group as a whole working intensively to process their problems, the more they may access modeling, social support, and other emotional and spiritual resources inherent in the group context.

A structured, time-limited format results in certain processes adapting to the time available (as has been noted for life tasks generally and in short-term or time-limited psychotherapy, e.g., Strupp & Binder, 1984). For instance, a hypothetical client in individual EMDR might take 60 minutes to process a certain event; but when informed that there will be a total of 30 minutes allotted, their system may unconsciously adapt its internal processing rhythms and algorithms and achieve similar results. This principle can apply at each stage: A client who may have taken three sets for SUDs to decline from 3 to 1, may do so in just one set after being informed that only one set will be done, and likewise for the VoC, Installation, and Body Scan.

This protocol builds on the robustness of the original EMDR approach (Shapiro, 2001), and on the fact that even incomplete sessions are highly therapeutic and provide an excellent basis for further work. Thus, we need not be overly concerned about clients who reach a SUD of 2 and with one or two more sets might have reached 0 to 1. They can continue with the protocol, and even if their VoC will only be 5 (or less), and their Body Scan not completely clear (as expected), they have gained much from the session. In subsequent sessions, using the same framework and time structure, they will be in even better position to benefit from the imposed short-term dynamic. Loyal to the basic, optimistic EMDR assumptions of maximum possibility of healing, we also remain open to the possibility of an SUDs of 2 not necessarily preventing a VoC of 6 to 7 or a clear Body Scan, whether because of continued emotional processing, separation of modalities, or other factors. It is likely that as more clinicians attempt to implement such group procedures, the very limitations it imposes will serve to further delineate the robustness of EMDR, its therapeutic mechanisms, the boundaries of what can be defined as "good enough EMDR," and its potential benefits for clients.

Structuring the Group

The proposed workbook format allows a range of possibilities on a dependence-independence continuum. On one end, the therapist can lead the group through each set of the protocol step-by-step, reading each question or instruction aloud, and waiting for client responses before proceeding together to the next step. This would even include having clients process for equal lengths of time every set, and moving together from one set to the next. On the other end, since clients have all instructions in front of them, the therapist can just let them work the workbook at their own pace, being present in case of questions or problems, and providing necessary support and structure. In this format, clients determine the length of each set of processing according to their individual needs.

The decision as to whether to have participants work independently or to structure the group for synchronous progression through the protocol depends on factors including group size, prior experience with individual and group EMDR, and the emotional and cognitive capacities of participants relative to the issues they are working on. A given group may first use the workbook in the more structured format, the leader reading each question aloud, providing guidance and clarification where needed, and the group proceeding together through the protocol step-by-step. The group's ability to handle the protocol is assessed in this initial session, and normally members will be able to handle increasingly independent work from session to session. Participants needing more support to achieve independent work can receive additional individual or small group preparatory sessions. Eventually, experienced groups will hopefully be able to use the workbook independently, allowing therapists to concentrate more on the content of individual processing and on the group meta-processing (processing of the processing).

On the technical side, the workbook format is currently being presented assuming that the form of BLS to be applied is tapping. Individual computer screens, light bars, audio equipment, and projection on a frontal screen could allow choices and combinations of tapping, audio stimulation, and eye movements, with implications for group process. Individual computer screens or light bars go better with a format designed for individual pace and independent processing, as each participant adjusts the visual stimulation to suit their preferences (speed, length of sets, etc.). Large-scale projection better suits the group structured to proceed together from set to set, at a uniform pace. If the group BLS does not suit a given client, they can use self-administered BLS during the same time intervals. Future research will hopefully help delineate what forms of group BLS are most helpful with different types of groups, individual clients, and situations.

Children and the Workbook Format

The workbook format can be used with children. Older children and adolescents of sufficient cognitive, reading and writing abilities can tackle the workbook just like adults, with additional support provided as necessary. Adolescents and many children may enjoy the increased privacy and sense of independence that the workbook format allows. For younger elementary school-age children, it is perhaps best applied when a family member works through their own workbook next to them, modeling and providing assistance as needed. With still younger children, family members can work with the child step-by-step through the applicable stages of the workbook. All of these possibilities allow important family-systems EMDR work, or multiple-family group work (Birnbaum, 2005a, 2005b). As in the application of EMDR with children generally, instructions need to be simplified to match the child's cognitive and linguistic abilities, and greater flexibility and support are required. Assessment phases focusing on negative and positive cognitions and VoC can be omitted, and SUDs can be rated using pictures rather than numbers (a placard may be easiest to refer to). Processing can be very fast, and children will tend to draw more than to write; it is often preferable to allow them an entire page for drawing after each set of BLS. It is important that the child receive strong positive reinforcement for their efforts with the workbook protocol, and that therapists supply a sufficiently supportive and flexible approach so that the child leaves the session feeling that their work and responses were accepted, respected, and appreciated.

Client History-Taking Guidelines

Optimally, history can be taken individually as in the Standard EMDR Protocol, and combined with the specific assessment of the client's suitability for group work and the workbook protocol. When circumstances do not allow for individual history taking and evaluation, much can be done in group format. This would be necessary, for instance, following natural or man-made catastrophic events, when numbers of people affected and low availability of therapists may dictate the need to improvise. In such emergency conditions, while attempting to adhere as closely as possible to ideal treatment modalities, adaptations such as substituting teachers and paraprofessional mental health workers for trained therapists in the EPT may be required and can be highly successful. Emergency group intervention represents a first level of (pre)intervention and helps identify those who need individual attention. Care and good judgment need to be exercised, however, when offering group EMDR after disaster. No treatment can be considered a panacea under any circumstances, and some victims of disaster were already fragile, or dealing with difficult issues and life situations. When disaster strikes, they may be overwhelmed with stress and loss, and therapists coming in to provide first aid may be unaware of their fragile condition. Thus, every effort needs to be made even under dire circumstances to provide for adequate client screening and staff support during and after group EMDR sessions (Jane Lopacka and Frances Yoeli, personal communication, February 6, 2005).

Several elements of history taking are particularly germane to group administration and can increase cost-efficiency and group cohesion in any situation. These include provision of information about EMDR, discussing selection criteria, indications and contraindications (e.g., stabilization, medical considerations, timing and readiness, secondary gains), administering the Dissociative Experiences Scale (DES)

(Carlson & Putnam, 1992) and other self-report instruments, obtaining informed consent, explaining the adaptive information processing model, and identification of treatment targets. For example, collecting a list of each participant's most positive and negative life experiences could be done as a group. Using clinical judgment, the therapist can open up certain of the above for brief discussion in group. Virtually all modes of presenting and explaining EMDR described in the initial sections of this volume can be utilized in group, followed by group responses and discussion.

Written Workbook for Individual or Group EMDR: Leader's Script

Phase 1: Client History

For the list of past traumas and of positive life experiences, for example,

Say, *"To help us decide about and prepare for work in the group, I'd like each of you to make a short list of traumatic life events and of especially significant positive life events you may have experienced at any point in your lives. We won't be going into detailed discussion of these right now; we'll just jot them down in the space provided and have them for future reference and possible work."*

Traumatic Life Events	Positive Life Events

Optional (use clinical judgment):

Say, *"People who have suffered trauma often feel alone. Let's go around and share some of the kinds of difficult life experiences you've written down. We won't go into detail, and no one should share anything they are not comfortable sharing at this point; and we don't want to compete about who has suffered most. But, if you have experienced something similar to others, you can just say so. For instance, do any of you have an accident or injury on your list?"*

Prompt for other types of trauma as necessary, going from least to most traumatic, and when appropriate shift the discussion to positive experiences.

Say, *"And what are some of the positive experiences you identified in your lives?"*

Prompt as necessary, and after an appropriate amount of time, conclude this segment.

Say, *"So now we know that we have all had difficult as well as positive life experiences, and that we share some of these in common. Let's continue preparing for group EMDR, which will allow us to process our difficult life events."*

Phase 2: Preparation (for Independent Work Version, see Supplement A in This Chapter)

Brief Explanation of EMDR

In the initial session(s), if necessary, use the following:

Say, *"When a disturbing event occurs, it can get locked in the brain with the original picture, sounds, thoughts, feelings, and body sensations.*

EMDR stimulates the information and allows the brain to process the experience. That may be what is happening in REM or dream sleep—the eye movements or tapping may help to process the unconscious material. It is your own brain that will be doing the healing and you are the one in control."

Mechanics

Delineate structure, time frame, and special arrangements for the group setting.

Say, *"We will have _____ (state time frame) today. Here are your workbooks and writing or drawing utensils. Our therapist team will include _____ (state names and, as appropriate, relevant titles, experience or connection to the therapist, group, or organization). We'll be circulating among you to help if you feel stuck, are going in circles, or if things get too tough. If we haven't noticed, just raise your hand and one of us will come over."*

Demonstrate the bilateral stimulation technique of tapping such as the *Butterfly Hug* (Jarero et al., 2006) or knee tapping, if necessary.

Say, *"It has been discovered that doing alternating bilateral stimulation can jump-start the brain and facilitate processing of material that was previously stuck and causing distress. One good way of doing this is knee tapping, in which you just tap your knees or legs alternately like this."*

Demonstrate knee tapping.

Say, *"Go ahead and try that for a few seconds. Good. Another method is what we call the Butterfly Hug; you cross your arms over your chest like this (demonstrate), and alternate the movement of your hands, like the flapping wings of a butterfly. Your eyes can be closed or partially closed looking toward the tip of your nose. Try that for a few seconds. Very good. In our processing today, you can use both knee tapping and the Butterfly Hug. You can also use squeezing instead of tapping, and vary the speed according to what works best for you in processing through difficult material."*

The Safe/Calm Place Protocol

Image

Say, *"I'd like you to think about some place you have been or could imagine being that feels very safe or calm. Perhaps sitting on the beach or by a mountain stream. Take 30 seconds to just find and be with the image of your own personal safe place. Then describe it in a sentence or two or draw a little sketch of your safe place in the space provided in your workbook."*

Emotions and Sensations

Say, *"As you continue to be in your safe place, take a few moments to notice what you see, hear, and feel there right now. Just notice it. Then jot it down with a few words, or draw."*

Enhancement

> Say, *"Focus on your safe place, on its sights, its sounds, its smells, and your body sensations. Connect to it even more deeply. If you like, you can add to what you wrote or drew before."*

Optional: Have group members briefly share their safe place and reactions. This also allows group members to share ideas on overcoming obstacles within a positive frame of reference, increasing cohesion, and making the group a better holding environment for the upcoming processing. Hopefully, the group itself will become its own version of a shared, group safe place for its members.

> Say, *"Let's go around and hear what kinds of places people have chosen for their safe place, and how their safe place feels."*
>
> Say, *"Now let's try to deepen our connection to our safe place by doing some bilateral stimulation. We'll try knee tapping first, and afterward we'll try the Butterfly Hug. Bring up the image of your safe place. Concentrate on where you feel the pleasant sensations in your body and allow yourself to enjoy them. Noticing your sensations, let's briefly do some tapping, and then write or draw a quick response."*

Model knee tapping, allow four to six sets, and then time for a very short response.

> Say, *"Okay, notice how you feel now. Focusing on the pleasant sensations, let's briefly do some Butterfly Hugs and then write or draw a quick response."*

Allow four to six sets and time for a short response.

Cue Word

> Say, *"Take a moment to choose a cue word or phrase for your safe place. When you have it, jot it down. (Pause) Now think of your safe place and your cue word, notice the pleasant sensations, and give yourself 10 seconds of tapping or Butterfly Hugs. (Pause) Good. Let's repeat that once more. (Pause) Very good. If you like, write or draw for a few seconds."*

Self-Cuing

> Say, *"Now just say your cue word or the phrase you chose for your safe place and notice how you feel. If you like, write or draw for a few seconds."*

Cuing With Disturbance

> Say, *"Now imagine a minor annoyance and how it feels. (Pause) Bring up your safe place with your cue word, and notice any shifts in your body. If you like, write or draw for a few seconds."*

Self-Cuing With Disturbance

> Say, *"Now I'd like you to think of another mildly annoying incident and then bring up your safe place by yourself. Again, especially notice any changes in your body when you have gone to your safe place. If you like, write or draw for a few seconds."*

Practice

Say, *"I'd like you to practice using your safe place between now and our next session, any time you feel a little annoyed. Keep track of how things go and we'll talk about it next time we meet. It's good to keep in mind that we can always go to our safe place to relax or feel better, and we can use it in EMDR if we need to take a break before continuing if the work gets very tough."*

Resource Connection

A similar approach to personal resource connection (Laub, 2001) has participants connect to a time they felt good about themselves or to a success they had, or to a significant other who represents a social resource (Emanuel, 2006), or to a musical resource (Birnbaum, unpublished research, July 29, 2006). These resources are written down or drawn, and reinforced with BLS.

For personal resources, say the following:

Say, *"Before continuing, take a moment to connect to a time when you felt really good about yourself, or to an experience of success in your life, perhaps where you overcame some obstacle or challenge, whether recently or a long time ago. The positive feelings may have lasted anywhere from a few moments to a long period of time. When was that time or what was the experience?"*

Say, *"Now choose a picture that represents that positive time, and notice the feelings you have inside in connection with it. Let yourself relive it, with all the thoughts, feelings, and sensations around it. Let yourself hear, see, and even smell or taste it, breathe it in and really connect with it. Then do some tapping to deepen your connection with this personal resource."*

Allow time for one or several short sets.

Say, *"Jot down what you connected with, or draw a picture."*

For social resources, say the following:

Say, *"Take another moment to bring up the image of someone important to you, past or present, someone who connects to feelings like caring, comfort, safety, protection, support, encouragement, acceptance, understanding, empathy, warmth or compassion, or with whom you are at your best. Write down the name of the person with whom you are connecting. Think of an event you shared with them and choose a picture that represents the best part of the event, or concentrate on the image of the person while you think of their name and notice the feelings you have inside. Then do some tapping to deepen your connection with this resource.*

Allow time for one or several short sets.

Say, *"Jot down what you connected with, or draw a picture."*

For creative arts resources, say the following:

Say, *"Take another moment to bring up a song or melody, poem, picture, or other artistic creation that carries positive meaning for you. Perhaps it is connected to a certain time or experience, recent or long past, and it brings up feelings like hope or inspiration, strength or courage, comfort or solace. Write down the name of the song or piece with which you are connecting. Bring up a picture that represents the piece, or hum it softly to yourself, and notice the feelings you have inside. Let yourself really connect with it; allow yourself to fully experience and take in its positive effect with all your senses, through the words, the beat, the melody, the image, and the message, through your thoughts, feelings, and your body. Then do some tapping to deepen your connection with this resource."*

Allow time for one or several short sets.

Say, *"Jot down what you connected with, or draw a picture."*

Say, *"Excellent. Now let's take a few minutes to share some of the resources we identified. Who is willing to share?"*

To end this segment,

Say, *"Thank you for sharing. Clearly there are a lot of resources in this group, and we can depend on them to help us deal with difficult emotions and issues and process them through."*

Set Up

Assuming the initial phases were done with members sitting in a circle, instruct the group about the preferred seating arrangement if changes are necessary. Possibilities include sitting in a circle, with EPT circulating outside (enhances group feeling and allows discussion without rotating chairs, but EPT and other participants are in the clients' visual field); a straight line, circle, or semicircle with participants facing *outward* (reduces mutual distraction and maximizes privacy, EPT circulate behind or inside; may be best if clients need to leave the room, with chairs positioned facing away from the path to the door). If one of the latter options is chosen, the group will need to move back into a regular circle facing inward, with the EPT rejoining the group for closure and possible discussion.

Metaphor

Say, *"In order to help you just notice the experience, imagine riding on a train, and the feelings, thoughts, and so forth are just the scenery going by. (Optional: may suggest other metaphors such as seeing memories on a TV screen, or through a thick window, etc.) We also remember that we have all our resources, and we can temporarily go to our safe place if we need to take a break."*

Specific Instructions

Say, *"After we focus in on our target for today and answer a few questions about thoughts and feelings surrounding it, we will begin processing using our bilateral tapping techniques. After each set of tapping we will briefly write or draw something about our response, and then continue tapping and processing. Sometimes things will come up or change, and sometimes they won't. There are no 'supposed to's' in this process. Just go with the flow and let whatever happens happen, without judging it. If you have a problem or feel you have to stop, raise your hand."*

Phase 3: Assessment

Past Incident

Say, *"What memory will you start with today? Please describe your target event briefly in the space provided."* (Pause)

Say, *"What picture represents the worst part of the incident? Please describe it briefly in the space provided."*

Negative Cognition (NC)

Say, *"Many people have negative thoughts after difficult life events. Some people might say things like, 'I am bad' or 'I am stupid' or 'I am guilty' and so forth. Fill in the words that go best with your difficult picture and that express your negative belief about yourself now.*
'I am . . .' " (Pause)

Positive Cognition (PC)

Say, *"When you bring up that picture or incident, what would you like to believe about yourself, now? You might say, 'I am good' or 'I am smart' or 'I did the best I could' for example.*
'I am . . .' " (Pause)

Validity of Cognition (VoC)

Say, *"When you think of the incident or picture, how true do those positive words feel to you now on a scale of 1 to 7, where 1 feels completely false, and 7 feels completely true?"*

1	2	3	4	5	6	7
(completely false)				(completely true)		

Say, *"When you bring up the picture* (or incident) *and the <u>negative</u> words that go with it, what emotion do you feel now? (Do you feel sad, angry, afraid, ashamed, etc.?) Go ahead and fill in what you feel."*

Subjective Units of Disturbance (SUD)

Say, *"On a scale of 0 to 10, where 0 is no disturbance or neutral and 10 is the highest disturbance you can imagine, how disturbing does it feel now?"*

0	1	2	3	4	5	6	7	8	9	10
(no disturbance)							(highest disturbance)			

Location of Body Sensation

Say, *"Where do you feel it* (the disturbance) *in your body?"* (Pause)

Phase 4: Desensitization

Say, *"Let's move on to processing. For each set, we'll do tapping or Butterfly Hugs for about 30 seconds, then we'll pause, take a deep breath together, and briefly jot down a few words or draw what we noticed in the space provided. Then we'll repeat: tapping . . . , deep breath . . . , writing or drawing. We'll do this for _____ (state the number of minutes). I'll let you know a couple of minutes before it's time to move on together to the next stage. So we'll begin with the target, and let ourselves go with whatever comes up. Go ahead and bring up the picture from your difficult event, those negative words you were saying about yourself, notice where you are feeling it in your body, and begin tapping."*

The group leader models tapping and Butterfly Hug and inserts supportive comments to individuals and to the group, to encourage and facilitate processing.

Say, *"That's it"* or *"Good"* or *"Just notice it"* or *"Go with that"* for example.

After approximately 30 seconds, say the following:

Say, *"Okay, let's take a deep breath . . . , and then just notice what you get now . . . , and take a few moments to write down a few words or draw."* (Allow about 30 seconds.)

Say, *"Okay, let's continue tapping and processing. Again, go with the flow, let whatever happens happen."* (Model continued tapping or Butterfly Hug, add positive comments as appropriate.)

Continue to repeat the above at about 30-second intervals or according to group response. Space has been provided in the workbook (see supplement A) for several sets of processing; therapist will decide on the number of sets to be used and give the appropriate amount of paper or copy the page in the workbook that has the instruction: *"Whatever came up, just go with it, and continue tapping. After about 30 seconds, or when you feel a change, take a deep breath, and write or draw something about what you noticed,"* at the top of the page and has a place to write or draw and then the same text again in the middle of the page. Give as many copies as needed, according to group needs and time constraints; responses to additional sets can also be recorded on reverse sides or extra pages—each set should be numbered in order to allow reconstruction of the process.

Two sets before the end of processing time, say the following:

Say, *"Okay, we can do two more sets of processing before moving on. Come on, let's go."*

Model bilateral stimulation (BLS). After about 30 seconds, say the following:

Say, *"Okay, deep breath, notice what you get now, and take a few moments to write or draw."* (Allow about 30 seconds.)

After about 30 seconds, say the following:

Say, *"Okay, let's do one last set for now. Go ahead."*

Model BLS. After about 30 seconds, say the following:

Say, *"Okay, deep breath, notice what you get, and write or draw."* (Allow about 30 seconds.)

Say, *"When you bring up the original experience, on a scale of 0 to 10, where 0 is no disturbance or neutral and 10 is the highest disturbance you can imagine, how disturbing does it feel to you now?"*

0	1	2	3	4	5	6	7	8	9	10

(no disturbance)   (highest disturbance)

Say, *"Let's do one set of tapping and let go of any residual disturbance we don't need to hold onto right now."*

Model BLS.

Say, *"Okay, how disturbing does it feel to you now?"*

0	1	2	3	4	5	6	7	8	9	10

(no disturbance)   (highest disturbance)

Phase 5: Installation

Say, *"Before we started processing, you chose a positive statement you wanted to believe about yourself. It's okay to change that statement if something else fits better for you now. When you think of the original incident, what would you like to believe about yourself now?"*

Say, *"As you think of the incident, how true do those words feel, from 1 (completely false) to 7 (completely true)?"*

1	2	3	4	5	6	7

(completely false)   (completely true)

Say, *"Think of the event, and hold it together with the positive words you chose. Let's do one set of tapping to let it feel as true as possible.*

Model BLS.

Say, *"What's your reading on how true it feels to you now?"*

1	2	3	4	5	6	7

(completely false)   (completely true)

Phase 6: Body Scan

Say, *"Now close your eyes and keep in mind the original incident and your positive thought. (Pause) Now bring your attention to the different parts of your body, starting with your head and working downward. Any place you find tension, tightness, or unusual sensation, just notice it and then start tapping. Keep tapping until you sense a change, and continue tapping as long as it seems to be helping you feel better. Good. We'll do this for the next couple of minutes."*

Guide and encourage as necessary and, after about 90 seconds, say the following:

Say, *"Okay, let's do another half minute of tapping and let go of any residual disturbance in our bodies that we don't need to hold onto right now."*

After another 30 seconds, say the following:

Say, *"Very good. Now take a deep breath, and jot down or draw what you noticed and how you feel now."*

Options for Blocked Processing

As during standard EMDR processing, clients can be encouraged individually to vary the form and speed of their self-administered BLS as a first strategy to release blocked processing. Clients who had been attempting to process with eyes open and were possibly distracted may be told to look at their last written response or drawing to help keep them focused during BLS. Other clients may be guided to incorporate eye movements utilizing two points on the page or on the wall in front of them instead of or in combination with their tapping. Using clinical judgment if the above are ineffective, there is also the option of closing eyes during BLS. Consider using the *Affect Scan*, or the *Float-Back Technique* to identify old targets related to blocks, anxieties, or fears. Continue processing of these targets, as time allows.

Float-Back Technique

Say, *"Bring up your picture from the disturbing event and the negative words that went with it. Notice what feelings are coming up for you, and where you are feeling them in your body, and just let your mind float back to an earlier time in your life—without searching for anything in particular—just let your mind float back and notice the earliest scene that comes to mind where you had similar thoughts or similar feelings, or felt similar sensations in your body. When you have identified the original scene, let yourself continue processing by tapping, and just let whatever happens—happen"* (based on Shapiro, 2006, p. 48).

Affect Scan

If, through direct questioning and the Float-Back Technique, the Touchstone Event has not been identified, the Affect Scan may be successful. Identify the emotions and body sensations that resonate with the negative belief. Once identified, have clients scan back to the last time they felt these emotions (based on Shapiro, 2006, p. 48).

Say, *"Bring up the last time you felt upset* (or had that emotion). *Hold the image in mind and notice the thoughts that come up about it.* (Pause) *Where do you feel it in your body?"*

Say, *"Hold in mind the image, emotion, and the sensation, and let your mind scan back to the earliest time you remember feeling that way."*

Say, *"Now that you have remembered the earliest memory that is related to your problem, the Touchstone Event, what are your future concerns about this problem?"*

Say, *"Now that you have identified your Touchstone Event and your future concerns, let yourself continue processing by tapping, and just let whatever happens—happen."*

Continue alternating sets of BLS and drawing or writing, until the time for processing is over, and continue with Phase 5 (Installation).

Other past events and current triggers are reprocessed in future sessions in the same manner as above. Clients who do not reach the end of channels in specific sessions and are in distress, or do not achieve completion of processing before termination of time-limited groups may require additional individual sessions. Experienced clients who complete processing early in a group session may be given the option of independently processing other events, present triggers, or moving on to a future template using the workbook. Alternatively, the group can be led through future template work together.

Future Template (Based on Shapiro, 2006, pp. 51–53)

Say, "When you have a good, strong connection between the original incident, your positive thought, and pleasant emotions and body sensations, you can further enhance your progress by incorporating a detailed template for trauma-free future action. Imagine yourself coping effectively in the future with a situation that used to be a problem for you. With your new positive belief _____ (fill in positive belief) and your new sense of _____ (fill in the positive resource you are feeling, like strength, clarity, confidence, calm), imagine stepping into this scene. Notice what you see and how you are handling the situation. Notice what you are thinking, feeling, and experiencing in your body. As you imagine this positive scene, continue your tapping. If there are any blocks, anxieties, or fears that arise as you think about this future scene, just notice them and continue tapping in order to process and feel as good as possible about the future picture. When you are ready, take a deep breath and write down or draw your picture of whatever came up."

If blocks are encountered, other elements of the future template protocol may be incorporated.

Say, "What would you need to feel confident in handling the situation? Write it down and continue tapping."

Consider utilizing client resources to enhance future template processing.

For Personal Resource Connection

Say, "Bring up the time or event you remembered in which you were successful or felt really good. Connect to it and then imagine how you could handle your future challenge. Write or draw, and continue tapping."

For Social Resource Connection

Say, "Bring up the person with whom you feel or have felt especially close, or with whom you are at your best. Connect to them, imagine what they might tell you about handling your future challenge, or how they might handle a similar situation. Write or draw, and continue tapping."

For Creative Arts Resource Connection

Say, "Bring up the song or melody, poem, picture, or other artistic creation that carries a positive meaning for you. Let yourself really connect to it (see the picture, hum the tune in your head, say or write the words . . .) and then imagine how you would handle your future challenge with that inspiration. Write or draw, and continue tapping."

Say, "When you can visualize the future scene with confidence and clarity, focus on the image, on your positive belief, and your positive sensations, and continue tapping as long as you feel improvement. If anything comes up, feel free to write or draw, and then continue."

Phase 7: Group Closure

Say, *"We will be stopping soon. You have done very good work, as individuals and as a group."*

Say, *"Let's end with a relaxation exercise (e.g., Safe Place, Light Stream)."*

For Safe Place, see the above section, "The Safe/Calm Place Protocol."

The Light Stream Technique (Shapiro, 2001)

Say, *"I would like you to scan your whole body now and note any unpleasant body sensations or tensions."*

_____

_____

Say, *"I'd like you to imagine that those sensations were energy.
If the energy had a _____ what would it be?
Write down your responses in the workbook."*

Shape

Size:

Color:

Temperature:

Texture:

Sound:

Say, *"What color does your body need today to heal?"*

Say, *"Imagine that this healing colored light is coming in through the top of your head and directing itself at the shape in your body. Let's pretend that the source of this light is the infinite cosmos so the more you use it, the more you have available. Allow the soothing, healing light to come in more and more, and direct itself at the shape. As it does so, let the light resonate and vibrate in and around it, more and more. And as it does, what happens to the shape?"*

_____

_____

Say, *"Continue to allow the light to flow into your head, neck, and shoulders. Let it flow into your chest and down your arms and out your fingertips. Let the soothing, healing light flow through your torso into your legs and out through your feet. Let the light flow into every part of your body. Let it completely fill you up, let it work wherever it is needed inside you, to heal you and make you stronger. Then, let it spill over and surround you, encompassing you in a healing, protective layer of light. Finally, imagine saying to yourself the positive words you most need to hear right now."*

Say, *"Now, as I count from one to five, I'd like you to bring yourself back here to the room. (Pause) So, bringing your whole and complete self back in the room now, one, two, (rising intonation) three, four, and five. Very good. How do you feel?"*

Say, *"Remember, there is as much light like that as you could ever need, and even as you take the good feelings with you today, you also take the knowledge that you can access this healing light whenever you need it."*

After relaxation is completed, say the following:

Say, *"What is the most important thing you are taking from today's session? Take a moment to write it down or draw something to represent it."*

If there is time, allow for sharing in the group. If not, or in order not to disturb processing effects, postpone sharing and discussion till next session.

Say, *"Hats off to you all for being brave enough to confront difficult issues and work toward resolving your problems together, in group."*

As in the EMDR Standard Protocol, state the following:

Say, *"The processing we have done today may continue after the session. You may or may not notice new insights, thoughts, memories, or dreams. If so, just notice what you are experiencing—take a snapshot of it—what you are seeing, feeling, thinking, and the trigger, and keep a log. Go to your safe place or do the light stream exercise if you need to rid yourself of any disturbance. We can work on such new material next time. If you feel it is necessary, call me."*

In certain ongoing groups, the therapist may consider adding the option to call other group members, or designated "buddies" or "sponsors" in case difficult reactions occur, with the possibility of contacting the therapist saved as a last resort.

Supplement A: Workbook Version: Directions for Participants

Note: This section is designed to be copied and distributed to clients for independent EMDR work under the immediate supervision of the accredited EMDR therapist and (for groups) the emotional protection team (EPT). The therapist will instruct and clarify directions as needed. Please ask if anything is unclear.

Phase 2: Preparation

What Is EMDR, How Can It Help You, and How Does It Work?

When a disturbing event occurs, it can get locked in the brain with the original picture, sounds, thoughts, feelings, and body sensations. EMDR stimulates the information and allows the brain to process the experience. That may be what is happening in REM or dream sleep—the eye movements or tapping may help to process the unconscious material. It is your own brain that will be doing the healing and you are the one in control.

The therapists will be circulating to help if you feel stuck, are going in circles, or if things get too tough. If we haven't noticed, just raise your hand and one of us will come over.

What Is Bilateral Stimulation?

It has been discovered that doing alternating bilateral stimulation can jump-start the brain and facilitate processing of material that was previously stuck, causing distress. One good way of doing this is knee tapping, in which you just tap your knees or legs alternately. Another method is the Butterfly Hug: Cross your arms over your chest, and alternate hand movements, tapping your arms or shoulders like the flapping wings of a butterfly. (Eyes can be closed or partially closed looking toward the tip of the nose.) In our processing today, you can try both knee tapping and the Butterfly Hug. You can also try squeezing instead of tapping, and vary the speed according to what works best for you to help you process through difficult material.

How Do I Create and Install My Safe/Calm Place?

Image

Think about some place you have been or could imagine being that feels very safe or calm. Perhaps sitting on the beach or by a mountain stream. Take 30 seconds to just find and be with your image of a certain safe place. Then describe it in a sentence or two or draw a little sketch of your safe place here:

_____

_____

Emotions and Sensations

As you continue to be in your safe place, take another half a minute to notice what you see, hear, and feel right now. Just notice it. Then jot it down with a few words, or draw.

Enhancement

Focus on your safe place, its sights, sounds, smells, and body sensations. Connect to it even more deeply. If you like, you can write or draw your response.

Bilateral Stimulation (BLS)

Bring up the image of your safe place. Concentrate on where you feel the pleasant sensations in your body and allow yourself to enjoy them. As you concentrate on those sensations, briefly do some tapping (up to 10 seconds), and then write or draw a quick response.

Notice how you feel now. Focusing on the pleasant sensations, briefly do some Butterfly Hugs (up to 10 seconds) and then write or draw a quick response.

Cue Word

Take a moment to choose a cue word or phrase for your safe place. When you have it, jot it down here.

Cue Word:_____

Now think of your safe place and your cue word, notice the pleasant sensations, and give yourself 10 seconds of tapping or Butterfly Hugs.

Repeat as long as the feeling improves.

If you like, write or draw your response.

_____

Self-Cuing

Now just say your cue word or the phrase you chose for your safe place and notice how you feel. If you like, write or draw for a few seconds.

_____

Cuing With Disturbance

Now imagine a minor annoyance and how it feels. Bring up your safe place with your cue word, and notice any shifts in your body. If you like, write or draw for a few seconds.

Self-Cuing With Disturbance

Now think of another mildly annoying incident and bring up your safe place by yourself. Again, especially notice any changes in your body when you have gone to your safe place. If you like, write or draw for a few seconds.

Practice

Practice using your safe place between now and next session, any time you feel a little annoyed. Keep track of how things go to discuss it next time. You can always go to your safe place to relax or feel better, and you can use it in EMDR if you need to take a break before continuing.

What Other Personal and Interpersonal Resources Do I Have That Can Help Me Make Progress?

Personal Resource Connection Exercise (Based on the Work of Brurit Laub, 2001)

Before continuing, take a moment to connect to a time when you felt really good about yourself, or to an experience of success in your life, perhaps where you overcame some obstacle or challenge, whether recently or a long time ago. The positive feelings may have lasted anywhere from a few moments to a long period of time. When was that time or what was the experience?

Now choose a picture that represents that positive time, and notice the feelings you have inside in connection with it. Let yourself relive it, with all the thoughts, feelings, and sensations around it. Let your self hear, see, and even smell or taste it, breathe it in and really connect with it.

Then do some tapping to deepen your connection with this personal resource.

Jot down what you connected with, or draw a picture.

Social Resource Connection Exercise
(Based on the Work of Yair Emanuel, 2006)

Take another moment to bring up the image of someone important to you, past or present, someone you associate with feelings such as caring, comfort, safety, protection, support, encouragement, acceptance, understanding, empathy, warmth, or compassion, or with whom you are at your best.

The person you are thinking of is your social resource.

The name of the person is _____.

Think of an event or time you shared with that person. Choose a picture that represents the best part of the event, or concentrate on your person's image, saying your person's name while you notice the feelings you have inside.

Then do some tapping to deepen your connection with this resource.

Jot down what you connected with, or draw a picture.

Creative Arts Resource Connection Exercise
(From the Work of Aiton Birnbaum, 2005a and 2005b)

Take another moment to bring up a song or melody, poem, picture, or other artistic creation that carries positive meaning for you. Perhaps it is connected to a certain time or experience, recent or long past, and it brings up feelings like hope or inspiration, strength or courage, comfort or solace.

Write down the name of the song or piece with which you are connecting.

_____

Bring up a picture that represents the piece, or hum it softly to yourself, and notice the feelings you have inside. Let yourself really connect with it, allow yourself to fully experience and take in its positive effect through all your senses, through the words, the beat, the melody, the image, or the message, as they reverberate through your body, your feelings, and your thoughts.

Then do some tapping to deepen your connection with this resource.

Jot down what you connected with, or draw a picture.

_____

What Can I Expect When I Do EMDR?

In order to help you just notice the experience while you process, you can imagine riding on a train, and the feelings, thoughts, and so forth, are just the scenery going by. (Or you could see memories as if on a TV screen, or through a thick window.) And there is always your safe place, and your resources to connect with if you need to take a break during processing.

After you focus in on your target for today and answer a few questions about your thoughts and feelings surrounding it, you will begin processing using your bilateral tapping techniques. After each set of tapping, you will briefly write or draw something about what you noticed about your response, and then continue tapping and processing. Sometimes, things will come up or change, and sometimes they won't. There are no 'supposed to's' in this process. Just go with the flow and let whatever happens—happen, without judging it. If you have a problem or feel you have to stop, raise your hand."

Phase 3: Assessment

What Is the Assessment Phase?

This is when we identify the target you will work on today, as well as thoughts, feelings, and body sensations connected with it. After that, we will begin the actual reprocessing.

Past Incident

What memory will you start with today? Briefly describe your target event.

_____

_____

_____

_____

What picture represents the worst part of the incident?

_____

_____

Negative Cognition (NC)

Many people have negative thoughts after difficult life events. What words best go with the difficult picture that express your negative belief about yourself now? Some people might say, 'I am bad,' or 'I am stupid,' or 'I am guilty'. What do you say?
I am _____.

Positive Cognition (PC)

When you bring up that picture or incident, what would you like to believe about yourself, now? You might say, 'I am good,' or 'I am smart' or 'I did the best I could'. What is right for you? I am _____.

Validity of Cognition (VoC)

When you think of the incident (or picture) *how true does the positive statement you just chose feel to you now on a scale of 1 to 7, where 1 feels completely false, and 7 feels completely true?*

1	2	3	4	5	6	7
(completely false)				(completely true)		

Emotions

When you bring up the picture (or incident) *and your <u>negative</u> statement, what emotion(s) do you feel now? Do you feel sad? Angry? Afraid? Ashamed? Disgusted?*
I feel _____.

Subjective Units of Disturbance (SUD)

On a scale of 0 to 10, where 0 is no disturbance or neutral and 10 is the highest disturbance you can imagine, how disturbing does it feel now?

0	1	2	3	4	5	6	7	8	9	10
(no disturbance)							(highest disturbance)			

Location of Body Sensation

Where do you feel it (the disturbance) *in your body?*

_____

_____

Phase 4: Reprocessing

You are about to begin processing at your own pace. Bring up the picture, your negative thought (write in your negative thought) _____
_____ *and the feelings you feel in your body*
(write them in) _____
_____ *and then do about 30 seconds of*
tapping, just letting whatever happens—happen.

Then you will take a deep breath, notice what comes up, and briefly write or draw about what happened during or after the tapping.

Then repeat, just going with the flow: After each set of tapping, take a deep breath, write or draw in the space provided, and then continue tapping.

I will let you know 2 minutes before we need to move on to the next stage together.

If you need help, raise your hand.

So go ahead, bring up the picture from your difficult event, those negative words you were saying about yourself, notice where you are feeling it in your body and begin tapping. After about 30 seconds, or when you feel a change, take a deep breath, and write or draw something about what you noticed.

_____

_____

_____

Whatever came up (or did not come up), *just go with it, and continue tapping.*
After about 30 seconds, or when you feel a change, take a deep breath, and write or draw something about what you noticed.

_____

_____

_____

Whatever came up, just go with it, and continue tapping.
After about 30 seconds, or when you feel a change, take a deep breath, and write or draw something about what you noticed.

_____

_____

_____

Whatever came up, just go with it, and continue tapping.

After about 30 seconds, or when you feel a change, take a deep breath, and write or draw something about what you noticed.

_____

_____

_____

Whatever came up, just go with it, and continue tapping.

After about 30 seconds, or when you feel a change, take a deep breath, and write or draw something about what you noticed.

_____

_____

_____

Whatever came up, just go with it, and let's continue tapping for two final sets right now. After about 30 seconds, or when you feel a change, take a deep breath, and write or draw.

_____

_____

_____

Go back to the original experience or incident. What do you get now?

_____

_____

Just notice it, and do a last set of tapping for any final processing right now. Then take a deep breath, and write or draw for a moment.

_____

_____

_____

Okay, when you bring up the experience, on a scale of 0 to 10, where 0 is no disturbance or neutral and 10 is the highest disturbance you can imagine, how disturbing does it feel to you now?

0   1   2   3   4   5   6   7   8   9   10
(no disturbance)   (highest disturbance)

Continue tapping and allow yourself to let go of any residual disturbance you don't need to hold onto.

What's your current reading on how disturbing it feels to you now?

0   1   2   3   4   5   6   7   8   9   10
(no disturbance)   (highest disturbance)

Options for Blocked Processing

Consider using the *Affect Scan*, or the *Float-Back Technique* to identify old targets related to blocks, anxieties, or fears. Continue processing of these targets, as time allows.

Float-Back Technique (Based on Francine Shapiro, 2006)

Bring up your picture from the disturbing event and the negative words that went with it. Notice what feelings are coming up for you, and where you are feeling them in your body, and just let your mind float back to an earlier time in your life—without searching for anything in particular—just let your mind float back and notice the earliest scene that comes to mind where you had similar thoughts or similar feelings, or felt similar sensations in your body. When you have identified the original scene, let yourself continue processing by tapping, and just let whatever happens—happen.

Affect Scan (Based on Francine Shapiro, 2006)

Bring up the last time you felt upset (or had that emotion). *Hold the image in mind and notice the thoughts that come up about it.* (Pause) *Where do you feel it in your body?*

_____

Hold in mind the image, emotion, and the sensation, and let your mind scan back to the earliest time you remember feeling that way.

_____

Now that you have remembered the earliest memory that is related to your problem, the Touchstone Event, what are your future concerns about this problem?

_____

Now that you have identified your Touchstone Event and your future concerns, let yourself continue processing by tapping, and just let whatever happens—happen.

Continue alternating sets of BLS and drawing or writing, until the time for processing is over, and continue with Phase 5.

Phase 5: Installation

What Is the Installation?

Installation is when you connect as strongly as possible with the most appropriate positive thought relevant to the original event.

Before processing, you chose a positive statement you wanted to believe about yourself relating to the original event. Does a different statement fit better now? When you think of the original incident, what would you like to believe about yourself now?

_____

As you think of the incident, how true do those words feel, from 1 (completely false) to 7 (completely true)?

1	2	3	4	5	6	7
(completely false)				(completely true)		

Think of the event, and hold it together with the positive words you chose. Do some tapping to let it feel as true as possible.

What's your reading on how true it feels to you now?

1	2	3	4	5	6	7
(completely false)				(completely true)		

Phase 6: Body Scan

What Is the Body Scan?

Here you check in and notice any residual body sensations that may be connected with the event, and process them until you feel as clear and comfortable as possible.

Now, close your eyes and keep in mind the original incident and your positive thought.

Next, bring your attention to the different parts of your body, starting with your head and working downward. Any place you find any tension, tightness, or unusual sensation, just notice it, and then start tapping.

Keep tapping until you sense a change, and then continue for the next couple of minutes, as long as it seems to be helping you feel better.

Now take a deep breath, and jot down or draw what came up.

_____

_____

_____

Future Template

What Is the Future Template?

When you have a good, strong connection between the original incident, your positive thought, and pleasant emotions and body sensations, you can further enhance your progress by incorporating a detailed template for trauma-free future action. Imagine yourself coping effectively in the future with a situation that used to be problematic for you. With your new positive belief (fill-in your positive belief) _____
_____ *and your new sense of* (fill-in the positive resource you are feeling, like strength, clarity, confidence, calm), _____*imagine stepping into this scene.*

Notice what you see and how you are handling the situation. Notice what you are thinking, feeling, and experiencing in your body. As you imagine this positive scene, continue your tapping. If there are any blocks, anxieties, or fears that arise as you think about this future scene, just notice them and continue tapping in order to process and feel as good as possible about the future picture. When you are ready, take a deep breath and write down or draw whatever came up.

_____

_____

_____

If you encounter any blocks, ask yourself the following:
What would I need to feel confident in handling the situation?
Write it down and continue tapping.

_____

_____

_____

Consider utilizing your resources to enhance your future template processing.

For Personal Resource Connection

Bring up the time or event you remembered in which you were successful or felt really good. Connect to it and then imagine how you could handle your future challenge. Write or draw, and continue tapping.

_____

_____

_____

For Social Resource Connection

Bring up the person with whom you feel or have felt especially close, or with whom you are at your best. Connect to them, imagine what they might tell you about handling your future challenge, or how they might handle a similar situation. Write or draw, and continue tapping.

_____

_____

_____

For Creative Arts Resource Connection

Bring up the song or melody, poem, picture, or other artistic creation that carries positive meaning for you. Let yourself really connect to it (hum the tune in your head, say or write the words . . .) *and then imagine how you would handle your future challenge with that inspiration. Write or draw, and continue tapping.*

_____

_____

_____

Say, *"Take another moment to bring up a song or melody, poem, picture, or other artistic creation that carries positive meaning for you. Perhaps it is connected to a certain time or experience, recent or long past, and it brings up feelings like hope or inspiration, strength or courage, comfort or solace. Write down the name of the song or piece with which you are connecting. Bring up a picture that represents the piece, or hum it softly to yourself, and notice the feelings you have inside. Let yourself really connect with it; allow yourself to fully experience and take in its positive effect with all your senses, through the words, the beat, the melody, the image, and the message, through your thoughts, feelings, and your body. Then do some tapping to deepen your connection with this resource."*

When you can visualize the future scene with confidence and clarity, focus on the image, on your positive belief, and your positive sensations, and continue tapping.

Continue as long as you feel improvement. If anything comes up, feel free to write or draw, and then continue.

_____

_____

_____

Phase 7: Group Closure

We will be stopping soon. If you have reached this point, you have done some good hard work. Write a few words about (or draw) *how you are feeling.*

_____

_____

_____

Take a few minutes to go to your safe place, connect to your resources, or do another relaxation exercise.

For safe place exercise, see above.

The Light Stream Technique

Scan your whole body now and note any unpleasant body sensations or tensions.

_____

_____

Imagine that those sensations were energy.

If the energy had a shape, what would it be? _____

If the energy had a size, what would it be? _____

If the energy had a color, what would it be? _____

If the energy had a temperature, what would it be? _____

If the energy had a texture, what would it be? _____

If the energy had a sound, what would it be? _____

*What color does your body need today to heal?*_____

Imagine that this healing colored light is coming in through the top of your head and directing itself at the shape in your body. Let's pretend that the source of this light is the infinite cosmos so the more you use, the more you have available. Allow the soothing, healing light to come in more and more, and direct itself at the shape. As it does so, let the light resonate and vibrate in and around it, more and more. And as it does, what happens to the shape?

_____

Continue to allow the light to flow into your head, neck, and shoulders. Let it flow into your chest and down your arms and out your fingertips. Let the soothing, healing light flow through your torso into your legs and out through your feet. Let the light flow into every part of your body. Let it completely fill you up, let it work wherever it is needed inside you, to heal you and make you stronger. Then, let it spill over and surround you, encompassing you in a healing, protective layer of light. Finally, imagine saying to yourself the positive words you most need to hear right now.

_____

Now, get ready to count from one to five, and to bring yourself back here to the room.

So, to bring your whole and complete self back in the room now: one, two, three, four, and five.

How do you feel? _____

Remember, there is as much light like that as you could ever need, and even as you take the good feelings with you today, you also take the knowledge that you can access this healing light whenever you need it.

Please write or draw: What is the most important thing you are taking from today's session?

_____

_____

_____

Good job for being brave enough to confront difficult issues and work toward resolving your problems here, together with the group.

What Will Happen Now?

The processing you did today may continue after the session. You may or may not notice new insights, thoughts, memories, or dreams. If so, just notice what you are experiencing—take a snapshot of it (what you are seeing, feeling, thinking, and the trigger) *and keep a log. If you like, you can do a safe place exercise or relaxation to help you feel better. We can work on this new material next time. If you feel it is necessary, call the person you identified as your primary contact in group, or call me.*

PART VIII

EMDR and Performance Enhancement

It is a noble endeavor to find ways to enhance and better our performance in our personal, professional, and recreational lives as it supports our feelings of self-worth, confidence, and joy. Hopefully our parents, extended family, teachers, coaches, and bosses are involved with the support of our well-being. However, as this is not always the case, mental health practitioners have found innovative ways to reinforce positive experience. The American Psychological Association has acknowledged these concerns by supporting divisions in the following areas: Psychology of Aesthetics, Creativity and Art, Industrial and Organizational Psychology, Humanistic Psychology, and Exercise and Sport Psychology.

In EMDR, performance enhancement is closely linked with resources and their development (see Part III: Creating Resources). Whether it is the notation of resources throughout the session, as in Brurit Laub's Resource Connection, the mapping of them through Elan Shapiro's Resource Map, or the simple installation of a positive experience during the week as Robbie Dunton did with her students, there are many ways to support the positive feelings, sensations, beliefs, and behaviors of our clients.

In this section, Sandra Foster, Jennifer Lendl, and John Hartung show how EMDR can support work in the area of performance enhancement and how this work can be extended into other areas. These chapters include a more comprehensive treatment of their subject in a form that is more manual than script. Both chapters focus on the importance of beginning at the other end of the 3-Pronged Protocol with the future template.

Working in the area of future goals and expectations and helping the clients focus themselves in this forward-looking direction underlines the importance of the positive cognition in Francine Shapiro's 11-Step Standard Procedure pointing in the direction of adaptive resolution. Engaging the type of population that seeks help for performance enhancement, the clinician is charged with focusing on the presenting issue. By solidly targeting the clear development of the goal and reinforcing the qualities needed to get there, the practitioner who works in the area of performance enhancement supports the experience of well-being and forward direction, only addressing present triggers and past issues as needed.

In this manner, EMDR is used to reinforce the future actions and present behaviors before venturing into the stormy waters of the past. It could be said that there really is no difference between a clinician working with performance enhancement and one addressing past trauma as both work to support the grounding of the client in their strengths before visiting their problems; however, with performance enhancement, it is a matter of much more focus on the presenting issue in the present and the enhancement of the future behaviors.

Enhancing Positive Emotion and Performance With EMDR

John Hartung

The scripts included in this chapter exemplify how an EMDR therapist might talk with a client when the focus is on positive psychology and performance enhancement: reaching for a goal not yet realized, looking for a way to strengthen a positive quality, or hoping to fine-tune existing skills. The scripts accompany a model that has been taught in a number of countries to therapists, coaches, and human resource advisors (Hartung, 2005a). The model combines elements of coaching and psychotherapy. Coaches attend to a client's skills and deficits, look for solutions that are behavioral and strategic, and focus on the present and future while downplaying the past. Psychotherapists, on the other hand, attend to the client's internal experience: emotions, self-talk, beliefs, and other not-so-observable factors. The focus is largely on the past and present.

It follows that the model will be most useful to persons who practice both coaching and psychotherapy. As a coach, the practitioner is familiar with the situation in which the client seeks to perform, whether the client hopes to run faster, lead more effectively, parent better, or study smarter. Competency issues for coaches have been detailed by Hays (2006). As a psychotherapist, the practitioner—it will be assumed—will be comfortable using EMDR in the treatment of traumatic memories and other matters that interfere with the client's personal growth (Shapiro, 2001).

Applications of the Model

There are a number of applications for this model that address the special needs of clients:

- Positive Focus. Many clients with *high achievement goals* will respond favorably to the Standard EMDR Protocol for trauma resolution. The model described in this chapter complements the Standard Protocol in several ways. *The primary focus is less on trauma and more on positive factors,* something relevant to all clients and especially important in performance work. This positive focus will be detailed below, particularly in the context of Phases 1, 2, and 8 of EMDR.

- Time-Limited Work. The model allows EMDR to be adapted to *emergencies, disaster work, and whenever time is limited*. As an example: A young cyclist asked this author to help him prepare for a competition in which he would participate the following day. Clearly, it would have been unwise to follow the Standard EMDR Protocol and initiate desensitization, but we were able to use EMDR with a focus on positive factors that he found beneficial.

- Group Format. The model can also be applied with effectiveness and safety *in a group format*. Even if there were sufficient time, it would be inappropriate to do Standard EMDR processing with a large group where the practitioner could not monitor the experiences of individual participants. This author was once asked to offer "an experience in healing" to a group of 300 high school students, and their teachers, in post-tsunami Sri Lanka. Virtually all had lost loved ones in the disaster. A community leader, Karu, and this author adapted the EMDR group protocol (Jarero, Artigas, & Hartung, 2006) so as to have an exclusively positive intention. Briefly, we first requested colored pencils, asked everyone to sketch purely positive memories and goals, then to add their favorite virtues and dreams, and finally to reflect on what they had drawn and written. When we could determine that all students and faculty were "100% in the positive," we guided them in an extremely careful and slow group Butterfly Hug (Jarero, Artigas, Mauer, López Cano, & Alcalá, 1999), with frequent breaks to resketch their drawings. For an hour we continued, adding in a number of local healing techniques, returning to the positive frequently. The group responded with a profound silence (that surprised everyone, we were later told).

- Fear of Therapy. *Some clients choose not to initiate desensitization.* This author recalls the executive who wanted to feel more comfortable with her peers, but for whom the notion of therapy was a taboo subject. Any client who chooses not to work through past issues can nonetheless benefit to some degree from a purely positive focus. Frequently, the person will opt to use EMDR for reprocessing later; a hypothesis is that the positive focus builds self-confidence, which then allows the person to confront a traumatic memory that earlier had been too frightening.

- Low Affect Tolerance. The performance model can also be applied with *clients not yet ready to undergo EMDR desensitization because of ego fragility, emotional latency*, or any other feature that suggests they cannot yet handle the affective intensity that accompanies EMDR processing. With these clients, a performance focus can be extremely valuable as preparation for future desensitization (and in this sense the model parallels resource development or RDI themes). In this regard the model can be applied to a person with addictions and a history replete with failure, as well as to an individual whose life has been relatively privileged and rewarding. Though this author will refer to high achievers in this chapter, the reader is invited to consider ways to apply the same scripts to persons who are primarily interested in resolving traumatic memories, healing symptoms, and desensitizing triggers, but who are not yet ready to begin this journey.

Enhancing Positive Emotion and Performance With EMDR Script

Phase 1: Clinical History

The usual EMDR clinical history is taken. Several additional themes deserve special attention. The first entries that follow have to do with the principle that "language shapes behavior," a particularly useful theme when we work with persons where the most subtle interferences can compromise performance. Special attention is also given to memories of success, and to memories of failure that sustain present-day triggers.

The Positive Focus or Framework of Enhancing Positive Emotion

Ask Clients to State the Goal in a Positive Way

Look for opportunities to restate a goal. If a client says, "I really would like to get that anxiety down," or speaks of overcoming an obstacle, say the following.

> Say, *"I'd like you to imagine being already free of anxiety. What would you feel instead?"*

_____

_____

_____

> Or say, *"Imagine you have already overcome that obstacle. What is it like for you now?"*

_____

_____

_____

Some clients have great difficulty with this task.

> Say, *"Tell me about a time when you were free of _____* (state the symptom), *or when you felt _____* (state a competing positive emotion). *Go back as far as you can in your life. Take your time. It doesn't have to be any special time, only a time when you felt _____* (state the competing positive emotion). *What is that like as you drift back and recall that special, positive moment?"*

_____

_____

_____

The initial phrasing of a goal need not be detailed or elaborate; it is most important that it be expressed positively, even if vague at first. Clients become more aware of their motivation as EMDR progresses, and fine-tuning or changing a goal statement is common.

Ask Clients to Talk About Successes

Clients (even high achievers) may arrive with a focus on failures. At the beginning of history taking, ask about small and large successes at reaching goals, plans for solutions, and other positive directions.

Say, *"So, you say you have not reached your goal yet. Let me ask if you could tell me about some of the times you have already tried to reach that goal. I already know that you have not been totally successful so far. What I would like you to tell me about now are the times you got close to the goal, and what you did to get down the road toward the goal."*

_____

_____

_____

An alternative might be to say, *"I'm curious about what you did that worked, at least partially. That is, I wonder if you could tell me about what you have done so far that you liked, or that you think you could do again, even though it was not enough to get you all the way to your goal. Go ahead and talk about anything that comes to mind, and I will take notes as I listen."*

_____

_____

_____

After the client responds, say something like the following:

Say, *"I wrote down a list of things as you were speaking, and it seems to me that it contains quite a few ideas and strategies that you might want to keep in mind to do again. Let me go over them and see what else you might recall doing that you liked and would want to keep doing."*

Read the list to the client and discuss.

Ask Clients About What They Have Thought of Doing That They Have Not Yet Tried

The therapist just asked the client to talk about what has worked in the *past*. Now ask about the *future*—about what she has considered as possible solutions, including creative and bold ideas.

Say, *"I am curious about what you have imagined doing to meet your goal, ideas you might not have tried out yet, but that you have thought might be feasible. Go ahead, and don't worry about editing anything for now."*

_____

_____

_____

Wonder aloud with the client about what internal resources might be reflected in this client's report about untested solutions.

Say, *"What internal resources might be reflected in what you have just told me about these untested solutions?"*

_____

_____

This is also a chance to listen to and question superstitions, fears, blocking beliefs, and dilemmas and to consider these for possible future targeting in Phase 4.

Say, *"Tell me about _____ (state any fears, blocking beliefs, or dilemmas the client mentioned above)."*

_____

_____

Teach Clients to Speak in Positive Language

Look for other signs of language that can interfere with success. A simple guide is to listen for "hot" versus "facilitative" words (Harmison, 2006).

Say, *"I have found that in my work it is important to talk about what I call 'hot' words. The reason is that hot words can interfere with performance, presumably because they are related to an overactivated, sympathetic branch (SNS) of the autonomic nervous system—which is to say, the fight-flight response. Fight-flight is accompanied by the emotions of anger, fear, and anxiety. While these emotions are useful in emergencies, and can improve performance in the short run, they compromise performance when they continue for too long, or are otherwise excessive. Hot words include no, never, always, must, fear, failure, perfection, resentment, and so forth. The point is not to eliminate these words entirely from your vocabulary, but rather to notice them when they appear and to recognize that they have power in the short term, and also that they may interfere with success when overused. In this case, it would be wise to replace them or at least supplement them with words that facilitate optimal performance. Do any of those words sound similar to the ones that you use?"*

_____

_____

_____

_____

To offer your client alternatives, say the following:

Say, *"Any idea about words that you could use instead?"*

_____

_____

At this point some clients will need to be coached on words that produce positive motivators and physiological coherence, concepts endorsed by peak performance consultants in the fields of sports, leadership, and the performing arts (Berman & Bradt, 2006; Hamilton & Robson, 2006; Harmison, 2006; Hays, 2002, 2006; Hays & Brown, 2004).

Say, *"Some of the words considered positive motivators are yes, want, will, passion, and confidence. Others are curious, dedicated, joyful, fun, and natural. Still others are deserving, abundance, spontaneous, and resilient. Can you think of any more?"*

_____

_____

When the client uses positive words spontaneously, ask that they be repeated.

Say, *"A short time ago you said* _____ (state something positive, e.g., 'I really love this sport'). *I wonder if you would say that again, and this time notice how it feels inside of you?"*

This simple experiment is done often enough for the client to feel the difference between negative and positive words. In other cases it is helpful to explain further.

Say, *"We find that the way we talk has a lot to do with how we feel and act. I wonder if you would try something out, which would be to say 'Yes I do,' and then 'No I don't,' and to notice any difference you feel as you say these phrases. What do you notice?"*

Most clients quickly get the point about language-shaping behavior, along with insights about their habitual way of talking.

Contextual Words

Some words can have a positive or negative impact depending on context, or degree of emphasis. The word "stress," for example, can be negative ("distress") or positive ("eustress"). Question whether a certain word challenges the client in healthy ways, or whether it causes damage (Everly & Lating, 2003; Selye, 1974). The following is an example of a way to introduce this concept (or use your own example that is more relevant to your client):

Say, *"For example, one athlete I worked with was unable to compete in an event because of '. . . too much contentment. I could not get my adrenaline going,' she said. In subsequent sessions, she practiced ways to feel physically energized after waiting for a long period of time before being called to perform. In a bicycling sprint, a competitive spirit and thoughts of winning might be useful, whereas the same attitudes could well interfere with a triathlon, a public speech, or an interview."*

When in doubt, we can question clients to see what their physiological response is to a word, how they personalize it, and what the context means.

Say, *"I notice you talk about how you get* _____ (state the words that the client uses such as stressed and competitive) *just before an event. What I cannot figure out is how these words make you feel, and whether they help you to be more successful, or whether they get in your way. I know that* _____ (state the word) *by itself, for example, is neither good nor bad: sometimes it helps us and sometimes it doesn't. Let's talk about this a bit to find out what it means to you."*

Failures and Triggers

After an initial positive focus, ask the client to recount failed attempts to reach the goal. The purpose is solely to identify present-day *triggers*. In performance enhancement, a trigger is often the *environment* or *demand situation* in which the client will be *challenged* to realize a goal.

Explain the concept of triggers to the client and look for specific examples.

> Say, *"I'm going to ask you to think about what is going on around you and within you when you feel those strong negative emotions that get in your way when you are trying to accomplish what you want to do. Let's work together to identify as much as we can of what gets you to feel the way you do. You don't all of a sudden get _____ (state the negative emotion(s)) for no reason when you _____ (mention the situation that triggers the negative emotion and thought, such as taking an exam, performing in front of a crowd, and so forth). Rather, there are certain things that trigger the feeling. Sometimes it's not easy to spot these triggers, so let's take some time to see what we can figure out today. When you think of the last time you _____ (repeat the situation), what do you recall?"*

_____

_____

Sometimes we need to be even more specific, as in this case with an academic overachiever.

> Say, *"For example, think of an academic overachiever who studies hard and is very self-critical of any grades less than perfection. She has twice failed to pass her licensing exam as a psychologist. She has just reported that she begins to sweat as soon as she touches a page from a practice exam. Using what we call the Float-Back Technique, I asked her the following: 'You know logically that a piece of paper is really just a piece of paper. The reason it makes you sweat is because for you it's no longer just paper, but rather what we call a trigger and things can trigger us, in this sense, only because they are somehow connected to our past. So what I am going to do now is invite you to float back into your past to see what memories come up that explain why the paper has become a trigger for you. Okay, look back at the scene of the last time you took the exam, and see what you can recall about what you were thinking and feeling . . . and now go back even further to find other times when you felt this same feeling, or something very similar. The reason we are looking for these memories is so that we can find out why a piece of paper can cause you to get sweaty so quickly and so automatically. Later on in our work, you can decide whether you want to target these memories with EMDR so that a piece of paper becomes just a piece of paper again, and so that you get back your control over things like an exam paper, and other things in the exam room. Do you have any questions about this?"*

_____

_____   _____

_____

Now say to your client the following:

Say, *"Now, let's try the Float-Back procedure with the situation that we just spoke about that triggers you. You know logically that _____ (state the trigger) is _____ (state what happens in response to the trigger). The reason it makes you _____ (state the negative response) is because it is no longer _____ (state the trigger) but rather what we call a trigger and things can trigger us, in this sense, only because they are sometimes connected to our past. So what I am going to do now is invite you to float back into your past to see what memories come up that explain why _____ (state the trigger) has become a trigger for you. Okay, look back at the scene of the last time you _____ (state the thought and affect), and see what you can recall about what you were thinking and feeling . . . and now go back even further to find other times when you felt this same feeling, or something very similar. The reason we are looking for these memories is so that we can find out why _____ (state the trigger) can cause you to _____ (state what happens to the client) so quickly and so automatically. Later on in our work, you can decide whether you want to target these memories with EMDR so that a _____ (state the trigger) becomes just a _____ (state the trigger) again, and so that you get back your control over things _____ (state the task the client wants to accomplish). Do you have any questions about this?"*

Always Return to the Positive Frame

To get the discussion back on a positive track, say the following:

Say, *"By the way, let's assume that you can work through these memories and put them in the past where they should be. Imagine now, if you will, how will it be for you the next time you _____ (state the next time the event occurs, such as repeating an exam or performing in the next event) and do NOT get triggered."*

_____

_____

_____

Continue the earlier example (or use your own).

Say, *"For example, my client who wanted to be able to take her exam said: 'Okay, I'm going to risk saying that I would like to take the exam with a smile. There, I've said it. After studying so much, you'd think I deserved at least that!'"*

Most clients find several triggers. Some therapists rate each trigger with the SUD scale, and use these baseline measures for later comparisons.

Phase 2: Preparation

Variations in Phase 2 to Enhance Positive Emotion

Informed Consent

At this juncture, most clients are content with a very simplified explanation of EMDR trauma work. In any case, whatever you say in this step to inform or instruct a client may well be forgotten by the time it becomes relevant. Therefore, it will be helpful to repeat information about desensitization later when it becomes relevant.

> Say, *"I'd like to talk a little bit about how we use EMDR to deal with traumatic memories and triggers. We're not going to do that yet and we might decide not to do it at all. But, as I've been saying, it seems that you're having trouble reaching your goal. Not because you haven't prepared for it. On the contrary, you're very well prepared, you rehearse and practice, and yet when you finally get to the event, something gets in the way of your performance. Well, that 'something,' as we have been saying, is most likely coming from your past, perhaps a memory of failure or something like that. You know what I'm talking about, because we already visited some of those memories when I asked you to float back to see where those strong feelings of _____ (state the client's feelings) come from when you think of the last time you faced one of your events. Well, in my experience, EMDR is simply the best way to fix those memories—to revisit them and to resolve them, or to desensitize them. I also said that this explains why we get triggered sometimes. So, another way to put this is to say that we can use EMDR to take the power out of those triggers. In your case, that would mean that _____ (fit the explanation to the situation, such as, a piece of paper would just become a piece of paper again)."*

> Say, *"If you do decide to use EMDR in this way, I will accompany you as you go back to those old memories. You will probably feel some of the same emotion you felt when the memory first took place, but we will go very slowly so that you can pace yourself and handle whatever comes up. I will also give you more information when we actually decide to do some memory work. For now, though, let's go back to being more focused on the positive, and on your goals."*

_____

_____

_____

Test the Bilateral Movements

Testing out the optional bilateral stimulation (eye movements, taps, sounds, mechanical devices) is done with a slightly different emphasis in performance work.

> Say, *"Now I'd like to show you some of the bilateral movements that we will be using. We'll be using these movements to help you develop more of the positive qualities that will help you to reach your goals. We use these back-and-forth movements when we work on memories, but we're not going to use them in that way just yet."*

> Say, *"So, there are different ways to do these movements. For example, I could move my hand back and forth in front of you as you follow with your eyes; that's what the eye movement in EMDR means. Or you might prefer to have me tap your hands, or to make sounds, first on one side, then the other. You also might want to tap yourself like this (demonstrate the Butterfly Hug on yourself briefly). How about if we start with my showing you the eye movements?"*

_____

_____

_____

The therapist then demonstrates the bilateral movements.

Renewed Statement of the Positive or Ideal Future Goal

There are many reasons for revisiting the positive goal from time to time.

> Say, *"Let's talk about the positive or ideal future goal that we spoke of earlier. Do you remember what you said?"*

_____

_____

_____

Note the reasons to revisit the positive goal: clients tend to talk in negative terms, so they can be helped to think in more positive and facilitative ways; motivation is often complex, in part because dilemmas are present, and in part because the unresolved traumatic past gets in the way of even contemplating success; some clients set goals that compromise achievement (*"I will* win"). One keynote speaker initially said during clinical history, "If I don't stop being so nervous in public I'm going to look for another career!"

> Say, *"Let's revisit your goal. Originally, you said that _____ (state the original goal and any others stated). How does that sound and feel to you now? And now that we've talked about the power of words, would you like to modify or change your goal?"*

_____

_____

_____

Focus on making sure that the goal is stated in a positive manner. For further suggestions on how to become more facile with this way of thinking, see Lombardo and Eichinger (2002). For example, when a client insisted that "winning" and "beating the competition" was the only goal she could accept, her therapist said:

> Say, *"I'd like to comment on what you just said about 'beating the competition.' Imagine, if you will, that there are 10 people in this race, 9 plus you. Each one has a personal coach, and each one is working toward beating the competition. Since only 1 can win, it seems to me that the other 9 will have to suffer some kind of defeat. This is why I wonder if you might look for another way to set your sights. Of course, if you win, you would reach your goal. But even if you came in second place you would fail to meet that goal. Do you see my point? Why set yourself up for potential failure?"*

_____

_____

_____

This client then talked about being able to feel good whether she wins the race or not

Client: "I remember that I began with 'I will win!' Egad, that sounds weird now, after I reflect on it. Tell me what you think of this, 'I move through my pain.' Hmmm, that's it, that's exactly it. It feels right, it's not tied to having to win, and it's something I know I can do better. I can win even if I don't win."

Skills Inventory

As mentioned, the model works best when the practitioner is a coach–psychotherapist. In this author's experience, skills tend to be ignored by therapists, and overemphasized by coaches. As with most issues, skills are necessary but not sufficient. Begin by asking *what skills the client already has*; then *inventory the skills* necessary for success; and that leads to an assessment of the *skills that the person has yet to learn*.

> Say, *"Well, you like the goal you've set for yourself, and I would say that it sounds feasible to me too. It's realistic, specific, and positive. So, how about if we look at what skills are required to meet the goal, and then do a bit of a survey of the skills you already have to get there? It's been said that success is part perspiration and part inspiration. Let's talk now about the perspiration part. What have you done so far to get yourself ready?"*

_____

_____

_____

_____

_____

_____

Clearly, clients need to be practiced in the discipline(s) in which they want to be successful, whether that is leadership, parenting, public speaking, athletics, or any other area. Not only do clients need to know their disciplines, the therapists need to think about the following questions: "What is the minimal for me to know about the client's field of discipline?" and "How much information is optimal for me to have."

With elite athletics, the practitioner will probably work with a sports coach. In leadership, it is essential to know about challenges and realities, and how to measure leadership qualities. For clients wanting to be authors, does the practitioner need to know how to find a publisher, or only to know where to refer for the answer? If a professional presumes to teach parenting skills, teamwork, interviewing, or physical fitness, does he also need to be a good parent or team leader, interview well, and be physically fit? There is still no consensus on answers to these questions any more than there is still no standard definition of optimal coaching, so the question of "best practices," in this context, must be answered by the practitioner.

Redefine the Goal as Goals Can Change

The purpose of redefining the goal from time to time is to capitalize on clients' increasing awareness of where they want to go, what might have kept them from getting there, and what they still need to do to optimize success. Once clients look realistically at their available skills, the goal may well be updated to reflect this new awareness.

> Say, *"You have taken a hard look at what you might need to work on as far as the skills you will need to accomplish your goal. With that in mind, let me give you another chance to look at the goals you set, and see if you might like to modify them again. If you do, that's fine. It's also fine if you want to keep the goals you set a few minutes ago. By the way, do you recall the words you used to describe your goals for today? What I wrote was _____ (state the goal). You then added _____ (state what was added). What do you think now?"*

_____

_____   _____

_____

Develop Positive Qualities *Related to the Goal(s)*

The focus now is on qualities that will assist clients in reaching the goal. The idea is to assist clients in feeling 100% positive about their goal(s). Underlying this step is the assumption introduced above that most high achievers who are skilled but who struggle with reaching their goals suffer from excessive anxiety, which is to say that their sympathetic nervous system (SNS) is overly active (Wolpe, 1969). Rarely, the high achiever is overresponsive in a parasympathetic way, which often indicates depression.

For most of these clients, then, the solution involves greater parasympathetic activity (PNS). We are not speaking *only* of stimulating parasympathetic responding, however, but rather of producing a balance or synchrony between these two branches of the autonomous nervous system, a sort of partnership between activity on the one hand, and calm or centeredness on the other. This physiological balance between these two important functions underlies the concept of cardiac coherence, as described in the Heartmath literature (McCraty, Atkinson, Tomasino, & Bradley, 2006). Cardiac coherence has been studied extensively and shown to correlate with a wide range of cognitive, emotional, mental, and performance indicators of health and optimal functioning. Cardiac coherence, fortunately, can also be learned and practiced. The team at the Heartmath Institute has developed a heart-based breathing strategy that will be introduced below. This strategy facilitates the SNS–PNS balance (or coherence) that can serve as a physiological basis for achievement. The focus now is not on the goal, but rather on the means necessary to achieve the goal. "Means" are positive qualities, internal resources, positive emotions, cognitive tools, attitudes, personal strengths, and so forth. The examples that follow will clarify.

As a therapist, watch and assess the impact of what the client does by looking for signs of physiological balance: deeper and more regular breathing, slower heart rate, a calmer expression, more positive words, and so on. As this author has noted, however, these examples just cited can be either under- or over-practiced. Too little calm can interfere with performance, but *too much calm* can also interfere! It may be worth repeating that we are seeking an SNS–PNS balance, not simply increased PNS activity. Because this balance can be difficult, if not impossible for most of us to detect simply by reflecting on our bodies, Heartmath manufactures a biofeedback device named the Freeze Framer. The Freeze Framer reads the client's heartbeat, heart rhythm, and coherence scores via a monitor placed on the fingertip or earlobe, and then displays the data on a laptop screen. Clients then observe the changes in scores as coherence exercises are practiced (see http://www.Heartmath.com; research articles are available at http://www.Heartmath.org).

If the client speaks of qualities that are too close to the goal, such as "*I am confident* that I can approach the exam with a peaceful feeling," ask the client to modify, distance, or even *distort* the quality until it produces a positive impact on the client. An example of this would be to restate the sentence more simply: "I feel confident when I think of the exam." The purpose here is *only to enable the client to arrive at a 100% positive experience,* whatever it takes.

To guide questioning, many practitioners use Arnold Lazarus's (1989) BASIC I.D., where each letter refers to one set of information about the client (behavior, affect, sensation, interpersonal, drugs, diet, or biological factors).

BASIC I.D.

These script examples follow the BASIC I.D. acronym.

B or Behavior as in BASIC I.D.

This script exemplifies how the therapist might teach the client to practice the very critical habit of optimal breathing to produce a state of system coherence just discussed. The value of posture changes is also discussed.

Say, *"I'd like to help you now to identify the positive qualities that will help you to get to your goal. We will spend as much time on this step as you need. When you find that you feel really good—let's say as close to 100% positive as you can—then I will give you a chance to think again about working toward the goal. I'll help you do this by reminding you of the triggers or challenges you told me about before. So that will be a sort of test to see how ready you are to go out and actually work on the goal. Does that make sense?"*

_____

_____

Say, *"Then we will repeat this process. You can work on feeling really good, then pairing up that feeling with the thought of one of the triggers. What happens is that your good feeling state will eventually wear down the power of the trigger, so that it doesn't produce the anxiety it did before. This happens physiologically, sort of automatically, basically like a reflex. The more you practice this, the weaker the triggers will get. What do you think so far?"*

_____

_____

Say, *"Okay, good. I'd like to start by talking about a behavior you do all the time, which is breathing. First, I'd like you simply to pay attention to how you are breathing without changing how you do it. Good. Just notice. Breathe naturally for a few breaths. I wonder if you could now continue to breathe normally and count the second you breathe in, and then count the second you breathe out. You can say one-thousand-one, one-thousand-two, and so forth. Okay, are you ready to inhale?"*

Say, *"Now just count, one-thousand-one, one-thousand-two. Okay. Now do the same as you exhale. What number did you get to on the inhale? And on the exhale?"*

_____

_____

_____

At this point, clients may express a new awareness of how they breathe and this feedback in itself can help, albeit only temporarily, to motivate the person to breathe more optimally.

Then say, *"What we find is that the exhale seems to be more effective for bringing a sense of calm. Do you recall when we talked about the _____ (state the negative affect) you feel? Well, when we are _____ (state the negative affect), we tend to breathe in a way that is shallow, irregular, and inefficient. When we are _____ (state the negative affect), we also spend more time inhaling than exhaling."*

It is helpful to begin with breath training and not give specific instructions at first, however, but simply ask clients to become aware of breathing (as above). Most clients will spontaneously enter into a deeper and more regular breathing pattern simply by paying attention to their breathing, so the therapist does not have to do more than ask questions at first. This allows clients to follow their own rhythm, and empowers them to develop their own resources. Since most clients will inhale longer than they exhale, there is usually an opportunity here to have clients practice longer exhales. These longer exhales, along with a more ordered respiratory rhythm, will produce a deeper sense of calm (while interfering with anxiety) through a natural physiological process called respiratory sinus arrhythmia. If clients are interested, at this point you can explain as follows:

> Say, *"The inhale is thought of as a sympathetic function* (designed to produce activity), *and exhaling as parasympathetic* (for calming and rest). *The goal here is to reach a balance between these two branches of the autonomic nervous system via increasing parasympathetic function with a more extended exhale."*

For further information, consult McCraty et al., 2006.

Other practitioners teach diaphragmatic breathing, because individuals with anxiety-related problems often show signs of hyperventilation or "overbreathing" (Holt & Andrews, 1989). When they are stressed, they may take rapid and shallow breaths in the region of the upper chest, disrupting the body's oxygen and carbon dioxide balance. Diaphragmatic breathing exercises can reduce hyperventilation by teaching the client to breathe slowly, regularly, and with the abdomen when they experience tension or stress.

> Say, *"Have you noticed that sometimes when you get anxious or fearful _____* (or any other negative affect), *you may take rapid and shallow breaths in the region of the upper chest. Did you know that this disrupts your body's natural balance between oxygen and carbon dioxide that is of crucial importance for your feeling of well-being? There is a technique that we use called diaphragmatic breathing that can help you with this overbreathing or hyperventilation. The way we do this is by learning to breathe slowly, regularly, and with your abdomen any time you feel tension or stress. Instead of teaching you, however, I am going to ask you to simply pay attention to how you are breathing now. To show you what I mean, I would like you now to continue breathing just as you have been, but now count as you inhale, and then count as you exhale. You can use one-thousand-one, . . ."*

Most performance clients will inhale longer (because of their relatively overactive sympathetic activity). As they notice the difference in the time they count between inhale and exhale, they naturally begin to modify breathing so that the numbers become more equalized. Not only does this approach empower the client, and increase the likelihood that the client will practice this later between sessions, but it also allows for personalizing the breathing practice. There is no guarantee that teaching a prescribed breathing procedure will be useful for any particular client; even though the procedure may be useful for some persons, there is no guarantee that it will be effective for everyone. In any case, if the client needs help with this procedure, the therapist can suggest additional ways for the client to become aware of breathing and hence to make helpful modifications.

For example, say the following:

> Say, *"Let me suggest something else for you. This time as you inhale, notice where your breath goes and follow it as you take it in through your throat, into your lungs, and now notice how far down it goes into your stomach. There is no need to push it or force it, just notice where it goes."*

This increased awareness will often be sufficient to enable the client to breathe spontaneously with the stomach and diaphragm. The therapist can also encourage the client, if necessary, to breathe more deeply into his or her stomach, to slow breathing, and to match inhale and exhale times. No matter how effective this procedure is, however, people generally are unable to sustain conscious patterned breathing for more than a minute or so at a time. To help a person to sustain optimal breathing, while adding elements to increase positive emotion in the process, the author finds more and more coaches relying on biofeedback to supplement the client's natural awareness of breathing. The author recommends the biofeedback system engineered by the Heartmath Institute and available on their Web site. This system, utilizing information about a client's heart rate, heart rate variability, and cardiac coherence, is particularly effective and user-friendly, as well as scientifically grounded. Whether one employs their biofeedback system or not, however, the breathing procedure pioneered by Heartmath can be learned and taught quickly (Childre & Martin, 1999).

Since we are still in the behavior category, we can consider other ways to help the client to utilize behavior to strengthen positive qualities.

Say, *"Can you show me how you would look if you were ready to _____ (state the goal)? Okay. How does that feel?"*

_____

_____

_____

Say, *"What would you like to change about your posture so that you feel even more the way you would like to feel?"*

_____

_____

_____

The therapist can make suggestions until clients begin to hold their head level and balanced over their shoulders, hold their hands and arms with strength, and sit or stand with confidence.

Say, *"It is often helpful to begin by holding your head straight and level as you think about balancing it over your shoulders. How does that feel now?"*

_____

_____

Say, *"Now what if you held your hands and arms in a way that focuses on their strength like when you _____ (state appropriate example for this client). How does that feel?"*

_____

_____

Say, *"Now what happens as you sit or stand up straight with your shoulders relaxed but back and your feet firmly planted on the ground? What is that like?"*

_____

_____

Ask how the new posture feels so as to measure the impact of the change.

Say, *"As you change your posture so that you feel more the way that you would like to feel, how do you feel with this new posture?"*

_____

_____

_____

Say, *"As you feel your new posture, notice what it is like to do one of your breathing exercises, too?"*

_____

_____

_____

Following the pattern of these examples, look for other ways to help the client to utilize behavior to develop and strengthen the qualities that will facilitate performance. Then continue inventorying other aspects of the BASIC I.D. acronym.

A or Affect (Emotion) as in BASIC I.D.

Let us look now at one example of a script designed to teach the client to focus on positive emotion.

Say, *"Now, what special feeling or emotion would you most like to experience as one of those positive qualities we have been discussing? Perhaps an emotion that goes along with your breathing?"*

_____

_____

_____

Many people will come up with their own positive emotion. If they have trouble, say the following:

Say, *"You know there have been studies conducted by the Heartmath Institute (McCraty et al., 2006), and they have found that the positive emotions most conducive to coherence are appreciation, gratitude, and love. They also found that when high achievers reflected on a moment of personal excellence, with a focus on a totally positive experience, they produced high heart coherence."*

S or Sensation as in BASIC I.D.

This does not mean, "Where do you feel the emotion?" as is said in the Standard EMDR Protocol, but rather refers to the five senses (with the visual getting its own category next).

Say, *"Now, let's talk about the five senses. Bring up any sensation you would like that helps you to deepen that feeling of _____ (state chosen affect(s)). Sensations that go along with your deep breathing could be a sound, a feel of something, a taste, or a smell. Some people like the gentle swaying of a tree, the feel of sand under their*

*feet, or warmth in some part of the body. What sensations go along
with your deep breathing?"*

I or Imagery as in BASIC I.D.

Say, *"Now I would like to invite you to visualize yourself with a picture
that deepens that feeling even further. It could be a symbol, or a color.
Make it your own. Tell me what you see."*

Some clients will find that beginning this process is difficult, so the therapist
can make direct suggestions at first.

Say, *"For example, what color represents the way you would like to
feel?"*

Say, *"Okay. Where is the color* _____ (state the chosen color) *in
your picture? Might you want to visualize it in the form of* _____
(state examples of objects or nature that represents the color)? *You
can decide. The important thing is to see what helps you to feel the
way you want to feel. What else do you see?"*

Say, *"Perhaps, you see a scene. Are you in the scene?"*

Say, *"Is anyone else or anything else in it?"*

Say, *"What does the color* _____ (state color) *do as you look at the
picture?"*

Say, *"How do you feel now with that color?"*

Say, *"Would you like to change it in any way?"*

_____

_____

In the present context, the term visualization is meant to serve as a means to *establish* a positive emotional and sensory state. Visualization can be used in another way; that is as a specific performance strategy frequently utilized by athletes and other high performers. It has been found that visualizing ourselves going through certain acrobatic or other movements utilizes the same neural circuits that will be employed when we actually perform the physical movement later on. Apparently, the circuits become more efficient (which is different from exercising the related muscles).

Note: This kind of visualization practice should be done only when the person is *already* experiencing a positive emotional and sensory state, that is, without excessive sympathetic activation.

C or Cognition as in BASIC I.D.

This category includes language, belief, self-talk, logic, and various forms of verbal and vocal expression, as discussed above in Phase 1.

Say, *"Another area that is helpful for us to discuss is cognition. Cognition includes the type of language, belief, self-talk, logic, and various forms of verbal and vocal expression that we say to ourselves that we spoke about earlier. For instance, one woman sought help because she could not get the promotion she craved. She began to realize that others saw her competitive spirit as aggressive, and as undermining team morale. It was suggested to her that she could substitute being recognized for those words of competitiveness and aggression instead and then she was asked to drift into the future and imagine being promoted or recognized in some other way and listen for positive words that come to her. Quite spontaneously she said, 'The world is abundant. I have abundance. I accept what is offered, and I am grateful, and in turn I share what I have. There is truly abundance in the world.' What is the belief or self-talk that you find yourself saying that may be getting in the way of your moving forward with your goal?"*

_____

_____

This does not have to be either complex or logical. When the client comes up with a more helpful verbalization, the therapist could say the following:

Say, *"Okay, now could you repeat the word several times?"*

_____

_____

Say, *"Great. Now, how about saying that more softly? What happens when you do that?"*

_____

_____

Say, *"And now, try it more slowly. What happens now?"*

_____

_____

Say, *"Is this one of the key words that you would like to strengthen so that it becomes more natural, familiar, and personal?"*

_____

_____

Say, *"Okay, now what happens as you say the word again and this time breathe into it?"*

_____

_____

Say, *"Is there something that you would like to change about it, or add to it so that you can feel more the way you want to feel?"*

_____

_____

Remember to check frequently to assess the impact of what the client is doing. Subsequently, you will ask clients to report how close to 100% positive they are feeling.

Say, *"Now when you say the word, how close to 100% are you feeling?"*

_____

_____

If the client is not yet at 100% positive, continue enhancing the positive using any strategies from the BASIC I.D.

I or Interpersonal as in BASIC I.D.

Some therapists worry that clients who include other people while developing this special state are promoting codependency; this is not necessarily true. The important thing is to help the client to feel fully positive, and to do what is necessary to get to that place. Later, in the protocol the client will take other action that has the benefit of strengthening independence and self-reliance.

D or Diet and Drugs as in BASIC I.D.

The "D" is for diet and drugs and also covers other aspects of health, medical condition, biology, chemical use, and so forth. It is recommended that a careful medical examination be conducted (either in Phase 1 or now) to rule out any biological or medical contributions to anxiety and underperformance. Some athletes, for example, are also anorexic and undernourished, or use performance-enhancing drugs that have paradoxical effects. Ask your clients directly and explain some of the effects of dietary and nutritional habits.

Say, *"Diet and nutrition can help or hinder performance. While one runner may find a dose of caffeine to increase performance in the short term, others may find that too much coffee generates a feeling of hyperactivity. Some people consume natural herbal stimulants. Their intention might be good, but they may find these supplements actually hurt them. Let me ask you for example, do you take any of these: ginkgo biloba, ginseng, gotu kola, guarana, ma huang, or yohimbine? How about perfumes? Do you notice that certain scents affect you in negative ways? In general, what do you eat or drink to make yourself feel different, either calmer or more energized?"*

Notice that the general format of the protocol, up to this point, could be followed by someone who does not practice, or even know about, EMDR. So far the focus has been on general principles of performance enhancement, coaching strategies, and techniques such as the Heartmath exercise that can be considered to be self-standing resources as well as tools in the service of EMDR.

What follows is how the dynamic EMDR method, including the classical application of EMDR to the resolution of traumatic memories, can be used to enrich the Enhancing Positive Emotion Protocol. Also, from this point on, several assumptions will be made: that the reader or user of the protocol is acquainted with EMDR; has experience in treating traumatized persons; and is willing to adjust the basic EMDR model in order to apply it in the subsequent steps. For further introductory comments on EMDR adaptations, see chapter 4 of Hartung & Galvin (2003).

The Ideal State

Strengthen the Ideal State With Eye Movements or Other Alternating Bilateral Movements (Similar to Safe Place)

Do not begin this step until the client is in a 100% positive state at this point. There is a slight but real risk for the client to shift out of the positive and into the negative, as many EMDR practitioners report while conducting the safe place exercise with their clients. If clients are first able to say that "I feel 100% positive," there is only a slight risk of having traumatic memory channels triggered by the eye movements or other bilateral stimulation (BLS).

Say, *"Tell me about the state that you are in now. Would you say that you are 100% in your positive state now? If not, how much?"*

_____

_____

_____

Once clients report feeling 100% positive, begin with a single bilateral movement, which means one eye movement from side to side, one pair of taps, or one pair of alternating bilateral sounds. There is no real down side to this caution—and it prevents much hardship because the alternative (having to slow down after starting too fast) is often too late, as some clients will have already decided that EMDR is too powerful and not for them.

Say, *"Okay, I am going to begin with a single bilateral movement. What do you notice?"*

_____

_____

_____

Stop immediately after the single movement, ask clients to take a deep breath to activate parasympathetic functioning further, ask what was noticed, and ensure that they are still in a positive state.

Say, *"Now, take a deep breath. What did you get?"*

_____

_____

_____

After clients respond briefly, say the following:

Say, *"How close to 100% positive are you now?"*

_____

_____

_____

If clients have accessed traumatic material and report less than 100% positive, stop the bilateral movements and spend more time developing the positive without bilateral movements, using strategies just described. Once clients are again at 100% positive, resume the bilateral movement and continue until the client reports no further change.

Some therapists prefer to have the client run a video or movie of the *next time* the client performs, and, if the feeling is still 100% positive, to do several sets of bilateral stimulation, repeating these as long as the positive feeling deepens and strengthens. If this technique is employed, it is recommended that it *not* be limited to visualization alone, but that the therapist includes other aspects of the BASIC I.D.

Say, *"I would invite you now to imagine being in this 100% positive state while you visualize yourself the next time you are asked to perform. I suggest you make up a movie of the next time, beginning with the first step in the process. And as you see yourself going through each step, continue to notice how you feel, and where you feel that in your body. Also whisper or say your positive words from time to time. Look for any colors or lights. Listen to sounds around you. See who might be there with you. Notice any smells or tastes that help you to feel even more positive. Anything and everything that helps you to deepen the positive feeling as you see yourself performing the next time. Go ahead and do that now. When you feel 100% in the positive, let me know, and I will do some bilateral stimulation to help you deepen that experience. Or, if you prefer, you can cross your arms over your chest and do bilateral taps on yourself, first one side, then the other."*

If offered, many clients will prefer to tap themselves with a Butterfly Hug. Besides increasing the client's sense of self-efficacy, this procedure teaches the clients a technique that can be practiced between sessions.

Say, *"What was that like for you?"*

_____

_____

Anchor the Positive State Once the Person Is at 100% Positive

An anchor or cue is usually a touch or sound that the person pairs with the special positive state. Later, when the person remembers to repeat the touch or sound, the body, which has learned to pair this with the positive state, will—to some degree at least—reproduce the positive feeling again. An example of associative learning, this method can be practiced repeatedly at this point to strengthen the bond between the anchor and the positive state. Obviously, we use the anchor *only* if the client remains 100% positive, otherwise, when the person reactivates the anchor at a future time, the body will remember the less-than-positive state.

Say, *"Some people like to develop a kind of cue or reminder at this point so that they can return to this positive state whenever they want.*

The cue or reminder I am talking about is a touch on the hand, or a word, or something else that you can do right now to link up with this positive experience. If you would like you could do that. What do you think?"

Say, *"Okay then, I will let you pick your reminder—which could be touching your hand or a finger, or coming up with a pleasant word like peace or calm—whatever feels right to you. What works for you?"*

Check for appropriateness. It would be inappropriate for an athlete who uses both hands for an event to touch one hand with the other; however, it might work to touch the thumbs softly to the index fingers. And the word "win" might produce too much adrenaline and a sympathetic response when used during a competition, whereas "flow" might produce just what the person needs.

Say, *"Let's check to see how that will work for you. Think of a time when you could use your reminder. How does that work for you as you think of yourself doing it while engaging in _____ (state the task)?"*

Caution: Subtle triggers often appear during this procedure. One client slipped out of 100% positive simply because the word perform was used, which was a trigger for her. Another person, connected to the Heartmath biofeedback device, produced chaotic heart waves when he said, "I see myself writing my dissertation . . . now sitting in front of the committee . . . now answering questions about the statistics . . ."
If and when this happens say the following:

Say, *"Well, this is great news, because we now know about one more trigger, something we can work on later. Nice work! Let me make a note of this for the future and put it to the side for now. So, let's go back to that 100% positive state. Just leave out any thought or picture or word that gets in your way, and concentrate only on those that allow you to feel 100% positive. Let's start with behavior again. Show me the posture that best brings you back to that feeling that you experienced before now, notice the positive emotion and see what you would call it. And now notice where you feel it in your body."*

Test: Link the Ideal State Visually to a Trigger (This Discussion Is Based on the Work of Pavlov as Described by Wolpe in His 1969 Text on Systematic Desensitization)

When the client is definitely in a 100% positive state, ask the client to pair the positive state with the trigger, then to measure any disturbance with the SUD scale.

Say, *"I would like you to notice this pleasant experience you are having as you look at me. And now I will ask you to imagine yourself*

_____ (state the trigger of the issue). *On a scale of 0 to 10, where 0 is no disturbance or neutral and 10 is the highest disturbance you can imagine, how disturbing does it feel now?"*

0	1	2	3	4	5	6	7	8	9	10
(no disturbance)								(highest disturbance)		

Say, *"Go with that."*

Do BLS.

Check the Result of Linking the Ideal State to the Trigger

Say, *"Now on a scale from 0 through 10 where 0 means that the trigger does not produce any anxiety whatsoever and 10 represents the most disturbance, what do you get?"*

0	1	2	3	4	5	6	7	8	9	10
(no disturbance)								(highest disturbance)		

If the SUD score reported is 0, it means that the ideal state is stronger (the trigger does not produce any anxiety whatsoever). In this case, do more eye or other bilateral movements to further strengthen the ideal state, and somatic coherence.

Say, *"Go with that."*

Do BLS.

If the SUD score is greater than 0, it means that the trigger is stronger. In this case, there are at least seven options. The first six options can be dealt with in the here and now in Phase 2. First, the procedures for managing options one through six.

Option #1: Your client may need to develop and practice skills

Say, *"What skill would you need to handle this challenge?"*

_____

_____

_____

If the client reports needing to develop a skill further, go back and work on the skill needed as above.

Option #2: Check for any need to redefine the goal further

Say, *"Do we need to redefine your goal further so it is even clearer than it is now? Might that be why you are having difficulty feeling comfortable when you think about actually going ahead with what you want to do?"*

_____

___ _____

_____

If so, go back to redefine the goal. See above.

Option #3: See if positive qualities need to be strengthened further

Say, *"Do any of the positive qualities that we have been working with such as _____ (state positive qualities) need further strengthening?"*

_____

_____

_____

If so, continue with the positive strengthening.

Say, *"Imagine the quality _____ and think of another time that you felt this way. When and what was that?"*

_____

_____

_____

Say, *"Go with that."*

Do BLS.

Continue working with strengthening the positive quality until the client can give a 0 on the SUDs while revisiting the trigger.

Option #4: Evaluate client motivation

Some clients at this point will talk about pursuing goals that are more important to others than to themselves; if their goal is to please others, or to meet some outside standard, they might well realize that this produces some of their anxiety and it would be helpful to seek other, more internal, motivation.

Say, *"Let's talk about your goals. Are they more important to others or are they more important to you?"*

_____

_____

_____

If they are more important to others, consider saying the following:

Say, *"If your goal is to please others or to meet some outside standard, how does that make you FEEL?"*

_____

_____

_____

If they do not make the connection between trying to meet some other criteria and feeling emotions that interfere with performance, consider saying the following:

Say, *"Often, when we are forced to meet other standards and not our own, it is a denial of who we are in a very basic way and can make us very distressed. Could that be going on with you?"*

_____

_____

Say, *"Go with that."*

Do BLS.

Option #5: Check for secondary gain

Say, *"What would it mean if you were able to handle _____ (state the trigger)? How would your life be different?"*

_____

_____

_____

Option #6: Check for dilemma

It was mentioned above that a goal does not need to be stated perfectly at first. Much of EMDR processing of performance issues, in fact, uncovers the client's ambivalence, hesitancy, or other yes–no or approach–avoidance conflicts. Whenever these appear, a dilemma procedure can be employed with usually quick and excellent results. Note that dilemmas are generally tied to the unresolved past, so using this procedure requires providing additional informed consent to the client.

Say, *"Hmmm. I hear you talking about this trigger from two sides, as it were. When you think of performing in the next event, you say you feel anxious. And then you say that you are somewhat conflicted about being successful. This sounds like quite a dilemma in that you do and don't feel ready for this. How would you like to work on this dilemma?"*

_____

_____

_____

Answer any questions and ensure the client does want to resolve the dilemma.

Say, *"Let me show you what we'll do. I will ask you to extend your hands out front and hold them open, palms up. Then I will ask you to take one side of this dilemma and place it in one of your hands—your choice—and close your hand. And then do the same with the other side. We will then do some bilateral stimulation very slowly, as you simply notice what you are experiencing in your hands. You might recall memories related to the dilemma, or you might simply experience what is happening in your hands. Do you have any questions?"*

_____

_____

This is generally sufficient for informed consent because the procedure is very well contained. Answer questions, guide the client as above, and then say the following:

Say, *"Now, just tell me what you notice in your hands."*

_____

_____

_____

To empower the client, allow any comment to be volunteered at first. Some clients will spontaneously report noticing that one hand feels lighter, warmer, or bigger. In these cases say the following:

Say, *"Okay. Just notice that as I do bilateral stimulation."*

Do only a few BLS movements and then stop.

Say, *"Okay. Take a breath. What do you notice in your hands now?"*

_____

_____

_____

Only when clients are unable to report spontaneously, say the following:

Say, *"For example, one hand might feel lighter, warmer, or even bigger. Or if your hands said something, or made a sound, what would that be? First, one hand, then the other? What color, symbol, shape, or taste represents that hand and the other?"*

_____

_____

_____

Each time the client responds, do a few BLS movements.

Say, *"Okay. Great. Go with that."*

Do BLS.

Continue in this way until the client reports no further change and one hand feels similar to the other.

Say, *"Okay. Good work. Now what would you like to do with your hands? Would you like to keep them apart, or would you like to connect them in some way? Or does something else occur to you?"*

_____

_____

_____

Some clients will spontaneously join their hands, perhaps placing one over the top of the other. You can then ask if that has any particularly meaning and do more BLS movements. You can also do a cognitive intervention.

Say, *"What would your hands say now if they had a voice?"*

_____

_____

_____

Say, *"Okay. Great. Go with that."*

Do BLS.

This may produce additional awareness that helps the client to understand and resolve the dilemma. It may also lead to a further fine-tuning of a goal statement. One high-achieving adult said at this point:

Client: "That's very interesting. The part of me that wants to be successful, my right hand, is now covering the other hand, the one that has been rebellious because I knew the people in charge—my parents, my boss, the faculty—also wanted me to be successful. Wow, to realize I have been holding myself back just so I would not please them! I think I'm ready to grow up."

Caution: The reader may conclude that this is actually an example of desensitization of a body memory and this author would agree. The reason the dilemma procedure can be conducted in Phase 2, without much additional information, evaluation, or concerns about abreactions, is because the questions generally contain the client's experience. The therapist asks the client to continue to focus on the hands, instead of asking, *"What comes up?"* more generally, which could take the client to additional memory networks. Nonetheless, even though risk is minimal, it is important for the clinician in this case to remain alert to the possibility that other feeder memories could arise, a matter which will be considered next.

We just reviewed six ways to respond when the client links the ideal state to a trigger and finds the trigger to be stronger than the client's ideal state. The client may need to develop skills further, strengthen positive qualities further, reexamine initial goals and motivation, and look for the possibility of secondary gain or dilemma.

Option #7: Feeder memories. See Phase 3.

The feeder memory is tied to unresolved memories and requires that EMDR treatment move into the desensitization phase of Phases 3 through 7. Only EMDR clinicians are trained to shift into the trauma desensitization format. Note that in the event that the dilemma procedure also taps into feeder memories, the clinician would also proceed to the next phases.

Phase 3: Evaluation

Feeder Memories

EMDR clinicians already know how to process traumatic memories. The next discussion suggests some special steps for processing feeder memories that appear in the course of conducting the performance enhancement protocol.

Option #7: Check for feeder memory(ies)

In this option, the trigger remains powerfully perturbing, and stronger than the client's ideal positive state, because the trigger is tied to an unresolved traumatic experience called a "feeder memory." The therapist guides clients to identify that feeder memory by employing the Float-Back Technique or Affect Bridge. That feeder memory is then reprocessed. The specific steps to take are next.

Informed Consent for Traumatic Processing

The therapist *must first* inform the client that they will be switching from the positive focus to a decidedly different one: desensitization of traumatic material.

> Say, *"It appears to me that you are discovering one of the reasons why you are having trouble getting to your goal. Do you remember talking about triggers?"*

_____

_____

Say, *"When you get triggered in this way, it is most likely that what you are thinking about is causing you to recall some old memory where something unpleasant happened to you. Whatever that old memory is, it still has the power to affect you, and it's getting in the way of your being successful. We have an opportunity here. This means that you can take on that memory, reprocess it with EMDR, and see about putting it in the past so that it stops keeping you from moving forward. I do need to remind you, however, that it is possible that you will feel some strong emotions if we do this. I will go very slowly as we work and accompany you through this, and it is most likely that the feeling will not be too strong, but nonetheless I want to make sure that you know what you would be getting into. In other words, there is a good chance for lots of gain, with not too much risk. What do you think of all this so far?"*

_____

_____

The therapist then proceeds with Phase 3, using the Float-Back or Affect Bridge.

Say, *"Okay. Now just pay attention to how you are feeling about* _____ (state the issue). *What might be a negative and irrational belief that goes with these emotions and sensations when you think of* _____ (state the trigger)."

_____

_____

Say, *"Okay, now think about* _____ (state the trigger), _____ (state the emotion(s)) *and* ____ (the NC or irrational belief) *and float back to a time that is related to this situation and seems to be connected to it. Notice how you feel right now. Let's go slowly into your history. I would like you to find as many times as you can where you felt this feeling before or something very similar to it. Look for early times when your had this feeling."*

_____

_____

_____

Continue with the Float-Back or Affect Bridge from the Standard EMDR Protocol until the client is able to identify the earliest Touchstone memory. Then use it as a target and follow the Standard EMDR Protocol.

As mentioned, whenever the use of the dilemma procedure produces feeder memories, switch into the same protocol just described.

Phase 4: Desensitization

Important Elements of Desensitization for the Enhancing Positive Emotion Protocol

Follow the Standard EMDR Protocol, while emphasizing the following two points:

Slow Bilateral Movements

This is important with certain high achievers who have views of themselves as being superhuman, and who harbor blocking beliefs such as "I cannot be weak," "I can overcome anything," or "It's a matter of mind over matter." Athletic coaches, executives, and other persons with extraordinarily high standards spend lots of time suppressing emotional distress, and can be surprised by the power of their emotions when they finally get around to tackling their traumatic memories. It is essential that these persons be allowed to pace themselves, however slowly, and to approach their memories little by little. Initiating bilateral movements slowly may mean beginning with one movement, as follows:

Say, *"Okay. Now I'd like you to return to that memory, with the words _____ (state the NC) notice where you feel it in your body, and now follow my fingers while I have you move your eyes just once from side to side."*

Then follow the 11-Step Standard Procedure ("Breathe, what do you get?" etc.). After the client has responded say the following:

Say, *"Okay. Let's continue. I did one movement at first. I can do another single movement or more if you would like."*

_____

_____

Continue in this way, empowering the client to be truly in charge of the session. Paradoxically, this starting slow invariably allows the client to feel success, less fear at approaching a shameful memory, and more confident to begin to work faster and faster. These comments are consistent with other clinician opinions that suggest intense emotional expression or reexperiencing (catharsis) is not needed to achieve effective treatment outcome with EMDR (Lee, Taylor, & Drummond, 2006; McCullough, 2002).

To clarify: The principle involved here is *not* to do EMDR desensitization slowly, but rather only to *begin* slowly. In this regard, this performance model is consistent with Shapiro's principle of producing bilateral movements (and hence emotional experiencing) with as much velocity, intensity, and speed as the client can tolerate. The start-slow principle is metaphorically like turning on a rheostat, providing a lower amount of power at first so the client can handle the initial emotional energy and brightness, and then slowly increasing the power. Too much intensity for clients at first risks retraumatization that could lead to premature termination from treatment. They may also fear initiating EMDR at all, believing that EMDR is too overwhelming. This could result in having to spend too much time in resource development, denying clients the chance to resolve handicapping traumatic memories.

Check for Blocking Beliefs

The second emphasis in desensitization with high achievers is to look for blocking beliefs, just described. This is less likely if you begin slowly as described, but can still become a salient issue. Consider inviting the client to state the blocking belief (e.g., "I cannot afford to fail") and use the Float-Back exercise to identify feeder memories, which can then be processed as usual.

Say, *"Okay. Now just pay attention to how you are feeling about _____ (state the issue). What might be a negative and irrational belief that goes with these emotions and sensations when you think of _____ (state the trigger)."*

_____

_____

_____

Say, *"Okay, now think about _____ (state the trigger), _____ (state the emotion(s)), and _____ (the NC or irrational belief) and float back to a time that is related to this situation and seems to be connected to it. Notice how you feel right now. Let's go slowly into your history. I would like you to find as many times as you can where you felt this feeling before, or something very similar to it. Look for early times when you had this feeling."*

_____

_____

_____

Continue with the Float-Back or Affect Bridge from the Standard EMDR Protocol until the client is able to identify the earliest or Touchstone memory. Then use it as a target and follow the Standard EMDR Protocol.

Phase 5: Installation

Positive Cognitions

With high achievers, particularly those such as athletes who depend on finely tuned physical movement or coordination, spend even more time to look for ways to define positive qualities that go beyond the positive cognition (which is to say the additional aspects of the BASIC I.D.). Shapiro (2001) has emphasized the fact that Phase 5 involves much more than cognitions, but the point bears repeating. For example, say the following:

Say, *"Before we continue into the positive, I would ask you to return to what you already worked on before when you told me about your positive goal. How much do you recall about the positive feelings, colors, and movements, all of those features that you practiced earlier? I would like you to return there again. We will do more eye movements after you have been able to return to that special place. Take as much time as you want before we do eye movements again. Okay. Are you ready now? Go with that."*

_____

_____

Phase 6: Body Scan

Positive Sensations

Many high achievers live in their heads a lot. Even though they may use their bodies for success, they may focus on muscle tone, physical strength, and what they might call signs of an adrenaline rush. They may be much less aware that their bodies are also used for signaling emotions. Use this opportunity to have them practice any of the positive exercises they have already learned, and guide them in the Body Scan that is described next.

Say, *"Close your eyes and keep in mind the original memory and the positive cognition. Then bring your attention to the different parts of your body, starting with your head and working downward. Any place you find any tension, tightness, or unusual sensation, tell me."*

Phase 7: Closure

Tactics for Self-Management

High achievers tend to value practical, concrete, and efficient strategies and are open to your teaching them special techniques that they can use between sessions to manage negative emotions and to strengthen positive experiences. This is particularly valuable for those unable to replicate in your office the triggers that will show up when they are in front of a crowd, surrounded by competitors, or inhaling the smells of a competitive environment.

More and more EMDR clinicians write about the wisdom and practicality of teaching special self-help techniques to their clients. Lobenstine (2007), for example, describes the use of a technique from applied kinesiology that he teaches his clients to use at home for self-soothing and stress reduction. Similar performance resources are described in Hartung (2002, 2005b) and Hartung and Galvin (2003).

What follows is an example of a simple yet powerful technique that the author teaches to virtually every high-performance client. The author learned the technique in Pune, India. There is a similar procedure, Tapas Acupressure Technique, which was developed independently of the author's approach. TAT is described on the TATLife Web site: http://www.tatlife.com

To teach the author's technique, say the following:

Say, *"I would like to teach you a simple method that helps my clients to feel calmer when they are in a challenging situation, and also to feel more focused on what it is they want to do. We can also see if it helps you. First, I want to show you how it goes and then ask if you would like to try it. I first place my thumb and fourth finger—my ring finger—on the bridge of my nose, as close to my eyes as possible without touching the eyes. Use either hand. Then I raise my fingers ever so slightly, just under the ridge of bone over my eyes. I don't push or cause pressure, only touch the skin slightly. That is often enough for some people. Others prefer to add something. They touch a point in the middle of their forehead either with their index finger or middle finger—your choice. That point is about a half inch above where their eyebrows would join. Again, a soft touch. If you can do this in private you can add one more thing, which is to place the other hand behind your head, thumb just under your skull, in the middle of the back of your head, and the palm covering both sides of your head. I say private because it looks a little weird to do it in public. Then you just say some positive words that feel right to you, like 'focus,' or 'centered.' We can experiment with the right words for you."*

The author recently taught this to an athlete who was world-class, in practice sessions, but consistently felt disruptive anxiety in competitions, in spite of having worked repeatedly with EMDR on both traumatic memories and future positive templates. He used the procedure just described at his latest competition, and reported feeling immediately calm and focused. Because of his level of fitness, talent, and the concentration he was finally able to enjoy using the technique. In a follow-up session he said, "I finally understood what it means to feel centered in a competition. Thinking of all those years of hard work, only to have it stunted by that unpredicted anxiety whenever I was in a competition. But last week I did that procedure we had practiced and the anxiety dissolved. I felt excited but not anxious. I can say that I truly enjoyed myself, finally. Oh, I set three world records."

The procedure is not magical, of course, but if your client is already skilled and well-intentioned, it can help to eliminate emotional interferences while generating focus, concentration, and positive emotion.

At the end of the session, say the following:

> Say, "*Things may come up or they may not. If they do, great. Write it down and it can be a target for next time. If you get any new memories, dreams, or situations that disturb you, just take a good snapshot. It isn't necessary to give a lot of detail. Just put down enough to remind you so we can target it next time. The same thing goes for any positive dreams or situations. If negative feelings do come up, try not to make them significant. Remember, it's still just the old stuff. Just write it down for next time. Then use the tape or the Safe Place exercise to let as much of the disturbance go as possible. Even if nothing comes up, make sure to use the tape every day and give me a call if you need to.*"

Phase 8: Reevaluation

Reality Check (In Vivo)

Information from any follow-up sessions will direct the therapist and client to the appropriate steps in the model, which can be repeated as necessary. Continue with the basic model until the client can feel comfortable while imaging the goal in a session and while meeting the goal in real life.

You can have the client walk through a recent experience, step-by-step, to identify both those behaviors (thoughts, feelings) that helped to get closer to the goal and those that did not. Celebrate success and analyze interferences. For example, say the following:

> Say, "*Let's have you imagine sitting in a movie theater walking through your recent experience, step-by-step, to identify the thoughts and feelings that helped you get closer to your goal and those that did not. What do you get?*"

_____

_____

_____

> Say, "*You were really able to do _____ (state successes). How do you feel when you think of that?*"

_____

_____

_____

Say, *"It is important to reinforce your successes and to notice what gets in the way of those successes. When those blocks to success occur, what other choices might you have?"*

_____

_____

_____

Say, *"Imagine this new choice and notice that while I guide you in a couple of eye movements. Go with that."*

Do BLS.

Say, *"What other choices might you have in that same situation? Think about those while I lead you in a few eye movements. Go with that."*

_____

_____

_____

Additional Skills

Sometimes, it becomes clear only with experience that additional skills may be lacking and may need to be learned and practiced.

Say, *"Now that you have had a chance to have some experience with the triggers we have been working with and found that it did not go quite the way that you wanted, what else do you think you need to learn and practice to do even better than before?"*

_____

_____

_____

Depending on what the client identifies as deficient skills, the therapist will spend time coaching the client to develop the abilities necessary to achieve the goal, whether this involves public speaking, athletics, or parenting. At such a point, the therapist will also inquire as to whether the client needs to consult with someone who specializes in the client's discipline—an issue particularly relevant in sports, leadership, first responding, and similar pursuits where the therapist may not have sufficient specialty knowledge.

Secondary Gain

Secondary gains (and losses) are often not apparent until after the person has achieved some success (the impact of success on the person's social world can be difficult to forecast).

Say, *"Now that you have had some success at _____ (state where the client has had the success), what has been the response of others and for you internally? Have you noticed any downside to this success?"*

_____

_____

_____

In the event of a yes, check for blocking beliefs.

Say, *"Are you noting any thoughts that keep getting in the way of your feeling good about your accomplishments and keep you from accomplishing what you want?"*

_____

_____

_____

Clients might discover that they feel successful only to notice that "I should not be so successful or should not be feeling this good," or "The only place to go from here is down," "No one in my family has gotten this far before." As before, you can use a Float-Back procedure to track down the feeder memories, then offer EMDR desensitization of those memories as an option.

Say, *"Okay, if you think of _____ (note the belief holding them back), notice what you feel as you think about that, and float back to an earlier time in your life. What other incident or memory connects you with this thought and feeling?"*

_____

_____

_____

As before, target the Touchstone memory and process with the Standard EMDR Protocol.

Dilemmas

Look for even more dilemmas and employ the dilemma procedure described above at the end of the Phase 2 discussion.

Say, *"Hmmm. I hear you talking about this trigger from two sides, as it were. When you think of performing in the next event, you say you feel anxious. And then you say that you are somewhat conflicted about being successful. This sounds like quite a dilemma, in that you do and don't feel ready for this. How would you like to work on this dilemma?"*

_____

_____

_____

Answer any questions and ensure the client does want to resolve the dilemma.

Say, *"Let me show you what we'll do. I will ask you to extend your hands out front and hold them open, palms up. Then I will ask you to take one side of this dilemma and place it in one of your hands—your choice—and close your hand. And then do the same with the other side. We will then do some bilateral stimulation very slowly, as you simply notice what you are experiencing in your hands. You might recall memories related to the dilemma, or you might simply experience what is happening in your hands. Do you have any questions?"*

_____

_____

This is generally sufficient for informed consent because the procedure is very well contained. Answer questions, guide the client as above, and then say the following:

Say, *"Now just tell me what you notice in your hands."*

_____

_____

_____

To empower the client, allow any comment to be volunteered at first. Some clients will spontaneously report noticing that one hand feels lighter, warmer, or bigger. In these cases say the following:

Say, *"Okay. Just notice that as I do bilateral stimulation."*

Do only a few BLS movements, then stop.

Say, *"Okay. Take a breath. What do you notice in your hands now?"*

_____

_____

_____

Only when clients are unable to report spontaneously, say the following:

Say, *"For example, one hand might feel lighter, warmer, or even bigger. Or if your hands said something, or made a sound, what would that be? First, one hand, then, the other? What color, symbol, shape, or taste represents that hand and the other?"*

_____

_____

_____

Each time the client responds, do a few BLS movements.

Say, *"Okay. Great. Go with that."*

Do BLS.

Continue in this way until the client reports no further change and one hand feels similar to the other.

Say, *"Okay. Good work. Now what would you like to do with your hands? Would you like to keep them apart, or would you like to connect them in some way? Or does something else occur to you?"*

_____

_____

_____

Some clients will spontaneously join their hands, perhaps placing one over the top of the other. You can then ask if that has any particular meaning, and do more BLS movements. You can also do a cognitive intervention.

Say, *"What would your hands say now if they had a voice?"*

_____

_____

_____

Say, *"Okay. Great. Go with that."*

Do BLS.

This may produce additional awareness that helps the client to understand and resolve the dilemma. It may also lead to a further fine-tuning of a goal statement.

Future Action Plan

Clients and therapist then develop an action plan for the future. Clients may end treatment at this point with the understanding that sessions can be requested at any future time, following the attitude of intermittent coaching and therapy. Some clients will ask to rehearse further before they terminate. Here is a series of scripts that can be used at this point.

Say, *"It is often helpful to rehearse the behaviors that are necessary for success. Some of my clients like to visualize a scene here in the office and then do more EMDR. Others like to rehearse in what we call in vivo, which means that I accompany them to a place where they are going to be when they work on their goal in real life. Would you like to do something like that?"*

_____

_____

_____

Say, *"You have accomplished the goals that we have set out to work on. Do you have any questions?"*

_____

_____

_____

Say, *"Please know that you are welcome to come back at any time when you think that there is something else that you would like to accomplish and think that some coaching (or therapy) would be helpful. In the meantime, it might be of use for us to talk about how you are going to track your progress. Some people keep a log of how things are going. How does that sound for you?"*

_____

_____

_____

Say, *"Some people like to practice some specific techniques they learned here, before taking a break from this work. You have learned _____ (for example, a particular breathing technique). If you would like, you could practice it here, and I could give you feedback on what*

I see, and whether I might have any other suggestions for you. Is there anything that you would like to do?"

_____

_____

_____

Say, *"I also want to tell you how grateful I have been for being able to collaborate with you along your journey. If at any point you think I can be of help again, please feel free to get in touch. I wish you the best on your journey."*

EMDR Performance Enhancement Psychology Protocol

Jennifer Lendl and Sandra Foster

EMDR-PEP Script Notes

The EMDR Performance Enhancement Psychology Protocol (EMDR-PEP) addresses performance anxiety, self-defeating beliefs, behavioral inhibition, posttraumatic stress, and psychological recovery from injury for creative and performing artists, workplace employees, and athletes. The EMDR-PEP can be very useful with every-day nonpathological complaints such as procrastination, fear of failure, setbacks, and life transitions.

Note: Clinicians, working with athletes require rigorous training in Sport Psychology and Sociology of Professional Sport.

The EMDR-PEP encompasses a full spectrum viewpoint (body, mind, and spirit) regarding optimal functioning at work and in life. This perspective inspires clients to identify their strengths as well as areas to improve and to prioritize their work accordingly. The EMDR-PEP approach draws upon Maslow's (1971) Human Potential Movement and Positive Psychology (Amen, 2002; Buss, 2000; Csikzentmihalyi, 1990; Seligman, 1998; Taylor, Kemeny, Reed, Bower, & Gruenwald, 2000), as well as Sport Psychology Research and Principles (Ievleva & Orlick, 1991; Kohl, Ellis, & Roenkerm, 1992; Mamassis & Doganis, 2004; Martin, Moritz, & Hall, 1999; Nideffer, 1976; Short & Short, 2005; Simons, 2000; Unestahl, 1982), and Health Psychology (Graham, 1995; Levine, 1991; Simonton & Creighton, 1982; Whiting & den Brinker, 1982). The first single subject series (Foster & Lendl, 1996) reported promising findings with four diverse work-related situations and was republished in APA's seminal coaching papers in Consulting Psychology, *The Wisdom of Coaching* (Foster & Lendl, 2007). Reduced anxiety and increased self-confidence were reported for mature performing artists launching an existing repertoire into a new arena (Foster, 2000) and in a controlled study of master swimmers (Linebarger, 2005).

Note: The Linebarger study included the Brief Intervention Focusing Protocol; the paper does not include inner advisor and mental room.

Special attention is given to performance elements such as ability, focus, and motivation. The types of questions that the therapist needs to find out are the following:

"What abilities are needed?"
"What deficits exist in education, training, or emotional management?"
"Do they have the ability to stay present?"
"What distractions impair focus?"
"What motivates them?"
"Do they have a sense of life purpose?"

While EMDR-PEP adheres faithfully to Shapiro's 3-Prong, 8-Phase Protocol, the emphasis is on performance and the future template. In essence, the practitioner works backward by visioning expected outcomes and uploading performance skills before reprocessing blocks.

A summary of the EMDR-PEP Protocol is as follows:

Phase 1: Client History

- Clinical intake
- Rule out significant pathology and refer for appropriate treatment before performance work
- Performance intake
- Include history of relational and performance success or failure and authority or control issues

Phase 2: Client Information and Preparation

- Create safe and quiet place
- Teach Brief Intervention Focusing Protocol for imminent performance situations
- Teach other performance skills, such as centering
- Create inner advisor and support team
- Install a *success* memory
- Create a mental theater room for running future template projections

Phase 3: Assessment Choice of Targets

- Performance clients are highly motivated and result oriented who usually prefer to start with the current day presenting performance issue related to sport, health, work, the arts, spirituality, or life transition
- Carefully note past difficulties relating to the goals to cover if they do not emerge spontaneously

Phases 4 Through 7: Desensitization Through Closure

- Follow the EMDR Standard Protocol, albeit focusing on the performance issues

Phase 8: Reevaluation

- After installing the positive cognition (PC), future template, and reprocessing any subsequent issues or blocks, proceed to the expanded future template.

EMDR Performance Enhancement Psychology Protocol Forms and Script

Phase 1: History Taking

Do a thorough clinical intake. Before proceeding with performance work, give priority to ruling out dissociative disorders, major trauma issues, active substance abuse disorders, neurological symptoms, or other Axis I and II symptomatology. If discovered, these clients should be referred out for treatment or, if appropriate, the performance coach or therapist can contract to do the clinical processing.

The following forms are included in the clinical intake for performance work: Trauma History and EMDR Readiness, Relationship History, School History, Employment History, Problem History, and a Performance Inventory (adapted from Lendl & Steidinger, 1997).

Trauma History and EMDR Readiness

Date:
Checklist:
Name:
Referral source:
Quick readiness:
Timing:
Stability:
Support:
Need for referral:
Referral to:

Age:
DOB:
Day time phone:
Night time phone:

Physical(s):
Last check-up:
Current medical problems (eyes, seizures, asthma, pregnancy, high blood pressure, etc.):
Medications:
Past medical problems:
Past medications:
Birth trauma:
Head injuries (including coma or other loss of consciousness, i.e., falls, accidents, fainting):
Operations:
Hospitalizations:
Other serious illness:
Seizures or seizurelike activity:
Allergies or drug intolerances:
Present height: _____ weight: _____
Last 6 months weight loss _____ weight gain _____
Mental health and medications:

    Get nervous?:
    Worries?:
    Gets stuck or procrastinates?:
    Gets down about?:
    Feels defensive about?:
    How reacts to stress?:
    How reacts to anger?:
    How becomes angry or shows anger?:
    How unwinds after work?:

Sleep behavior (nightmares, recurrent dreams), difficulties (falling asleep, staying asleep, going back to sleep):
Dissociation (use screening tool):
Therapy? _____ years (outcome or results):
Hospitalizations:
Suicide ideation:
Suicide attempts:
Suicide resolution:

Alcohol and drug history (and family history) including first incident,
   recent, normal week:
Caffeine:

   Coffee: _____
   Tea: _____
   Soda: _____
   Chocolate: _____

Nicotine (cigarettes, cigar, tobacco chew):

   First date: _____
   Per day: _____
   Past: _____
   Present: _____

Attempts to stop or interventions:
Abuse (past and present both self and family):
Physical:
Sexual, rape, or molestation:
Emotional:
Grief experience (death, disaster, loss):
Near-death experience:
Legal problems:
Current family problems:
Current work or corporate problems:
Learning, school difficulties:
Military service:
Support system (family, friends, colleagues, groups, pets):
Religious history:
Sexual history (if comfortable): (First experience age, # of sexual part-
   ners, sexually transmitted disease, abortion):
Describe your relationship with friends:
Describe your weaknesses:
Describe your strengths:

Relationship History

Name: _____
Current relationship status:
Satisfaction 0–10:
Important dates:
First date:
Marriage:
Separations:
Divorces:
Death:
Past relationship (first love, other partners):
Home history (birthplace, moves to present):
Heritage (family origin or culture):
Parents (names, DOB, death, married, divorced, separated—dates, education, occupation, physical and mental health, functioning, family history including: birth order, early history, family mental health, strengths):
Siblings (same as above):
Children (same as above):
Friends (same as above):
Colleagues (same as above):

Rapport with client	(parents, siblings, partners, children):
Express anger	(same as above):
Express love	(same as above):
Releases stress/unwinds	(same as above):
Competition	(same as above):
Support	(same as above):
Best experience	(same as above):

School History

	Grammar	Middle	High	College
Grade average				
Positive subjects				
Negative subjects				
Sports History and Outcome				
Extracurricular History and Outcome				

Degrees and colleges attended:
Learning problems:
Oral reports:
Writing:
Math:
Reading:

Learning strengths:
Attention problems:
Social skills or relationship difficulties:
Negative authority figures:
Positive authority figures:
Negative experiences (teasing, bullying, shaming):

   Did same to others:

Positive experiences (validation, recognition, awards):
Greatest achievements:
What teachers would say about you:
Negative cognitions or beliefs mentioned:

Employment History

Past Employment

Favorite and why:
Least favorite and why:
Negative experiences (loss, abuse, harassment, firings):
Negative authority figures:
Personality clashes:
Major failures:
Positive experiences (promotions, validation, awards, recognitions):
Positive authority figures:
Positive teamwork situations:
Greatest achievement:
What your boss would say about you:

Present Employment

Start date:
First position:
Job progressions or promotions:
Relationship with co-workers: positive and negative:
Skill strengths:
Needing improvement:
Negative experience:
Fears:
Mentor:
Greatest achievement:
What your boss would say about you:

Negative or beliefs spontaneously mentioned:

Problem History

Name: _____
Occupation: _____
Education: _____

Presenting Issue

How tried to solve:
What are job or task requirements?:

Have all needed skills and abilities?:
Performed successfully ever? last time?:
Consequences, if solved?:
Reason not to solve?:
System impact (work and family):
What's needed to accomplish task?:
New skills?:
Outside resources?:
Communication?:
Other?:
What will or can sabotage?:

EMDR Targets

Present: First (When started):
Worst:
Triggers:
Symptoms:
Past: First (Ever happened before? How about when very young? Jr. high?):

(This feeling, emotion, sensation is not new. When did it first come up ?):

Worst:
Future (desired results):

Negative Cognitions or Beliefs (list any mentioned spontaneously):

Performance Inventory

(Adapted from Lendl and Steidinger, 1997)

1. What is your job or sport? Position?
2. Why did you choose this area?
3. What do you like about it?
4. What keeps you motivated?
5. How does fun fit into your regimen?
6. How do you feel about competition or challenge?
7. At present, what level are you?
8. What are your goals, long- and short-term?
9. What would stop you from getting there?
10. What help or changes do you need to get there?
11. What personal records or markers help you measure improvement?
12. Are those measures realistic and timely?
13. Do they focus on a current event or goal?
14. Do you have trouble staying in the moment?
15. Are you easily distracted?
16. Do you procrastinate?
17. Are you concerned about what others think about you?
18. Do you get stuck on failures, losses, or mistakes?
19. How do you respond to criticism?
20. What do you do when you make a mistake or lose?
21. What was your greatest failure or loss?
22. What is your greatest achievement?
23. How successful do you feel?
24. Any difficulty with choking, consistency, or slumps?
25. Do you have any dreaded competitors? Who? Why?
26. Who is your role model or hero?
27. Who is the "star" in your family?
28. How is your relationship with your coach, trainer, boss, or manager?
29. How do you respond to their directives?
30. Do you feel pressure from your parents, significant other, coach, trainer, manager?
31. Do you feel you have met their expectations?
32. How do you respond to pressure?
33. Do you feel performance anxiety? Have you ever?

34. Do you ever get angry at work or while playing?

35. Are you having difficulty with any of your skills?

36. In what areas do you feel most competent?

37. How does your job or sport involvement affect other relationships? Problems? Support?

38. Any problems with resources?

39. Any problems managing your time?

40. If travel is required for your job or sport, how do you manage "travel stress"?

41. What is it like when you reach new levels, goals, or get promoted?

42. Is recognition important to you? Do you get enough? From whom?

43. How does aging or getting older affect doing your sport or job?

44. Have you had any injuries or illnesses? What?

45. How do you handle injury or illness?

46. What do you think or do when someone cheats, lies, or is unfair?

47. How do you handle bad calls or reviews?

48. Do you ever have negative thoughts such as the following:

    I can't

    I'm stuck

    I always

    I never

    I hate losing or failing

    I'm not as good as . . .

    I'm an imposter

    I'm too (short, slow, old, young, weak)

    It's not fair

49. Do you ever have slogans such as

    More is better

    No pain no gain

    Just do it

50. What do you do in your spare time?

51. What are your eating habits?

52. Sleep habits?

53. Exercise routine?

54. What would your coach or boss say about you?

55. What's the biggest risk you've taken?

Phase 2: Preparation

Creating a Safe/Calm Place

Use Shapiro's 8-step Safe/Calm Place Protocol (Shapiro, 2007, and see chapter 7). You can add a step 9 by having the client imagine utilizing the protocol for a stressful performance situation.

> Say, *"Imagine using your Safe/Calm Place for _____ (state the stressful performance situation)."*
> Say, *"How did that work for you?"*

_____

_____

If the client is deemed appropriate to start performance work, timing of resources and interventions must be determined. Urgent performances, competitions, or presentations may need the use of the Brief Intervention Focusing Protocol.

Brief Intervention Focusing Protocol for Performance Enhancement Purpose

The Brief Intervention Focusing Protocol for Performance Enhancement may be used when consultation time is very limited or when the consultant wishes to assist the client in quickly building confidence. The protocol is suitable for platform speakers, stage performers, athletes, musicians, artists, students, or poets who have upcoming engagements or tests, and business people who are preparing for a sales or marketing presentation.

Intention

In this protocol, the consultant focuses on the client's forthcoming performance rather than the clearing of emotional blocks, the effects of past trauma, or recent setbacks. Anything outside of the task at hand is considered an intrusion. Internal distractions such as crowd noise and environmental conditions are put aside as expediently as possible so that the client can fully focus on the performance.

Brief Intervention Focusing Protocol for Performance Enhancement Script

1. Establish the hours available to do the intervention and explain the protocol to the client.

   > Say, *"We can work on past issues when we have more time. For now, we'll focus on what you <u>can</u> do for <u>this</u> event. We will set aside any distractions and concentrate on the specific elements of your upcoming performance and what you are already prepared to do for it."*

2. Quickly identify internal and external distractions. Have the client determine each distraction's importance and immediacy in regards to the upcoming performance.

   > Say, *"What thoughts or distractions get in the way of your having confidence in your upcoming event? Examples of distractions*

might be something like, 'I'm worried about my sick child,' 'I have a toothache,' or 'I'm not prepared'."

_____

_____

_____

_____

_____

_____

Say, *"Can you put them in order of importance?"*

_____

_____

_____

_____

_____

_____

3. Help the client problem solve around each distraction and do short saccades while they visualize the solution.

Say, *"What is the problem that is getting in the way of* _____ (state what the goal is)*?"*

_____

_____

Say, *"What can you do to take care of* _____ (state what the issue is) *before the event?"*

_____

_____

Say, *"Good. Imagine* _____ (state the solution)*."*
   Do bilateral stimulation (BLS).

_____

_____

Say, *"What can you do during the event to make sure that* _____ (state the issue) *is taken care of?"*

_____

_____

Say, *"Good. Imagine* _____ (state the solution)*."*
   Do BLS.

_____

_____

Examples

Example 1

Say, *"What are you doing to help your child now and who will help him during your event?"*

Answer: *"He saw the doctor today and my mother can babysit during my event."*

Say, *"Good, imagine him seeing the doctor and following the doctor's directions."*

Do BLS.

Say, *"Now imagine your mother babysitting your event."*

Do BLS.

Example 2

Say, *"What are you doing for your toothache?"*

Answer: *"I'll try to get to the dentist before the event. If not I can make a later appointment and take aspirin to help with the pain."*

Say, *"Good, imagine that."*

Do BLS.

Example 3

Say, *"What have you done to prepare for the event?"*

Answer: *"I have practiced or worked out for _____ days and I worked with my coach on strategy."*

Say, *"Imagine your workouts and strategy sessions."*

Do BLS.

4. Assist the client in letting go of the distractions when they intrude.

   Say, *"Think of your event. When an intrusion comes up, ask yourself 'Is this thought useful right now'? Remember your solution _____ (state the solution). Then refocus on the task by saying 'What is my job right now for this event'?"*

   Do BLS.

   Say, *"Remember how important it is to stay focused on the event. There is limited time. You need to stay present and let go of any concerns to get the best possible results. To this end it is useful to hold the intention: 'I will move through my performance, staying on task, no matter what comes up.'"*

   Note: There has been NO focus on the body up, to this point in time to avoid eliciting the emotional material that needs to be processed at a later, more appropriate time.

5. Assist the client with installing an Expanded Future Template as follows:

> Say, *"Please imagine the entire performance. When a distraction intrudes, ask yourself 'Is this useful right now'? Build in a plan. Go back on task by saying 'What is my job right now'? and continue until you can visualize the entire event. Imagine the event as fully as possible: notice your posture, muscle movements, voice quality, gestures, and so forth. Let me know when a distraction arises and we'll use BLS to help move it to the background by putting a plan in place and returning to the task."*

_____

_____

Continue this until the client can move smoothly through the entire performance.

6. Using BLS, install the entire performance from start to finish with the client staying focused on the task throughout.

> Say, *"Now that you have your distractions under control please run your performance from start to finish feeling your body fully. We will use BLS. Let me know when you're finished."*

Do BLS.

_____

_____

Note: For resource installation, it is usual to do slower saccades (6–12). However, performances often run longer than 6–12 saccades and the clients seem quite capable of stopping on their own.

This is the end of the Brief Performance Protocol Script.

Useful Resources for EMDR-PEP

When time is not constricted, there are several other resources that can be useful in EMDR-PEP. In keeping with RDI work (Korn & Leeds, 2002; Leeds & Shapiro, 2000), use one or two short sets of bilateral stimulation (6–12 saccades for eye movement) to install each resource. The following scripted resources are from EMDR Peak Performance Specialty Training Materials (Foster, 2001) as published in the Emdria Newsletter (Foster & Lendl, 2002).

Creating the Inner Advisor

> Say, *"Imagine an actual person or virtual being who can be an inner resource for you, like an inner coach. This may be some part of yourself, like your Higher or Wiser Self. Imagine this person's or being's voice, calming you when you are upset or frustrated and reminding you of your strengths, talents, and positive qualities. Go ahead and do that now and let me know what you find."*

_____

_____

Say, *"Great. Go with that."*

Do slow BLS.

Say, *"Do you feel stronger or more positive?"*

_____

_____

Say, *"Do you need to add or delete anything to make it more positive?"*

_____

_____

If yes, say the following:

Say, *"Go ahead and do that now. Go with that."*

Do slow BLS.

Creating an Inner Team of Support People

Say, *"Imagine this inner coach and others who give you support and encouragement as your inner team, like your own personal cheering section. Hear and see them now as they rally around you, calling out words of encouragement, smiling at you, and offering advice when you need it. Go ahead and do that now and let me know what you find."*

_____

_____

Say, *"Great. Go with that."*

Do slow BLS.

Say, *"Does this help you feel stronger or more positive?"*

_____

_____

Say, *"Do you need any changes?"*

If yes, say the following:

Say, *"Go ahead and do that now. Go with that."*

_____

_____

Success Review

Say, *"Think back to the times when you felt more powerful, more in control, or more pleased with the results you reached at the end of the day. Notice the emotions and physical sensations that come up when you think of these successful experiences. Imagine deliberately bringing these successful times to mind when you are feeling discouraged in order to change your state of mind to one more powerful and positive. Go ahead and do that now and let me know what you find."*

_____

_____

Say, *"Great. Go with that."*

Do slow BLS.

Say, *"Does that help to empower you or do you need to make any adjustments?"*

_____

_____

If yes, say the following:

Say, *"Go ahead and do that now. Go with that."*

_____

_____

Mental Theater Room

Say, *"In your mind's eye, imagine an internal space like a comfortable room or a beautiful space outdoors in which you can sit in a favorite chair or on the grass under the trees. Imagine a large projection screen in front of you on which you can see the images of yourself doing the things well that you wish to do in the future. Go ahead and do that now and let me know what you create."*

_____

_____

Say, *"Great. Go with that."*

Do slow BLS.

Say, *"Do you need to make any adjustments?"*

_____

_____

If yes, say the following:

Say, *"Go ahead and do that now. Go with that."*

Do slow BLS.
Then, say the following:

Say, *"Please practice these performance resources during the week and remember to report the results to me at the following consult sessions."*

Phase 3: Assessment

Target: Start With the Problem History

In EMDR-PEP, the client usually starts with a present-day issue, but you can leave the decision to the client.

Say, *"In the history we took earlier, you mentioned the issue of _____ (state the reason in treatment) as the reason for seeking performance consultation at this time.*

Several other issues arose during our talks. Where would you like to start?"

_____

_____

Image

Say, *"What image best represents the _____ (name of the performance issue)?"*

_____

_____

_____

_____

Negative Cognition (NC)

Say, *"What words go best with that picture that express your negative belief about yourself <u>now</u>?"*

_____

_____

Positive Cognition (PC)

Say, *"When you bring up that picture or incident, what would you like to believe about yourself <u>now</u>?"*

_____

_____

Validity of Cognition (VoC)

Say, *"When you think of that picture or incident, how true do those words _____ (clinician repeats the positive cognition) feel to you now on a scale of 1 to 7, where 1 feels completely false and 7 feels completely true?"*

1	2	3	4	5	6	7
(completely false)				(completely true)		

Examples of Cognitions

Negative cognitions	Positive cognitions
I go blank	I am well prepared and can stay present.
I'm not as good as __	I can stay focused on my job.
I'm a loser	I can stay focused on the task and let go of the outcome.
I'm an imposter	I am competent. I've been doing this ___ _____ for _____ __ months/years.
I'm out of control	I can center myself with anger. I can use my breathing and think rationally.

Note: In EMDR-PEP, the negative emotional thinking is redirected to positive behavioral thoughts or actions.

Emotions

Say, *"When you bring up that picture or incident, and those words _____ (repeat the NC), what emotion(s) do you feel now?"*

_____

_____

Subjective Units of Disturbance (SUD)

Say, *"On a scale of 0 to 10, where 0 is no disturbance or neutral and 10 is the highest disturbance that you can imagine, how disturbing does it feel to you now?"*

0   1   2   3   4   5   6   7   8   9   10
(no disturbance)   (highest disturbance)

Location of Body Sensation

Say, *"Where do you feel it in your body?"*

_____

_____

Phase 4: Desensitization

Keep in mind that although you may be starting with a present-day issue, the goal is to help the client integrate past experiences underlying the present performance problem so as to minimize future upsets. Most past memories will surface during the reprocessing. However, if looping occurs or past memories are compartmentalized and do not emerge, you may want to use an Affect Bridge or cognitive interweave.

Say, *"When you see yourself stuck in _____ (state the performance situation), when have you had that _____ (state negative cognition) or _____ (state feeling in your body)?"*

If the time permits, return to the Intake History and reprocess as many of the aforementioned negative beliefs and disturbing incidents using the EMDR Standard Protocol.

Phase 5: Installation

Say, *"Do the words _____ (repeat the PC) still fit, or is there another positive statement you feel would be more suitable?"*
Say, *"Think about the original incident and those words _____ (repeat the selected PC), from 1 (completely false) to 7 (completely true), how true do they feel?"*

1   2   3   4   5   6   7
(completely false)   (completely true)

Say, *"Hold them together."*

Do a set of BLS and ask again.

Say, *"On a scale of 1 to 7, how true do those words _____ (state PC) feel to you now when you think of the original incident?"*

1	2	3	4	5	6	7
(completely false)				(completely true)		

Continue repeating this process (BLS and checking VoC) as long as the material is becoming more adaptive. If client reports a 7, do BLS again to strengthen and continue until it no longer strengthens. Go on to Phase 6.

Phase 6: Body Scan

Say, *"Close your eyes and keep in mind the original memory and the ___ (repeat the PC). Now bring your attention to the different parts of your body, starting with your head and working downward. Any place you find any tension, tightness, or unusual sensation, tell me."*

_____

_____

If any sensation is reported, do a set of BLS.

If a positive or comfortable sensation, do BLS to strengthen the positive feeling. If a sensation or discomfort is reported, reprocess until discomfort subsides and then repeat the Body Scan procedures.

Phase 7: Closure

The goal is to ensure client stability at the completion of any EMDR session whether the session is complete (VoC = 7; SUD = 0) or incomplete (VoC < 7; SUD > 0). In EMDR-PEP, the client is encouraged to practice performance skills.

Say, *"Between this session and the next, please practice your Safe/Calm Place, Inner Advisor, Support Team, Success Review, Mental Room, and or Brief Intervention Focusing Protocol. Notice when you are uncomfortable during the week and take a moment to do your exercise. If you cannot find time during the day, make time at night to review your day adding the exercise in whenever a difficult issue arises."*

While future templates are installed upon completion of EMDR targets (VoC = 7; SUD = 0), positive templates are useful as a resource to install learned behaviors. The above performance resources can be visualized with short BLS using 6–12 saccades or without BLS (Lendl, 2005, 2007).

Phase 8: Reevaluation

When the reprocessing is complete, the installation and Body Scan are clear (VoC = 7, SUD = 0), use The Expanded Future Template with its emphasis on the full-body experience to illicit any remaining discomfort or doubts and provide practice for confidence.

The Expanded Future Template

Say, *"This time when you imagine your performance, visualize yourself doing it confidently and successfully and notice how that*

<u>feels</u> *in your body. Pay attention to your muscle tension, posture, movements, and voice quality* (if relevant) *as you competently perform your task. Let me know whenever any discomfort arises. We will stop the visualization and reprocess any discomforts until you can imagine the task with a positive full-body experience."*

_____

_____

_____

After processing any physical or mental blocks, doubts, or discomfort that arise, be sure to reprocess any concerns about sustaining success once it has been achieved. This is a good point to remind them of the Mental Room established earlier.

Demonstrate this in the session.

Say, *"Imagine being in that space in which you can picture and mentally rehearse your goals and plans. See that projection screen in front of you. Now imagine that you can see images of yourself projected on to that screen* (state whatever task needs to be done)." (Foster, 2001)

_____

_____

Lastly, with performance work, it is sometimes beneficial to work in situ (physically go to the performance site and reprocess there).

PART IX

EMDR
and Clinician
Self-Care

Becoming a mental health practitioner is not for the faint of heart. Whereas the rewards are huge, a profession that pulls for all of the negative emotions and behaviors that, often, society prefers to ignore, can take its toll on its practitioners. As a result, clinicians need to make sure that they not only take care of their clients but they also take care of themselves.

Known for its impact on trauma, EMDR practitioners, in particular, are amongst those who are called on to deal with the worst of the worst. As seen in this volume, our clients are victims of war, natural disasters, catastrophic illnesses, or nightmares; the list is endless. We need to be alert, responsive, empathic, and mindful of ourselves as the instruments through which change can evolve in partnership with our clients.

Neal Daniels, a psychologist for many of his years, had seen the range of psychology practice from noncombatant soldier in a medical unit, to structural family therapist, to chief psychologist on an inpatient unit and later head of the PTSD unit at the Philadelphia Veterans Administration. Understanding the effects of secondary PTSD, Neal began to use EMDR on himself on his "peskies" and suggested to his team that they do the same. His chapter on Self-Care for EMDR Practitioners is a testimony to his concern about taking care of himself, as well as his staff. If he were here, he would invite you to do the same.

Mark Dworkin (2005), a social worker, with a talent for understanding the importance of interpersonal dynamics has written an excellent book, *EMDR and the Relational Imperative: The Therapeutic Relationship in EMDR Treatment,* on how this applies to the practitioner and his client. He has created a questionnaire to assist clinicians in uncovering what triggers them when working with their clients, and how to go about processing this material so that they can regain their sense of equilibrium or understand how the effects of their clients' issues could be affecting them. This is a tool that can be used by clinicians themselves or by consultants in their consultancy practice.

Self-Care for EMDR Practitioners

Neal Daniels

This protocol was derived from the notes of Neal Daniels, a clinical psychologist who was the director of the PTSD Clinical Team at the Veterans Affairs Medical Center in Philadelphia, Pennsylvania. Always concerned about the welfare of clients and practitioners, he put together a short, simple, and effective protocol for the practitioner, on the completion of any session where there was negative affect remaining.

Self-Care Script Notes

In Neal's words, "The procedure is short, simple, effective. Right after the session or later on in the day when it is possible, bring up the image of the patient; do 10–15 eye movements; generate a positive cognition and install it with the patient's image and another 10–15 movements. Once the negative affects have been reduced, realistic formulations about the patient's future therapy are much easier to develop. Residual feelings of anger, frustration, regret, or hopelessness have been replaced by clearer thoughts about what can or cannot be done. Positive, creative mulling can proceed without the background feelings of unease, weariness, and ineffectiveness. Daily, weekly, or even career-long "burn-out" can be viewed as the accumulated residual of negative feelings that were not dealt with effectively when they occurred." The idea was to work on the material right after the session or later in the day when time allowed.

Clinician Self-Care Script

Say, *"Bring up the image of the patient."*

_____

_____

Do 10–15 eye movements.

Say, *"Notice whatever positive cognition comes to mind."*

_____

_____

Say, *"Now install the positive cognition* _____ (state the positive cognition) *with the patient's image."*

Do 10–15 eye movements.

Say, *"What do you notice?"*

_____

_____

Once the negative affects have been reduced, realistic formulations about the patient's future therapy are much easier to develop. Residual feelings of anger, frustration, regret, or hopelessness have been replaced by clearer thoughts about what can or cannot be done. Positive, creative mulling can proceed without the background feelings of unease, weariness, and ineffectiveness.

Daily, weekly, or even career-long burn-out can be viewed as the accumulated residual of negative feelings that were not dealt with effectively when they occurred.

The Clinician Awareness Questionnaire in EMDR

Mark Dworkin

The Clinician Awareness Questionnaire
Script Notes

Whenever an EMDR treatment session becomes problematic, consider this self-administered instrument when reflecting on this session. EMDR consultants can also use this measure in their consulting groups to assist consultees in understanding when work with clients have an impact on the clinician.

The purpose of using the Clinician Awareness Questionnaire includes the following:

- To assist in raising awareness of what may be triggering the clinician;
- To assess what may be coming from the clinician and what may be coming from the client;
- To develop EMDR Relational Strategies.

Different problems can arise in different phases of the protocol. Sometimes, problems for the clinician may occur in Phase 1 when a client shares information that evokes negative arousal; or Phase 2 when the client has trouble understanding the elements of preparation or *wants to get going* processing trauma prematurely and the clinician has a negative response; or Phase 3 when there is a problem structuring the Assessment piece. Sometimes, client information may not evoke negative arousal in the clinician until Phase 4 when the client is actively processing. Often times, the clinician's triggers are from old memories. These memories may be explicit; at other times, implicit (somatosensory). As clinicians begin to notice these moments in themselves, they may aid themselves and their clients in continuing productive processing by using the Clinician Awareness Questionnaire.

Clinician Awareness Questionnaire Script

Background Information

Say, *"How many times have you seen this client?"*

_____

_____

Say, *"What is the client's gender?"* M ___ F ___

Say, *"What is the marital status?"* M D S W

Say, *"How many children do you have?"*

_____

_____

Say, *"What are their gender and ages?"*

_____

_____

Say, *"What is the occupation of the client?"*

_____

_____

Say, *"What is the religious or spiritual affiliation of the client?"*

_____

_____

Protocol Questions

1. Say, *"Is this the first time you have felt activated by this client?"* Y __ N __

2. If no, say the following:

   Say, *"Think back, perhaps there is another time when you were activated concerning this same issue with this or any other client. When or what might that have been?"*

3. Say, *"Do you get activated by the same issue with other clients?"* Y __ N __

4. Say, *"Have you ever been traumatized?"* Y __ N __

   Say, *"Could your old trauma be triggered?"* Y __ N __

5. Say, *"Do you believe that you are struggling with Compassion Fatigue, Vicarious Traumatization, or Secondary Traumatic Stress?"* Y __ N __

6. Say, *"Describe the clients presenting problem* (or present-day referents).*"*

   _____

   _____

   _____

   _____

7. Say, *"What old trauma(s) of the client are related to Question 6?"*

_____

_____

_____

_____

8. Say, *"Describe what is activating dysfunctional ego states in you with this client NOW. How are you activated?"*

_____

_____

_____

_____

9. Say, *"How do you know that you are being activated NOW? Which ego states of yours are activated? What old state dependent memories are activated by this client?"*

_____

_____

_____

_____

10. Say, *"What makes this client unusually challenging for you NOW? To which ego states of the client are you or your own ego states explicitly or implicitly reacting?"*

_____

_____

_____

_____

11. Say, *"What is it about this client's style of struggle with their problem _____* (state whatever it is that the clinician is having difficulty with, i.e., external-izing, intellectualizing, substance abusing) *that may activate you NOW. Why NOW? Please describe it."*

_____

_____

_____

_____

12. Say, *"Describe this client's presentation style; for instance it could be avoid-ant, aggressive, straightforward, shameful, guilt ridden, and so forth."*

_____

_____

_____

_____

13. Say, *"What activates you about their style of struggle, and their presentation style?"*

_____

_____

_____

_____

14. Say, *"When you think of the problem you are experiencing with this client, what picture comes to your mind NOW?"*

_____

_____

_____

_____

15. Say, *"When you see this picture in your mind, what negative cognition do you get about yourself NOW?"*

_____

_____

16. Say, *"When you link the picture with the negative cognition, what unpleasant sensations do you experience right NOW? Where in your body do you experience these sensations?"*

_____

_____

17. Say, *"When you picture the client in your mind's eye, who does this client remind you of? Check as many as fit."*

❑ Mom

❑ Dad

❑ Sibling (which) _____

❑ Clergy

❑ Teacher

❑ Relative (which) _____

❑ Other(s) (whom)

18. Say, *"What old memories emerge and dysfunctional ego states emerge NOW?"*

_____

_____

_____

_____

If there is a problem connecting with old memories, use the Float-Back Technique (based on Shapiro, 2006, p. 48).

19. Say, *"Now please bring up that picture of* _____ (repeat client's disturbing image) *and those negative words* _____ (state the negative cognition). *Now, notice what feelings are coming up for you, and where you are feeling them in your body, and just let your mind float back to an earlier time in your life—don't search for anything—just let your mind float back and tell me the earliest scene that comes to mind where you had* _____ *similar thoughts of* _____ (repeat negative cognition), *and feelings of* _____ (repeat emotions), *and where you feel it in your body?"*

   _____

   _____

   _____

   _____

20. Say, *"What negative cognitions go along with these old memories? When you link the picture of the most disturbing part of the memory with this negative cognition, what feelings and sensations arise in you RIGHT NOW? Where do you feel these sensations in your body?"*

   NC: _____

   Picture: _____

   Feelings and sensations: _____

   SUD: 0   1   2   3   4   5   6   7   8   9   10
         (no disturbance)   (highest disturbance)

   Body Location: _____

21. Say, *"Does your client notice your getting activated?"* Y __ N __

22. Say, *"If yes, how does the client's activated ego state/s deal with you and/or your ego state/s?"*

   ❏ Ignore: ___

   ❏ Anxiety: ____

   ❏ Annoyance: ____

   ❏ Attack: ____

   ❏ Guilt: ____

   ❏ Shame: ____

   ❏ Curiosity: ____

   ❏ Suspicion: ____

23. Say, *"What does your client do with their reactions to your reactions? To do this, reconstruct a piece of process that became problematic between the two of you."*

   _____

   _____

   _____

   _____

_____
_____
_____
_____
_____
_____

24. Say, *"After examining this piece of process, how would you NOW reconceptualize this treatment problem?"*

_____
_____
_____
_____
_____
_____

25. Say, *"What relational strategy(ies) can you develop NOW to overcome this problem and re-attune to your client?"*

_____
_____
_____
_____
_____
_____

Practicum

Note: When this questionnaire is part of a workshop or study group, you may have the option of processing this issue to possible closure, including debriefing. Consider using the Float-Back Technique when stuck in the present without old memories available.

1. Say, *"What is the Present Day Referent* (or Presenting Problem) *in the treatment moment?"*

_____

_____

_____

Picture

2. Say, *"What picture represents that moment in the treatment room?"*

_____

_____

_____

Negative Cognition (NC)

3. Say, *"When you bring up that moment, what words best go with the picture that express your negative belief about yourself now?"*

_____

_____

Positive Cognition (PC)

4. Say, *"When you bring up that picture or incident, what would you like to believe about yourself, now?"*

_____

_____

Validity of Cognition (VoC)

5. Say, *"When you think of the incident* (or picture), *how true do those words* _____ (clinician repeats the positive cognition) *feel to you now on a scale of 1 to 7, where 1 feels completely false and 7 feels completely true?"*

1	2	3	4	5	6	7
(completely false)				(completely true)		

Emotions

6. Say, *"When you bring up the picture* (or incident) *and those words* _____ (clinician states the negative cognition), *what emotion do you feel now?"*

_____

_____

Subjective Units of Disturbance (SUD)

7. Say, *"On a scale of 0 to 10, where 0 is no disturbance or neutral and 10 is the highest disturbance you can imagine, how disturbing does it feel now?"*

    0   1   2   3   4   5   6   7   8   9   10
    (no disturbance)   (highest disturbance)

Location of Body Sensation

8. Say, *"Where do you feel it* (the disturbance) *in your body?"*

    _____

    _____

If there is a problem connecting with old memories, use the Float-Back Technique (based on Shapiro, 2006, p. 48).

9. Say, *"Now please bring up that picture of* _____ (repeat clinician as client's disturbing image) *and those negative words* _____ (state the negative cognition). *Now notice what feelings are coming up for you, and where you are feeling them in your body, and just let your mind float back to an earlier time in your life—don't search for anything—just let your mind float back and tell me the earliest scene that comes to mind where you had similar thoughts of* _____ (repeat negative cognition), *and feelings of* _____ (repeat emotions), *and where you feel it in your body and what old dysfunctional ego states emerge?"*

    _____

    _____

    _____

    _____

10. Say, *"Based on your experiential work, how do you NOW reconceptualize this problem? How does this answer differ from question #21?"*

    _____

    _____

    _____

    _____

11. Say, *"What relational strategy might you consider NOW to help work this problem out?"*

    _____

    _____

    _____

    _____

Note

Reproduced with permission of Taylor and Francis Group via the Copyright Clearance Center for reprinting pp. 247–252, from *EMDR and the Relational Imperative: The Therapeutic Relationship in EMDR Treatment* by Mark Dworkin, for The Clinical Self Awareness Questionnaire, Copyright 2005.

Past Memory Worksheet Script (Francine Shapiro, 2001, 2006)

Phase 3: Assessment

Incident

Say, *"The memory that we will start with today is _____ (select the next incident to be targeted)."*

_____

_____

_____

Say, *"What happens when you think of the _____ (state the issue)?"*

_____

_____

_____

Or say, *"When you think of _____ (state the issue), what do you get?"*

_____

_____

Picture

Say, *"What picture represents the entire _____ (state the issue)?"*

_____

_____

_____

If there are many choices or if the client becomes confused, the clinician assists by asking the following:

Say, *"What picture represents the most traumatic part of _____ (state the issue)?"*

_____

_____

_____

Negative Cognition (NC)

Say, *"What words best go with the picture that express your negative belief about yourself now?"*

_____

_____

Positive Cognition (PC)

Say, *"When you bring up that picture or _____ (state the issue), what would you like to believe about yourself, now?"*

_____

_____

Validity of Cognition (VoC)

Say, *"When you think of the incident* (or picture), *how true do those words _____* (clinician repeats the positive cognition) *feel to you now on a scale of 1 to 7, where 1 feels completely false and 7 feels completely true?"*

1	2	3	4	5	6	7
(completely false)				(completely true)		

Emotions

Say, *"When you bring up the picture or _____* (state the issue) *and those words _____* (clinician states the negative cognition), *what emotion do you feel now?"*

_____

_____

Subjective Units of Disturbance (SUD)

Say, *"On a scale of 0 to 10, where 0 is no disturbance or neutral and 10 is the highest disturbance you can imagine, how disturbing does it feel now?"*

0	1	2	3	4	5	6	7	8	9	10
(no disturbance)								(highest disturbance)		

Location of Body Sensation

Say, *"Where do you feel it* (the disturbance) *in your body?"*

_____

_____

Phase 4: Desensitization

To begin, say the following:

Say, *"Now, remember, it is your own brain that is doing the healing and you are the one in control. I will ask you to mentally focus on the*

target and to follow my fingers (or any other BLS you are using). *Just
let whatever happens, happen, and we will talk at the end of the set.
Just tell me what comes up, and don't discard anything as unimportant. Any new information that comes to mind is connected in some
way. If you want to stop, just raise your hand."*

Then say, *"Bring up the picture and the words* _____ (clinician repeats the NC) *and notice where you feel it in your body. Now follow
my fingers with your eyes* (or other BLS).*"*

Phase 5: Installation

Say, *"How does* _____ (repeat the PC) *sound?"*

_____

_____

Say, *"Do the words* _____ (repeat the PC) *still fit, or is there another positive statement that feels better?"*

_____

_____

If the client accepts the original positive cognition, the clinician should ask for
a VoC rating to see if it has improved:

Say, *"As you think of the incident, how do the words feel, from 1
(completely false) to 7 (completely true)?"*

1	2	3	4	5	6	7
(completely false)				(completely true)		

Say, *"Think of the event and hold it together with the words* _____
(repeat the PC).*"*

Do a long set of bilateral stimulation (BLS) to see if there is more processing
to be done.

Phase 6: Body Scan

Say, *"Close your eyes and keep in mind the original memory and the positive cognition. Then bring your attention to the different parts of your
body, starting with your head and working downward. Any place you
find any tension, tightness, or unusual sensation, tell me."*

_____

_____

Phase 7: Closure

Say, *"Things may come up or they may not. If they do, great. Write it
down and it can be a target for next time. You can use a log to write
down what triggers, images, thoughts or cognitions, emotions and
sensations; you can rate them on our 0-to-10 scale where 0 is no
disturbance or neutral and 10 is the worst disturbance. Please write
down the positive experiences, too."*

"If you get any new memories, dreams, or situations that disturb you, just take a good snapshot. It isn't necessary to give a lot of detail. Just put down enough to remind you so we can target it next time. The same thing goes for any positive dreams or situations. If negative feelings do come up, try not to make them significant. Remember, it's still just the old stuff. Just write it down for next time. Then use the tape or the Safe Place exercise to let as much of the disturbance go as possible. Even if nothing comes up, make sure to use the tape every day and give me a call if you need to."

Phase 8: Reevaluation

There are four ways to reevaluate our work with clients.

1. Reevaluate what has come up in the client's life since the last session.

   Say, *"Okay. Let's look at your log. I am interested in what has happened since the last session. What have you noticed since our last session?"*

   _____

   _____

   _____

   Say, *"What has changed?"*

   _____

   _____

   _____

   If the client has nothing to say or does not say much, say the following:

   Say, *"Have you had any dreams or nightmares?"*

   _____

   _____

   _____

   Say, *"What about _____ (state symptoms you and client have been working on) we have been working on, have you noticed any changes in them? Have they increased or decreased?"*

   _____

   _____

   _____

   Say, *"Have you noticed any other changes, new responses, or insights in your images, thoughts, emotions, sensations, and behaviors?"*

   _____

   _____

   _____

Say, *"Have you found new resources?"*

_____

_____

_____

Say, *"Have any situations, events, or other stimuli triggered you?"*

_____

_____

_____

Use the material from your reevaluation to feed back into your case conceptualization and help decide what to do next concerning the larger treatment plan.

2. Reevaluate the target worked on in the previous session. Has the individual target been resolved? Whether the previous processing session was complete or incomplete, use the following instructions to access the memory and determine the need for further processing:

Say, *"Bring up the memory or trigger of* _____ (state the memory or trigger) *that we worked on last session. What image comes up?"*

_____

_____

_____

Say, *"What thoughts about it come up?"*

_____

_____

Say, *"What thoughts about yourself?"*

_____

_____

Say, *"What emotions did you notice?"*

_____

_____

Say, *"What sensations do you notice?"*

_____

_____

Say, *"On a scale of 0 to 10, where 0 is no disturbance or neutral and 10 is the highest disturbance you can imagine, how disturbing does it feel now?"*

0   1   2   3   4   5   6   7   8   9   10
(no disturbance)   (highest disturbance)

Evaluate the material to see if there are any indications of dysfunction. Has the primary issue been resolved? Is there ecological validity to the client's resolution of the issue? Is there associated material that has been activated that must be addressed?

If you are observing any resistance to resolving the issue, say the following:

Say, *"What would happen if you are successful?"*

_____

_____

If there are no indications of dysfunction, and SUD is 0, do a set of BLS to be sure that the processing is complete.

Say, *"Go with that."*
Say, *"What do you get now?"*

_____

_____

Check the positive cognition.

Say, *"When you think of the incident* (or picture) *how true do those words* _____ (clinician repeats the positive cognition) *feel to you now on a scale of 1 to 7, where 1 feels completely false and 7 feels completely true?"*

1   2   3   4   5   6   7
(completely false)   (completely true)

If the VoC is 7, do a set of BLS to be sure that the processing is complete.

Say, *"Go with that."*
Say, *"What do you get now?"*

_____

_____

If there are any signs of dysfunction such as a new negative perspective(s) or new facets of the event or the SUD is higher than 0, say the following:

Say, *"Okay, now please pay attention to the image, thoughts, and sensations associated with* _____ (state the memory or trigger) *and just go with that."*

_____

_____

Continue with the Standard EMDR Protocol until processing is complete. If the VoC is less than 7, say the following:

Say, *"What is keeping it from being a 7?"*

_____

_____

Note the associated feelings and sensations, and resume processing.

Say, *"Go with that."*

Continue with the Standard EMDR Protocol through the Body Scan until processing is complete.

If a completely new incident or target emerges, say the following:

Say, *"Are there any feeder memories contributing to this problem?"*

_____

_____

Do the Assessment Phase on the appropriate target and fully process it. It is not unusual for another aspect of the memory to emerge that needs to be processed.

If the client claims that nothing or no disturbance is coming up (or he can't remember what was worked on in the previous session), and the therapist thinks that the work is probably still incomplete and that the client is simply not able to access the memory, say the following:

Say, *"When you think of _____ (state the incident that was worked*
    on) *and the image _____ (state the image) and _____*
    (state the NC), *what body sensations do you feel now?"*

_____

_____

Say, *"Go with that?"*

_____

_____

Continue processing with the Standard EMDR Protocol.

If the client wants to work on a *charged* trigger that came up since the last session instead of the target from the previous session, say the following:

Say, *"Yes, this IS important information. Tell me about what came up*
    for you."

_____

_____

Then assess the magnitude of the trigger. If it is indeed a severe critical incident, then proceed accordingly, using the Assessment Phase to target the new material and return to the original target when possible.

If it is not, then say the following:

Say, *"Yes this is important, however, it is important that we finish our*
    work on _____ (state what you are working on) before mov-
    ing to another target. It is like what happens when you have too
    many files open on your computer and it slows down, or finishing
    the course of antibiotics even if you feel okay (or any other appropri-
    ate metaphor for your client).*"*

Fully reprocess each target through the Body Scan and Reevaluation before moving on to the next in order to ensure optimal results.

3. At various critical points in treatment (before moving on to the next symptom, theme, goal, etc.), reevaluate what has been effectively targeted and resolved and what still needs to be addressed.

Say, *"Now that we have finished this work, let's reevaluate our work so far. Remember _____ (state the work you have done). On a scale of 0 to 10, where 0 is no disturbance or neutral and 10 is the highest disturbance you can imagine, how disturbing does it feel now?"*

0	1	2	3	4	5	6	7	8	9	10

(no disturbance)   (highest disturbance)

If the SUD is higher than 0, evaluate what else needs to be done by continuing to work with the disturbance in the framework of the Standard EMDR Protocol.

Also evaluate whether the client has been able to achieve cognitive, behavioral, and emotional goals in his life.

Say, *"Have you accomplished all of the goals that we had contracted to work on such as _____ (read the list of agreed upon goals)?"*

_____

_____

_____

If not, evaluate what still needs to be targeted such as feeder memories.

Say, *"Please scan for an earlier memory that incorporates _____ (state the negative cognition). What do you get?"*

_____

_____

_____

Use the Standard EMDR Protocol to process any feeder memories.
Check if previously identified clusters of memories remain charged.

Say, *"Are there any memories left concerning _____ (state the cluster of memories previously worked on)?"*

_____

_____

_____

If so, work on the memory(ies), using the Standard EMDR Protocol. Make sure to incorporate the positive templates for all previously disturbing situations and projected future goals. See the Future Template Worksheet Script.

4. Before termination, reevaluate targets worked on over the course of therapy and goals addressed during treatment.

Say, *"Before we end our treatment, let's reevaluate our work to make sure that all of the targets are resolved and goals are addressed. Are there any PAST targets that remain unresolved for you?"*

_____

_____

_____

Or say, *"These are the past targets with which we worked, do any of them remain unresolved? What about the memories that we listed during our history taking and over the course of treatment."*

_____

_____

_____

Check with the SUDs for any disturbance.

Say, *"On a scale of 0 to 10, where 0 is no disturbance or neutral and 10 is the highest disturbance you can imagine, how disturbing does it feel now?"*

0   1   2   3   4   5   6   7   8   9   10
(no disturbance)   (highest disturbance)

Check the major negative cognitions to see if there are any unresolved memories still active.

Say, *"These are the main negative cognitions with which we worked. Hold _____ (state one of the cognitions worked with) and scan for any unresolved memories. Does anything surface for you?"*

_____

_____

If there is more unresolved material, check with BLS to see if the charge decreases. If not, use the Standard EMDR Protocol.

Say, *"Now scan chronologically from birth until today to see if there are any other unresolved memories. What do you notice?"*

_____

_____

If there is more unresolved material, check with BLS to see if the charge decreases. If not, use the Standard EMDR Protocol.

Progressions can occur during other events or during the processing of a primary target; use your clinical judgment whether it is important to return and reevaluate these memories.

Clusters are related memories that were grouped together during treatment planning and can be scanned to identify any memories that were not involved through generalization of treatment effects.

> Say, *"Let's check the _____ (state the cluster), we worked on earlier. When you think about it, are there any other memories that were not involved that you are aware of now?"*

_____

_____

If there is more unresolved material, check with BLS to see if the charge decreases. If not, use the Standard EMDR Protocol.

Participants are significant individuals in the client's life who should be targeted if memories or issues regarding them remain disturbing.

> Say, *"Let's check if there are any remaining concerns or memories concerning _____ (state whoever the client might be concerned about). Is there anything that still is bothering you about _____ (state the person's name)?"*

_____

_____

If there is more unresolved material, check with BLS to see if the charge decreases. If not, use the Standard EMDR Protocol.

> Say, *"Are there any PRESENT or RECENT triggers that remain potent?"*

_____

_____

_____

> Say, *"Are there any current conditions, situations, or people that make you want to avoid them, act in ways that are not helpful, or cause you emotional distress?"*

_____

_____

If there is more unresolved material, check with BLS to see if the charge decreases. If not, use the Standard EMDR Protocol.

> Say, *"Are there any future goals that have not been addressed and realized?"*

_____

_____

_____

Make sure to use the Future Template for each trigger, new goal(s), new skill(s), issues of memory, or incorporating the client's new sense of himself. See Future Template Worksheet Script in this Appendix.

Present Trigger Worksheet Script

Target and reprocess present triggers identified during history taking, reprocessing, and reevaluation. Steps for working with present triggers are the following:

1. Identify the presenting trigger that is still causing disturbance.
2. Target and activate the presenting trigger using the full Assessment procedures (image, negative cognition, positive cognition, VoC, emotions, SUD, sensations).
3. Follow Phases 3 through 8 with each trigger until it is fully reprocessed (SUD = 0, VoC = 7, clear Body Scan) before moving to the next trigger. Note: In some situations, a blocking belief may be associated with the present trigger requiring a new Targeting Sequence Plan.
4. Once all present triggers have been reprocessed, proceed to installing Future Templates for each present trigger (e.g., imagining encountering the same situation in the future). (See Future Template protocols.)

Present Stimuli That Trigger the Disturbing Memory or Reaction

List the situations that elicit the symptom(s). Examples of situations, events, or stimuli that trigger clients could be the following: another trauma, the sound of a car backfiring, or being touched in a certain way.

> Say, *"What are the situations, events, or stimuli that trigger your trauma* _____ (state the trauma)? *Let's process these situations, events, or stimuli triggers one-by-one."*

Situations, Events, or Stimuli Trigger List

_____

_____

_____

_____

_____

Target or Memory

> Say, *"What situation, event, or stimulus that triggers you would you like to use as a target today?"*

_____

_____

Picture

> Say, *"What picture represents the* _____ (state the situation, event, or stimulus) *that triggers you?"*

_____

_____

If there are many choices or if the client becomes confused, the clinician assists by asking the following:

Say, *"What picture represents the most traumatic part of the _____ (state the situation, event, or stimulus) that triggers you?"*

_____

_____

When a picture is unavailable, the clinician merely invites the client to do the following:

Say, *"Think of the _____ (state the situation, event, or stimulus) that triggers you."*

_____

_____

Negative Cognition (NC)

Say, *"What words best go with the picture that express your negative belief about yourself now?"*

_____

_____

Positive Cognition (PC)

Say, *"When you bring up that picture or the _____ (state the situation, event, or stimulus) that triggers you, what would you like to believe about yourself now?"*

_____

_____

Validity of Cognition (VoC)

Say, *"When you think of the _____ (state the situation, event, stimulus, or picture that triggers you), how true do those words _____ (clinician repeats the positive cognition) feel to you now on a scale of 1 to 7, where 1 feels completely false and 7 feels completely true?"*

1   2   3   4   5   6   7
(completely false)   (completely true)

Sometimes, it is necessary to explain further.

Say, *"Remember, sometimes we know something with our head, but it feels differently in our gut. In this case, what is the gut-level feeling of the truth of _____ (clinician states the positive cognition), from 1 (completely false) to 7 (completely true)?"*

1   2   3   4   5   6   7
(completely false)   (completely true)

Emotions

Say, "*When you bring up the picture* (or state the situation, event, or stimulus) *that triggers you and those words* _____ (clinician states the negative cognition), *what emotion do you feel now?*"

_____

_____

Subjective Units of Disturbance (SUD)

Say, "*On a scale of 0 to 10, where 0 is no disturbance or neutral and 10 is the highest disturbance you can imagine, how disturbing does it feel now?*"

0	1	2	3	4	5	6	7	8	9	10

(no disturbance)   (highest disturbance)

Location of Body Sensation

Say, "*Where do you feel it* (the disturbance) *in your body?*"

_____

_____

Continue to process the triggers according the Standard EMDR Protocol.

Future Template Worksheet (Francine Shapiro, 2001, pp. 210–214; 2006, pp. 51–53)

The future template is the third prong in the Standard EMDR Protocol. Work with the future template occurs after the earlier memories and present triggers are adequately resolved and the client is ready to make new choices in the future concerning their issue(s). The purpose of it is to address any residual avoidance, any need for further issues of adaptation, to help with incorporating any new information, and it allows for the actualization of client goals. It is another place, in this comprehensive protocol, to catch any fears, negative beliefs, inappropriate responses, and so forth, to reprocess them and also to make sure that the new feelings and behavior can generalize into the clients' day-to-day lives.

There are two basic future templates:

1. Anticipatory Anxiety
   Anticipatory anxiety needs to be addressed with a full assessment (Phase 3) of the future situation.

2. Skills Building and Imaginal Rehearsal
   These do not need a full assessment of target and can begin directly with "running a movie."

Future Template Script

Check the Significant People and Situations of the Presenting Issues for Any Type of Distress

It is helpful to check to see if all the material concerning the issue upon which the client has worked is resolved or if there is more material that has escaped detection so far. The Future Template is another place to find if there is more material that needs reprocessing.

Significant People

When the client's work has focused on a significant person, ask the following:

Say, "*Imagine yourself encountering that person in the future* _____ (suggest a place that the client might see this person). *What do you notice?*"

_____

_____

_____

Watch the client's reaction to see if more work is necessary. If a client describes a negative feeling in connection with this person, check to see if it is reality based.

Say, "*Is* _____ (state the person's name) *likely to act* _____ (state the client's concern)*?*"

_____

_____

If the negative feeling is not matching the current reality, say the following:

Say, *"What do you think makes you have negative feelings toward _____ (state the person in question)?"*

_____

_____

If the client is unsure, use the Float-Back or Affect Scan to see what other earlier material may still be active.

If the negative feelings are appropriate, it is important to reevaluate the clusters of events concerning this person and access and reprocess any remaining maladaptive memories. (See Past Memory Worksheet.)

Significant Situations

It is important to have the client imagine being in significant situations in the future; this is another way of accessing material that may not have been processed.

Say, *"Imagine a videotape or film of how _____ (state current situation client is working on) and how it would evolve _____ (state appropriate time frame) in the future. When you have done that, let me know what you have noticed."*

_____

_____

If there is no disturbance, reinforce the positive experience.

Say, *"Go with that."*

Do BLS.

Reinforce the PC with the future situation with BLS as it continues the positive associations. For further work in the future, see below.

If there is a disturbance, assess what the client needs: more education, modeling of appropriate behavior, or more past memories for reprocessing.

Say, *"On a scale of 0 to 10, where 0 is no disturbance or neutral and 10 is the highest disturbance you can imagine, how disturbing does it feel now?"*

0   1   2   3   4   5   6   7   8   9   10
(no disturbance)   (highest disturbance)

Anticipatory Anxiety

When the SUD is above a 4, or when the desensitization phase is not brief, the clinician should look for a present trigger and its associated symptom and develop another Targeting Sequence Plan using the 3-Pronged Protocol. (See worksheets on Past Memories and Present Triggers.)

When there is anticipatory anxiety at a SUD level of no more than 3 to 4 maximum, it is possible to proceed with reprocessing using the future template. The desensitization phase should be quite brief.

Say, "What happens when you think of _____ (state the client's anticipatory anxiety or issue)?"

_____

_____

_____

Or say, "When you think of _____ (state the client's anticipatory anxiety or issue), *what do you get?*"

_____

_____

_____

Picture

Say, *"What picture represents the entire* _____ (state the client's anticipatory anxiety or issue)*?"*

_____

_____

_____

If there are many choices or if the client becomes confused, the clinician assists by asking the following:

Say, "What picture represents the most traumatic part of _____ (state the client's anticipatory anxiety or issue)?"

_____

_____

_____

Negative Cognition (NC)

Say, *"What words best go with the picture that express your negative belief about yourself now?"*

_____

_____

Positive Cognition (PC)

Say, *"When you bring up that picture or* _____ (state the client's anticipatory anxiety or issue), *what would you like to believe about yourself now?"*

_____

_____

Validity of Cognition (VoC)

Say, *"When you think of* _____ (state the client's anticipatory anxiety or issue) *or picture, how true do those words* _____ (clinician repeats the positive cognition) *feel to you now on a scale of 1 to 7, where 1 feels completely false and 7 feels completely true?"*

1	2	3	4	5	6	7
(completely false)				(completely true)		

Emotions

Say, *"When you bring up the picture or* _____ (state the client's anticipatory anxiety or issue) *and those words* _____ (clinician states the negative cognition), *what emotion do you feel now?"*

_____

_____

Subjective Units of Disturbance (SUD)

Say, *"On a scale of 0 to 10, where 0 is no disturbance or neutral and 10 is the highest disturbance you can imagine, how disturbing does it feel now?"*

0	1	2	3	4	5	6	7	8	9	10
(no disturbance)								(highest disturbance)		

Location of Body Sensation

Say, *"Where do you feel it* (the disturbance) *in your body?"*

_____

_____

Phase 4: Desensitization

To begin, say the following:

Say, *"Now remember, it is your own brain that is doing the healing and you are the one in control. I will ask you to mentally focus on the target and to follow my fingers (or any other BLS you are using). Just let whatever happens, happen, and we will talk at the end of the set. Just tell me what comes up, and don't discard anything as unimportant. Any new information that comes to mind is connected in some way. If you want to stop, just raise your hand."*

Then say, *"Bring up the picture and the words* _____ (clinician repeats the NC) *and notice where you feel it in your body. Now, follow my fingers with your eyes (or other BLS)."*

Continue with the Desensitization Phase until the SUD = 0 and the VoC = 7.

Phase 5: Installation

Say, *"How does* _____ (repeat the PC) *sound?"*

_____   _____

_____   _____

Say, *"Do the words* _____ *(repeat the PC) still fit, or is there an-other positive statement that feels better?"*

_____

_____

If the client accepts the original positive cognition, the clinician should ask for a VoC rating to see if it has improved.

Say, *"As you think of the incident, how do the words feel, from 1 (completely false) to 7 (completely true)?"*

1	2	3	4	5	6	7
(completely false)				(completely true)		

Say, *"Think of the event and hold it together with the words* _____ *(repeat the PC)."*

Do a long set of BLS to see if there is more processing to be done.

Phase 6: Body Scan

Say, *"Close your eyes and keep in mind the original memory and the positive cognition. Then bring your attention to the different parts of your body, starting with your head and working downward. Any place you find any tension, tightness, or unusual sensation, tell me."*

_____

_____

Make sure that this anticipatory anxiety is fully processed before returning to the Future Template.

The Future Template for appropriate future interaction is an expansion of the Installation Phase; instead of linking the positive cognition with the past memory or trigger, the PC is linked to the future issues. Once the client's work has been checked and the other known issues in the past and present have been resolved, each client has the choice to do a more formal future template installation. The first option is to work with the situation or issue as an image.

Image as Future Template: Imagining Positive Outcomes

Imagining positive outcomes seems to assist the learning process. In this way, clients learn to enhance optimal behaviors, to connect them with a positive cognition and to support generalization. The assimilation of this new behavior and thought is supported by the use of bilateral stimulation (BLS) into a positive way to act in the future.

Say, *"I would like you to imagine yourself coping effectively with or in* _____ *(state the goal) in the future. With the positive belief* _____ *(state the positive belief) and your new sense of* _____ *(state the quality: i.e., strength, clarity, confidence, calm), imagine stepping into this scene."*
"Notice what you see and how you are handling the situation."

"Notice what you are thinking, feeling, and experiencing in your body."

_____

_____

_____

Again, here is the opportunity to catch any disturbance that may have been missed.

Say, *"Are there any blocks, anxieties, or fears that arise as you think about this future scene?"*

_____

_____

_____

If yes, say the following:

Say, *"Then focus on these blocks and follow my fingers* (or any other BLS).*"*
Say, *"What do you get now?"*

_____

_____

_____

If the blocks do not resolve quickly, evaluate if the client needs any new information, resources, or skills to be able to comfortably visualize the future coping scene. Introduce needed information or skills.

Say, *"What would you need to feel confident in handling the situation?"*
Or say, *"What is missing from your handling of this situation?"*

_____

_____

If the block still does not resolve and the client is unable to visualize the future scene with confidence and clarity, use direct questions, the Affect Scan, or the Float-Back Technique to identify old targets related to blocks, anxieties, or fears. Remember, the point of the 3-Prong Protocol is not only to reinforce positive feelings and behavior in the future but again to catch any unresolved material that may be getting in the way of an adaptive resolution of the issue(s). Use the Standard EMDR Protocol to address these targets before proceeding with the template (see Worksheets in Appendix A).

If there are no apparent blocks and the client is able to visualize the future scene with confidence and clarity, say the following:

Say, *"Please focus on the image, the positive belief, and the sensations associated with this future scene and follow my fingers* (or any other BLS).*"*

_____

_____

Process and reinforce the positive associations with BLS. Do several sets until the future template is sufficiently strengthened.

Say, *"Go with that."*

_____

_____

Then say, *"Close your eyes and keep in mind the image of the future and the positive cognition. Then bring your attention to the different parts of your body, starting with your head and working downward. Any place you find any tension, tightness, or unusual sensation, tell me."*

_____

_____

If any sensation is reported, do BLS.

Say, *"Go with that."*

If it is a positive or comfortable sensation, do BLS to strengthen the positive feelings.

Say, *"Go with that."*

If a sensation of discomfort is reported, reprocess until the discomfort subsides.

Say, *"Go with that."*

When the discomfort subsides, check the VoC.

Say, *"When you think of the incident* (or picture), *how true do those words* _____ (clinician repeats the positive cognition) *feel to you now on a scale of 1 to 7, where 1 feels completely false and 7 feels completely true?"*

1   2   3   4   5   6   7
(completely false)   (completely true)

Continue to use BLS until reaching the VoC = 7 or there is an ecological resolution. When the image as future template is clear and the PC true, move on to the movie as future template.

Movie as Future Template or Imaginal Rehearsing

During this next level of future template, clients are asked to move from imagining this one scene or snapshot to imagining a movie about coping in the future, with a beginning, middle, and end. Encourage clients to imagine themselves coping effectively in the face of specific challenges, triggers, or snafus. Therapists can make some suggestions in order to help inoculate them with future problems. It is helpful to use this type of future template after clients have received needed education concerning social skills and customs, assertiveness, and any other newly learned skills.

Say, *"This time, I'd like you to close your eyes and play a movie, imagining yourself coping effectively with or in _____ (state where client will be) in the future. With the new positive belief _____ (state positive belief) and your new sense of _____ (strength, clarity, confidence, calm), imagine stepping into the future. Imagine yourself coping with ANY challenges that come your way. Make sure that this movie has a beginning, middle, and end. Notice what you are seeing, thinking, feeling, and experiencing in your body. Let me know if you hit any blocks. If you do, just open your eyes and let me know. If you don't hit any blocks, let me know when you have viewed the whole movie."*

_____

_____

If the client hits blocks, address as above with BLS until the disturbance dissipates.

Say, *"Go with that."*

If the material does not shift, use interweaves, new skills, information, resources, direct questions, and any other ways to help clients access information that will allow them to move on. If these options are not successful, usually it means that there is earlier material still unprocessed; the Float-Back and Affect Scan are helpful in these cases to access the material that keeps the client stuck.

If clients are able to play the movie from start to finish with a sense of confidence and satisfaction, ask them to play the movie one more time from beginning to end and introduce BLS.

Say, *"Okay, play the movie one more time from beginning to end. Go with that."*

Use BLS.

In a sense, you are installing this movie as a future template.

After clients have fully processed their issue(s), they might want to work on other positive templates for the future in other areas of their lives using the above future templates.

Note

Reprinted from *EMDR New Notes on Adaptive Information Processing with Case Formulation Principles, Forms, Scripts and Worksheets* by Francine Shapiro, PhD, with permission from The EMDR Institute, Copyright 2006.

Appendix B: Expanding the 11-Step Procedure

Unconsolidated Sensory Triggers and Desensitization: Running the Tape
Gene Schwartz

Based on clinical observation over many years, this author has found that processing an event using the Standard EMDR Protocol may leave affect-laden sensory material associated with the event unprocessed. The initial observation came from the treatment of a Vietnam veteran who reported being triggered by a noise following the completed processing of a combat trauma. Initial work developed into two different uses of running a tape to look for arousal.

The veteran reported being triggered back to the original event after what was thought to have been the successful resolution of the event. He reported the noise from a door banging took him back to the event with the same high level of affect. He said, "You know a shell doesn't go boom, it goes crack." The veteran processed the sound by replaying it in his mind while the therapist used bilateral stimulation (BLS) until he reported no further disturbance.

On a hunch, the man was asked to run a tape of the event starting at the beginning and looking for any other sounds that caused disturbance. If he found one, he was to stop the tape and tell this author. He eventually identified several other sounds such as men yelling, guns going off, helicopters coming in, and so forth. Each time he stopped at a sound, he was asked to hear it and BLS was used until the disturbance went to 0 on a SUD scale.

He was then asked to back the tape up past where the work had been done and start running the tape again. This checked the trigger sound again as the tape went forward. He was asked to do this until he could run the whole tape listening for sound without noticing a disturbance.

Again, on a hunch, he was asked to start the tape running looking for pictures that caused any disturbance. The work was continued as above with pictures until the tape of pictures was clear. Smell, taste, and physical sensations were also done in the same way. Several sessions were needed until he could watch a tape of the event in "living color" with pictures, sound, taste, smells, and physical sensations without disturbance. At that point, he was asked to watch the tape thinking of the positive cognition.

Since then as the last step of Phase 4 or the Desensitization Phase, this author asks clients to run a tape of the event and look for disturbance. Clinical judgment determines how fully clients are asked to review the tape. When working on an event of negative learning without extreme affect, the client is just asked to watch the tape. For events heavily affect-laden clients, they are asked to review the tape for each sensory mode individually.

Running the Tape With Triggers That Occur After Processing

Another clinical case led to a second use of running the tape. An adult client completed the processing of a sexual assault he experienced as a 10-year-old. Weeks later he reported experiencing a lot of arousal while attending a social event. Focusing on the arousal and negative cognition went back to the assault again but at a different age. He had processed the original event and run the tape looking at each sensory mode separately. The event should have been completed. The current affect was being driven by a triggered memory of friends calling each other names when he was about 14 years old. A friend called him queer. This type of teasing is not unfamiliar to young men, but in this case the teasing had particular impact. He had participated, although unwillingly, in the behavior his brain associated with the teasing. This second event was processed using the Standard EMDR Protocol. On a hunch he was asked to run a tape. He was to take the original assault, run a tape quickly through his life, and see if anything came up that connected. He stopped the tape at the point in his life when he was a married father of three children. His wife wanted to send the kids to a camp. The Standard EMDR Protocol was used here to process this until the SUDS were 0 and then he was asked to backup the tape and start again finding several other triggers before finishing the work.

This use of running the tape is particularly useful in many situations where an event has lasting impact on a person's life.

Case Example

A man was in an accident while driving a truck pulling a trailer. His wife, daughter, and his daughter's friend were in the truck with him. A car crossed the median and hit him head on. Both vehicles burst into flame. He and the occupants of his truck were pulled out by witnesses and they were taken to shock trauma.

The event was processed starting at the worst part, the impact with a negative cognition of "We are going to burn to death." The event as represented by "the worst part" resolved to SUDS of 0. The client was then asked to run the tape using each sensory mode separately. Three sessions were needed to complete the work. He was triggered for example by: sounds of the crash, yelling, sirens, smells of burning, spilled fuel, bandages, taste of blood, dirt, pictures of flames, his family on the ground, his daughter not moving, physical sensations of being thrown against the steering wheel, pain, heat, and so forth.

After the accident processing was finished, he was asked to run a tape up to the time he was seen for treatment. He was triggered by memories of multiple trips back to shock trauma for infections, sounds of a doctor telling him he could lose a foot, fighting with an insurance company about the value of his loss, and worry if the other driver burned to death. As much work was completed as possible at the time. He was told the therapist would finish the work when the legal fight with the insurance company was completed. He returned several months later after the settlement and the effect surrounding the legal case was resolved. At that time he brought in a death certificate for the other driver showing death was due to a heart attack most likely the cause of his crossing the medium. A year later he returned for another issue. He reported no effect associated with memories of the accident.

Script for Running the Tape to Identify and Process Unconsolidated Sensory Triggers

This is a step that is added at the end of Phase 4 (Desensitization) to assure the processing of any affect-laden sensory material associated with the event that was left unprocessed.

The therapist needs to use clinical judgment here for events of less emotional impact as a last step in Phase 4: Desensitization, the therapist asks the client to run a tape of the event being sure to check all sensory modes (smell, taste, etc.). If a disturbance comes up, use BLS until the disturbance goes down and the SUD is 0. Then backup the tape past that stop and run the tape again until the tape is clear and then go on to Installation.

For events that have higher arousal or are more traumatic, the therapist can start with whatever modality seems most salient for the client, for example, it is possible to start with taste if that is the modality that seems most relevant, and so forth.

Sensory Triggers: Images, Sounds, Taste, Touch, Smells, Balance

Say, *"I would like to ask you to review the tape of the original event and see if there are any _____ (state the modality that you are using) that cause any disturbance. Please start at the beginning of the event and run a tape forward checking only for _____ (state the modality that you are using) and stopping the tape if the _____ (state the modality that you are using) causes you any distress."* (Pause)

If the patient stops the tape, say the following:

Say, *"What did you notice?"*

_____

_____

Say, *"Okay. Now focus on the _____ (focus on whatever stopped the tape) while I _____ (state the BLS that you use), until the disturbance becomes neutral. Let me know when that happens."*

_____

_____

Say, *"Now, backup the tape and run it forward looking for any distress that you might still have. Go ahead and do that now."*

Wait for the client to let you know that they have found another disturbance, or if the tape is clean go to the next sensory modality.

Say, *"What do you notice? Is the _____ (state the modality that you are using) that you talked about still a cause for distress?"*

_____

_____

If a disturbance comes up, say the following:

Say, *"Let's go through it, sit with it, until the distress level is down to 0 on our scale. Let me know when the distress is down."* (Pause)

Wait until the client is finished.

Say, *"What is your experience now?"*

_____

_____

When all of the affect-laden sensory data has been reprocessed with running the tape, the client is asked to run the tape of the event in living color with all of the sensory data that had been reprocessed until there is no disturbance.

Say, *"Okay, now I would like you to run the tape of this event in living color with all of the sensory data that we have reprocessed _____ (state the modalities used) until there is no disturbance. Go ahead and do this now and let me know when you are finished."*

_____

_____

When the tape is clean and there is no distress, *running the tape* is completed. If there is more material that comes up, continue to work with the material until there is no distress. If there is any new material that arises such as a blocking belief, it can be processed using the Standard EMDR Protocol.

The next step is to check the original positive cognition to make sure that it is still accurate or if it needs to be replaced. Then, install the positive cognition while *running the tape* again.

Say, *"Does your original positive cognition _____ (state the original positive cognition from the EMDR Standard Protocol) still fit or is there one that fits better?"*

_____

_____

Run the tape again with the new or original positive cognition.

Say, *"Let's run the tape again while you think about the positive cognition _____ (state the positive cognition). Let me know when you have completed it."* (Pause)

Wait until the client has completed the tape.

Say, *"What did you notice?"*

_____

_____

After installation of the positive cognition is completed, move on to Phase 6: Body Scan. This phase moves much quicker after using running the tape.

New Triggers

Catching sensory triggers so that the Standard EMDR Protocol is complete can be helpful in other scenarios as well. When there is an incident that is processed, it is often advantageous to *run the tape* taking the original target and negative cognition and then running the tape quickly through the time line of the client's life to see if anything comes up that is connected. If there is new material, the Standard EMDR Protocol can be used on the target. After this, backup the tape and find any other triggers that are left.

Say, *"Okay, now take the target about* _____ (state the target worked on) *and* _____ (state the negative cognition) *and run the tape quickly through your life to see if there is anything that comes up that is connected. Go ahead and do that."*

_____

_____

Allow ample time for the client to do this.

If the client comes up with anything, process it using the Standard EMDR Protocol until the SUD is 0. Then say the following:

Say, *"Now backup the tape to the beginning of the work about* _____ (state original work) *and look for any other triggers that might be left. Let me know when you have completed this."*

_____

_____

If there are more triggers, again use the EMDR Standard EMDR Process to reprocess the material. If not, continue with the installation of the positive cognition, body scan, and closure phases of the target.

Appendix C: EMDR Worldwide Associations and Other Resources

In the Beginning

The EMDR Institute

Web site: (http://www.emdr.com/)
Contact Person: Robbie Dunton (rdunton@emdr.com)

EMDR Worldwide Associations Contact Information

Africa

Kenya

Contact Person: Alice Blanshard (alice@swiftkenya.com)
Gisela Roth (dr.roth.ac@aimint.net)

South Africa

Association: EMDR South Africa/Africa
Contact Person: Reyhana Seedat-Ravat (rravat@iafrica.com)

Asia

Bangladesh

Contact Person: Shamim Karim (shamim.karim@gmail.com)

Cambodia

Contact Person: Jane Lopacka (jane@ppcounselling.org)

China—Mainland

Contact Persons: WeiLi (Wu-lilywu22@yahoo.com)
Yuchuan Yang (yuchuany@yahoo.com.cn)
Li Fang (hxfangli@hotmail.com)

Hong Kong

Association: The EMDR Association of Hong Kong (email@hkemdr.org)
Contact Person: Atara Sivan

India

Contact Person: Sushma Mehrotra (mehrotrasushma@gmail.com)

Indonesia

Association: EMDR Indonesia
(http://www.emdrindonesia.org)

Japan

Association: Japan EMDR Association
(http://www.emdr.jp/)

Korea

Association: Korean EMDR Association [KEMDRA]
(http://emdrkorea.com/fine/)

Pakistan

Association: EMDR Pakistan
(www.emdrpakistan.com)

Singapore

Association: EMDR Singapore Coordinating Committee
Contact Person: Matthew Woo (matthew woo@imh.com.sq)

Sri Lanka

Association: EMDR Sri Lanka
Contact Person: George Fernando (geo-fern@eureka.lk)

Thailand

Association: EMDR Thailand Coordinating Committee
Contact Person: Dr. Nanthaphan Chinlumprasert (nanthaphanchn@au.edu)

Vietnam

Contact Person: Dr Carl Sternberg (pv.carl@gmail.com)
International SOS Clinic Hanoi

Australia

Association: EMDR Association of Australia
(http://www.emdraa.org/)

Europe

EMDR Europe Association: An association of European National EMDR Associations
(www.emdr-europe.org)

Austria

Association: EMDR-Netzwerk Osterreich
(http://www.emdr-institut.at/)

Belgium

Association: EMDR Belgium (Website under construction)
Contact Information: emdr-belgium@telenet.be

Denmark

Association: EMDR Denmark
(http://www.emdr.dk/)

Finland

Association: Suomen EMDR-vhdistys
(http://www.emdr.fi)

France

Association: Association EMDR France
(http://www.emdr-france.org/)

Germany

EMDRIA Deutschland
(http://www.emdria.de)

Greece

Association: EMDR Greece
(http://www.emdr.gr)

Israel

Association: The EMDR Israel Association
(http://www.emdr.org.il)

Italy

Association: EMDR Italie
(http://www.emdritalia.it)

Netherlands

Association: Vereniging EMDR Nederland
(http://www.emdr.nl)

Norway

Association: EMDR Norge
(http://www.emdrnorge.com/)

Serbia

Association: EMDR Serbia
(http://www.emdr-se-europe.org)

Spain

Association: Asociacion E.M.D.R. Espana
(http://emdr-es.org)

Sweden

Association: EMDR Sverige
(http://www.emdr.se/)

Switzerland

Association: EMDR Schweiz-Suisse-Svizzera-Switzerland
(http://www.emdr-ch.org/)

Turkey

Association: EMDR Turkiye
(http://www.emdr-tr.org)

United Kingdom and Ireland

Association: EMDR Association United Kingdom and Ireland
(http://www.emdras sociation.org.uk)

Ibero-America

(Includes Mexico, South and Central Americas, Spanish Caribbean, and the Iberian
Peninsula)
Association: EMDR-Iberoamerica
(http://emdriberoamerica.org/)
Another EMDR Latin America association is as follows:
Association: EMDR Latinoamerica
(http://www.emdr.org.ar)

Argentina

Association: EMDR Iberoamerica Argentina
(http://www.emdribargentina.org)

Brazil

Association: EMDR Brasil
(http://www.emdrbrasil.com.br)

Colombia

Association: EMDR Colombia
(http://emdrcolombia.org/)

Ecuador

Association: EMDR Ecuador
(http://emdrecuador.org/)

Guatemala

Association: EMDR Ibero-America Guatemala
Contact: Ligia Barascout (ligiabps@yahoo.com)

Mexico

Association: EMDR Mexico
(http://www.emdrmexico.org)

Portugal

Association: EMDR Portugal
(http://www.emdrportugal.com)

Uruguay

Association: EMDR Uruguay
(http://emdruruguay.org.uy)

North America

Canada

Association: EMDR Canada
(http://www.emdrcanada.org)

United States

Association: EMDR International Association
(http://emdria.org)

Related EMDR Humanitarian Associations

Europe

HAP-Europe

Association: HAP-Europe (Web site under construction)

France

Association: HAP-France
(http://www.hap-france.org)

Germany

Association: Trauma Aid
(http://www.hap-trauma-aid.org)

Ibero-America

Argentina

EMDR-Programa de Programa de Ayuda Humanitaria–Argentina
(http://emdrasistenciahumanitaria@fibertel.com.ar)

Iberoamerica

EMDR Iberoamerica
(http://emdriberoamerica.org/)

Mexico

Asociacion Mexicana para Ayuda Mental en Crisis A.C.
(http://www.amamecrisis.com.mx)

North America

United States

EMDR Humanitarian Assistance Program [EMDR-HAP]
(http:// www.emdrhap.org)

The Francine Shapiro Library

Francine Shapiro Library's EMDR Bibliography
(http://library.nku.edu)

EMDR Journals and E-Journals

The Journal of EMDR Practice and Research—The official publication of the EMDR International Association
(http://www.springerpub.com/emdr)

The EMDR Practitioner—The official journal of the European EMDR Association
(http://www.emdr-practitioner.net/)

EMDR-IS Electronic Journal
(http://www.emdr.org.il)

Related Traumatology Information

The Australian Trauma Web—Professor Grant Devilly's Trauma Pages
(http://www.swin.edu.au/bioscieleceng/neuropsych/ptsd)

David Baldwin's Trauma Pages
(http://www.trauma-pages.com)

Children and War
(http://www.childrenandwar.org)

European Federation of Psychologists Associations Task Force on Disaster Psychology [EFPA]
(http://www.disaster.efpa.be)

European Society for Traumatic Stress Studies
(http://www.estss.org)

International Society for the Study of Dissociation
(http://www.issdt.org)

The International Critical Incident Stress Foundation
(http://www.icisf.org)

References

Adúriz, M., Bluthgen, C., Gorrini, Z., Maquieira, S., Nofal, S., & Knopfler, C. (in press). The flooding in Santa Fé, Argentina. *Journal of Psychotraumatology for Iberoamérica.*

Amen, D. G. (2002). *Healing the hardware of the soul.* New York: The Free Press.

American Psychiatric Association (APA). (2000). *Diagnostic and statistical manual of mental disorders* (4th ed.). Washington, DC: Jaypee.

Artigas, L., & Jarero, I. (in press). The Butterfly Hug. In M. Luber (Ed.) *Eye movement desensitization and reprocessing (EMDR) scripted protocols: Special populations.* New York: Springer.

Artigas, L., Jarero, I., Mauer, M., López Cano, T., & Alcalá, N. (2000, September). *EMDR and traumatic stress after natural disasters: Integrative treatment protocol and the butterfly hug.* Poster presented at the EMDRIA Conference, Toronto, Ontario, Canada.

Bar-Sade, E. (2003a) *Early trauma: Revisited and revised through EMDR, the narrative story and the implementation of attachment theory.* Paper presented at the EMDR European Annual Conference, Rome.

Bar-Sade, E. (2003b). *EMDR and children.* The International Trauma Conference, Jerusalem.

Bar-Sade, E. (2005a). *"Attachment cues" as resources in affect regulation enhancement in children's EMDR Processing.* EMDR European Conference, Stockholm.

Bar-Sade, E. (2005b). EMDR and the challenge of working with children. *EMDR-Israel E-Journal.* Retrieved February 23, 2009, from www.emdr.org.il (Hebrew).

Bar-Sade, E. (2005c). EMDR with children. *EMDR-Israel E-Journal.* Retrieved February 23, 2009, from www.emdr.org.il (Hebrew).

Beere, D. B. (1997). The memory line: A measure of amnesia and continuity of memory. In L. Van De Creek (Ed.), *Innovations in clinical practice: A source book 15* (pp. 83–95). Sarasota, FL: Professional Resource Exchange, Inc.

Berman, W. H., & Bradt, G. (2006). Executive coaching and consulting: "Different strokes for different folks." *Professional Psychology: Research and Practice, 37,* 244–253.

Birnbaum, A. (February, 2005a). *Group EMDR with children and families in South Thailand post-tsunami.* Invited presentation at Bangkok Children's Hospital, Bangkok, Thailand.

Birnbaum, A. (February, 2005b). *Group EMDR with children and families following the tsunami in Thailand.* Invited presentation at the EMDR-Israel Humanitarian Assistance Program Conference, Ra'anana, Israel.

Birnbaum, A. (July, 2006). *Group EMDR: Theory and practice.* Invited presentation at the EMDR-Israel Humanitarian Assistance Program Conference, Netanya, Israel.

Birnbaum, A. (2007, February). *Group EMDR in critical incident stress debriefing with IDF casualty notification officers: A pilot study.* Invited presentation at the EMDR-Israel Conference on EMDR in the Second Lebanese War, Netanya, Israel.

Bisson, J. I. (2006). *Plenary presentation, early treatment intervention.* EMDR Conference, June 9–11, 2006, Istanbul, Turkey.

Blore, D. C. (1997). Reflections on "A day when the whole world seemed to be darkened" changes. *International Journal of Psychology and Psychotherapy, 15*(2), 89–95.

Browning, C. J. (1999, September). Float-back and float-forward. *EMDRIA Newsletter,* 12–13.

Buss, D. (2000). The evolution of happiness. *American Psychologist, 55,* 15–23.

Carlson, E. B., & Putnam, F. W. (1992). *Manual for the Dissociative Experiences Scale.* Lutherville, MD: Sidran Foundation.

Cemalovic, A. (1997). *A saga of Sarejevo children: Coping with life under siege.* Stockholm: KTH Hogkoletryckeriet.

Chemtob, C. M., Nakashima, J., Hamada, R. S., & Carlson, J. G. (2002). Brief-treatment for elementary school children with disaster-related posttraumatic stress disorder: A field study. *Journal of Clinical Psychology, 58,* 99–112.

Childre, D., & Martin, M. (1999). *The HeartMath solution.* San Francisco, CA: Harper.

Cocco, N., & Sharpe, L. (1993). An auditory variant of eye movement desensitization in a case of childhood post-traumatic stress disorder. *Journal of Behavior Therapy and Experimental Psychiatry, 24,* 373–377.

Csikszentmihalyi, M. (1990). *Flow: The psychology of optimal experience.* New York: Harper Collins.

De Jongh, A., Ten Broeke, E., & Renssen, M. R. (1999). Treatment of specific phobias with eye movement desensitization and reprocessing (EMDR): Protocol, empirical status, and conceptual issues. *Journal of Anxiety Disorders, 13,* 69–85.

DeMaria, R., Weeks, G., & Hof, L. (1999). *Focused genograms: Intergenerational assessment of individuals, couples and families.* New York: Bruner-Routledge.

Dworkin, M. (2005). *EMDR and the relational imperative: The therapeutic relationship in EMDR Treatment.* New York: Routledge.

Emanuel, Y. (August, 2006). Integrating EMDR and a narrative approach in treatment of complex trauma. *EMDR-Israel E-Journal,* www.emdr.org.il (Hebrew).

Errebo, N., Knipe, J., Forte, K., Karlin, V., & Altayli, B. (2008). EMDR-HAP training in Sri Lanka following 2004 tsunami. *Journal of EMDR Practice & Research, 2*(2), 124–139.

Escudero, A. (2003). *Healing by thinking: Noesitherapy (Biological basis)* (4th ed.). Valencia, Spain: Impreso en Signo Grafico.

Everly, G. D., & Lating, J. M. (2003). *A clinical guide to the treatment of the human stress response* (2nd ed.). New York: Kluwer Academic/Plenum Publishers.

Fernandez, I., Gallinari, E., & Lorenzetti, A. (2004). A school-based intervention for children who witnessed the Pirelli building airplane crash in Milan, Italy. *Journal of Brief Therapy, 2,* 129–136.

Foster, S. (2000). Peak performance EMDR: Adapting trauma treatment to positive applications for enhancing performance in athletes. *Journal of Applied Sport Psychology, 7*(Suppl.), 63.

Foster, S. (2001). *From trauma to triumph: EMDR and advanced performance enhancement strategies* (self-published training manual). San Francisco, CA: Success at Work.

Foster, S., & Lendl, J. (1995). Eye movement desensitization and reprocessing: Initial applications for enhancing performance in athletes. *Journal of Applied Sport Psychology, 7*(Suppl.), 63.

Foster, S., & Lendl, J. (1996). Eye movement desensitization and reprocessing: Four case studies of a new tool for executive coaching and restoring employee performance after setbacks. *Consulting Psychology Journal, 48,* 155–161.

Foster, S., & Lendl, J. (2002). Peak performance EMDR: Adapting trauma treatment to positive psychology outcomes and self-actualization. *EMDRIA Newsletter, 7*(1), 4–7.

Foster, S., & Lendl, J. (2007). Eye movement desensitization and reprocessing: Four of a new tool for executive coaching and restoring employee performance after setbacks. In R. Kilburg & R. Diedrich (Eds.), *The wisdom of coaching* (pp. 407–412). Washington, DC: American Psychological Association. (Republished from [1996] *Consulting Psychological Journal, 48*(3), 155–161.)

Gelbach, R., & Davis, K. (2007). Disaster response: EMDR and family systems therapy under communitywide stress. In F. Shapiro, I. Jarero, L. Artigas, N. Alcalá, T. López Cano, & M. Mauer (1999, November). *Children's post traumatic stress after natural disasters: Integrative treatment protocol.* Poster presented at the annual meeting of the International Society for Traumatic Stress Studies, Miami, FL.

Gelinas, D. J. (2003). Integrating EMDR into phase-oriented treatment for trauma. *Journal of Trauma and Dissociation, 4,* 91–135.

Graham, H. (1995). *Mental imagery in health care: An introduction to therapeutic practice.* London: Chapman and Hall.

Grainger, R. D., Levin, C., Allen-Byrd, L., Doctor, R. M., & Lee, H. (1997). An empirical evaluation of eye movement desensitization and reprocessing (EMDR) with survivors of a natural disaster. *Journal of Traumatic Stress, 10,* 665–671.

Greenwald, R. (1993a). Magical installations can help clients to slay their dragons. *EMDR Network Newsletter, 3*(2), 16–17.

Greenwald, R. (1993b). Treating children's nightmares with EMDR. *EMDR Network Newsletter, 3*(1), 7–9.

Greenwald, R. (1994). Applying eye movement desensitization and reprocessing to the treatment of traumatized children: Five case studies. *Anxiety Disorders Practice Journal, 1,* 83–97.

Greenwald, R. (1998). Eye movement desensitization and reprocessing (EMDR): New hope for children suffering from trauma and loss. *Clinical Child Psychology and Psychiatry, 3,* 279–287.

Greenwald, R. (1999). *Eye movement desensitization and reprocessing (EMDR) in child and adolescent psychotherapy.* Northvale, NJ: Jason Aronson Press.

Greenwald, R., & Rubin, A. (1999). Brief assessment of children's post-traumatic symptoms: Development and preliminary validation of parent and child scales. *Research on Social Work Practice, 9,* 61–75.

Hamilton, L. H., & Robson, B. (2006). Performing arts consultation: Developing expertise in this domain. *Professional Psychology: Research and Practice, 37,* 254–259.

Harmison, R. J. (2006). Peak performance in sport: Identifying ideal performance states and developing athletes' psychological states. *Professional Psychology: Research and Practice, 37,* 233–243.

Hartung, J. (2002). Energy psychology in the service of EMDR. *The EMDRIA Newsletter, 7*(3), 3–4.

Hartung, J. (2005a). *Enhancing performance and positive emotion with EMDR.* Paper presented at the EMDR International Association Annual Conference, Seattle, Washington.

Hartung, J. (2005b). *Reaching further: How to remove obstacles to personal excellence.* Colorado Springs: Colorado School of Professional Psychology Press.

Hartung, J., & Galvin, M. (2003). *Energy psychology and EMDR: Combining forces to optimize treatment.* New York: W. W. Norton.

Hays, K. F. (2002). The enhancement of performance excellence among performing artists. *Journal of Applied Sport Psychology, 14,* 299–312.

Hays, K. F. (2006). Being fit: The ethics of practice diversification in performance psychology. *Professional Psychology: Research and Practice, 37,* 223–232.

Hays, K. F., & Brown, C. H. (2004). *You're on! Consulting for peak performance.* Washington, DC: American Psychological Association.

Hofmann, A. (2004). *EMDR-Arbeitsbogen: Anamnese.* Cologne, Germany: EMDR-Institut Deutschland.

Hofmann, A. (in press). The Absorption Technique. In M. Luber (Ed.), *Eye movement desensitization and reprocessing (EMDR) scripted protocols: Special populations.* New York: Springer Publishing.

Holt, P. E., & Andrews, G. (1989). Hyperventilation and anxiety in panic disorder, social phobia, GAD and normal controls. *Behaviour Research and Therapy, 27,* 453–460.

Ievleva, L., & Orlick, T. (1991). Mental links to enhance healing: An exploratory study. *The Sport Psychologist, 5,* 25–40.

Ironson, G. I., Freund, B., Strauss, J. L., & Williams, J. (2002). A comparison of two treatments for traumatic stress: A pilot study of EMDR and prolonged exposure. *Journal of Clinical Psychology, 58,* 113–128.

Jarero, I., Artigas, L., & Hartung, J. (2006). EMDR integrative group treatment protocol: A post-disaster trauma intervention for children and adults. *Journal of Traumatology, 12,* 121–129.

Jarero, I., Artigas, L., Mauer, M., López Cano, T., & Alcalá, N. (1999, November). *Children's post traumatic stress after natural disasters: Integrative treatment protocols.* Poster presented at the annual meeting of the International Society for Traumatic Stress Studies, Miami, FL.

Jarero, I., Artigas, L., & Montero, M. (2008). The EMDR integrative group treatment protocol: Application with child victims of mass disaster. *Journal of EMDR Practice & Research, 2*(2), 97–105.

Johnson, K. (1998). *Trauma in the lives of children.* Alameda, CA: Hunter House.

Jones, R. T., Fletcher, K., & Ribbe, D. R. (2002). *Child's reaction to traumatic events scale-revised (CRTES-R): A self-report traumatic stress measure.*

Knipe, J. (in press). Dysfunctional Positive Affect: To assist clients with unwanted avoidance defenses. In M. Luber (Ed.), *Eye movement desensitization and reprocessing (EMDR) Scripted Protocols: Special Populations.* New York: Springer Publishing.

Kohl, R. M., Ellis, S. D., & Roenkerm, D. L. (1992). Alternating actual and imagery practice: Preliminary theoretical considerations. *Research Quarterly for Exercise and Sport, 63,* 162–170.

Konuk, E., Knipe, J., Eke, I., Yuksek, H., Yurtsever, A., & Ostep, S. (2006). The effects of eye movement desensitization and reprocessing (EMDR) therapy on posttraumatic stress disorder in survivors of the 1999 Marmara, Turkey, earthquake. *International Journal of Stress Management, 13*(3), 291.

Korkmazlar-Oral, U., & Pamuk, S. (2002). Group EMDR with child survivors of the earthquake in Turkey. *Association of Child Psychology and Psychiatry (ACPP).* Occasional Papers No. 19, 47–50.

Korn, D. L., & Leeds, A. M. (2002). Preliminary evidence of efficacy for EMDR resource development and installation in the stabilization phase of treatment of complex posttraumatic stress disorder. *Journal of Clinical Psychology, 58*(12), 1465–1487.

Korn, D. L., Weir, J., & Rozelle, D. (2004). *Looking beyond the data: Clinical lessons learned from an EMDR treatment outcome study.* Paper presented at the EMDR International Association Conference, Montreal, Canada.

Krakow, B., & Krakow J. (2002). *Turning nightmares into dreams.* Albuquerque, NM: The New Sleepy Times.

Kristal-Andersson, B. (2000). *Psychology of the refugee, the immigrant and their children: Development of a conceptual framework and applications to psychotherapeutic and related support work.* Lund, Sweden: University of Lund Press.

L'Abate, L. (2004). *A guide to self-help mental health workbooks for clinicians and researchers.* Binghamton, NY: Haworth.

Laub, B. (2001). The healing power of resource connection in the EMDR protocol. *EMDRIA Newsletter,* (special edition), 21–28.

Laub, B., & Weiner, N. (2007). The pyramid model—dialectical polarity in therapy. *Journal of Transpersonal Psychology, 39*(2), 199–221.

Lazarus, A. (1989). *The practice of multimodal therapy.* New York: McGraw-Hill.

Lee, C., Gavriel, H., Drummond, P., Richards, J., & Greenwald, R. (2002). Treatment of PTSD: Stress inoculation training with prolonged exposure compared to EMDR. *Journal of Clinical Psychology, 58,* 1071–1089.

Lee, C. W., Taylor, G., & Drummond, P. D. (2006). The active ingredient in EMDR: Is it traditional exposure or dual focus of attention? *Clinical Psychology & Psychotherapy, 13*(2), 97.

Leeds, A. M. (1995, June 24). *EMDR case formulation symposium.* Paper presented at the 1995 EMDR Conference: Research and Clinical Applications, Santa Monica, CA.

Leeds, A. M. (2006, September). *Installation when treating complex posttraumatic stress syndromes.* EMDRIA Conference, Philadelphia, PA.

Leeds, A. M., & Shapiro, F. (2000). EMDR and resource installation: Principles and procedures for enhancing current functioning and resolving traumatic experiences. In J. Carlson & L. Sperry (Eds.), *Brief therapy strategies with individuals and couples.* Phoenix, AZ: Zeig/Tucker.

Lendl, J. L. (2005). *Future template.* Presentation with B. Parrett, C. Kong, J. Lendl, & P. Levin. Facilitator Training Day at EMDRIA Conference, Seattle, WA.

Lendl, J. L. (2007). *Back to basics: The positive template.* Paper presented at the EMDIA Conference, Dallas, TX.

Lendl, J., & Foster, S. (1997). *EMDR 'performance enhancement' for the workplace: A practitioner's guide.* San Jose, CA: Performance Enhancement Unlimited.

Lendl, J., & Steidinger, J. (1997). Sport psychology. In *WISE athletic training manual.* Ventura, CA: Women Involved in Sport Evolution.

Levine, S. (1991). Additional visualization for emotional and physical pain contained. In *Guided meditation, explorations, and healing.* New York: Doubleday.

Linebarger, H. (2005). *Performance enhancement with competitive adult swimmers utilizing eye movement desensitization and reprocessing.* Unpublished doctoral dissertation, University of California–Davis.

Lobenstine, F. E. (2007). What is an effective self-soothing technique that I can teach my client to use at home when stressed? *Journal of EMDR Practice and Research, 1*(2), 122–124.

Lombardo, M. M., & Eichinger, R. W. (2002). *For your improvement: A development and coaching guide for learners, supervisors, managers, mentors, and feedback givers.* Minneapolis, MN: Lominger Limited.

Lovett, J. (1999). *Small wonders: Healing childhood trauma with EMDR.* New York: The Free Press.

Luber, M. (1986). *Peak experiences in childhood and adolescence.* Unpublished doctoral dissertation, Bryn Mawr College, PA.

Luber, M. (2001). *Handbook for EMDR clients.* New Haven, CT: EMDR HAP.

Luber, M. (2006). In celebration of Neal Daniels: A life well-lived. *EMDRIA Newsletter, 11*(3), 18, 19, 28, 29.

Mamassis, G., & Doganis, G. (2004). The effects of a mental training program on juniors' pre-competitive anxiety, self-confidence, and tennis performance. *Journal of Applied Sport Psychology, 16*(2), 118–137.

Manfield, P., & Shapiro, F. (2003). The application of EMDR to the treatment of personality disorders. In J. F. Magnavita (Ed.), *Handbook of personality: Theory and practice.* New York: Wiley.

Martin, K., Moritz, S., & Hall, G. (1999). Imagery use in sport: A literature review and applied model. *The Sport Psychologist, 13,* 245–268.

Martinez, R. (1991). EMDR: Innovative uses. *EMDR Network Newsletter, 1*(2), 7.

Maslow, A. (1971). *The farthest reaches of human nature.* New York: Viking.

Maxfield, L. (2008). EMDR treatment of recent events and community disasters. *Journal of EMDR Practice & Research, 2*(2), 74–78.

McCraty, R., Atkinson, M., Tomasino, D., & Bradley, T. (2006). *The coherent heart: Heart-brain interactions, psychophysiological coherence, and the emergence of system-wide order* (Publication No. 06–022). Boulder Creek, CA: HeartMath Research Center, Institute of HeartMath.

McCullough, L. (2002). Exploring change mechanisms in EMDR applied to "small t- trauma" in short term dynamic psychotherapy: Research questions and speculations. *Journal of Clinical Psychology, 58,* 1465 1487.

McGoldrick, M., Gerson, R., Petry, S. (2008). *Genograms: Assessment and intervention* (3rd ed.). New York: Norton Professional Books.

Meichenbaum, D. (1994). *A clinical handbook/practical therapist manual for assessing and treating adults with post-traumatic stress disorder (PTSD).* Waterloo, Canada: Institute Press.

NICE (National Institute for Clinical Excellence). (2005). *PTSD clinical guidelines.* United Kingdom: NHS.

Nideffer, R. (1976). *The inner athlete.* New York: Crowell.

Ogden, P., & Minton K. (January, 2000). Sensorimotor psychotherapy: One method for processing traumatic memory. *Traumatology, VI*(3), 149–173.

Pellicer, X. (1993). Eye movement desensitization treatment of a child's nightmares: A case report. *Journal of Behavior Therapy and Experimental Psychiatry, 24,* 73–75.

Pennebaker, J. W. (1997). Writing about emotional experiences as a therapeutic process. *Psychological Science, 8*(3), 162–168.

Perkins, B., & Rouanzoin, C. (2002). A critical examination of current views regarding eye movement desensitization and reprocessing (EMDR): Clarifying points of confusion. *Journal of Clinical Psychology, 58*(1), 77–97.

Pillai-Freedman, S. (in press). EMDR protocol for treating sexual dysfunction. In M. Luber (Ed.), *Eye movement desensitization and reprocessing (EMDR) scripted protocols: Special populations.* New York: Springer Publishing.

Popky, A. J. (1994, February). *EMDR protocol for smoking and other addictions.* Paper presented at the EMDR Networker, Sunnyvale, CA.

Popky, A. J. (2005). DeTUR, an urge reduction protocol for addictions and dysfunctional behaviors. In R. Shapiro (Ed.), *EMDR solutions: Pathways to healing* (pp. 167–188). New York: W. W. Norton.

Puffer, M. K., Greenwald, R., & Elrod, D. E. (1998). A single session EMDR study with twenty traumatized children and adolescents. *Traumatology, 3*(2) Article 6.

Reddemann, L. (2001). *Imagination als heilsam.* Kraft. Klett-Cotta, Stuttgart, Germany: Pfeiffer bei Klett-Cotta.

Reddemann, L. (2008). *Psychodynamisch imaginative Traumatherapie-PITT-Das Manual* (14th ed.). Klett-Cotta, Stuttgart.

Russell, A., & O'Connor, M. (2002). Interventions for recovery: The use of EMDR with children in a community-based project. *Association for Child Psychiatry and Psychology.* Occasional Paper No. 19, 43–46.

Samec, J. (2001, December). The use of EMDR safe place exercise in group therapy with traumatized adolescent refugees. *The EMDRIA Newsletter.* Special Edition, pp. 32–34.

Scheck, M. M., Schaeffer, J. A., & Gillette, C. S. (1998). Brief psychological intervention with traumatized young women: The efficacy of eye movement desensitization and reprocessing. *Journal of Traumatic Stress, 11,* 25–44.

Seligman, M. (1998). *Learned optimism: How to change your mind and your life.* New York: Pocket Books.

Selye, H. (1974). *Stress without distress.* Philadelphia: Lippincott.

Shalev, A. (2007). *Jerusalem trauma outreach and prevention study (J-TOPS).* Paper presented at the American College of Neuropsychopharmacology 46th Annual Meeting, Florida. Reported in *Medscape Psychiatry* by Shapiro, E. (2007), 4 elements exercise, *Journal of EMDR Practice and Research, 2,* 113–115.

Shani, Z. (2006, July). *Group EMDR with school children following a traumatic event.* Invited presentation at EMDR-Israel HAP conference, Netanya, Israel.

Shapiro, E., & Laub, B. (2008a). Early EMDR intervention (EEI): Summary, a theoretical model, and the recent traumatic episode protocol (R-TEP). *Journal of EMDR Practice and Research, 2*(2), 79–96.

Shapiro, E., & Laub, B. (2008b, May). *Unfinished-traumatic episode protocol (U-TEP): A new protocol for early EMDR interventions.* Paper presented at the EMDR Europe Annual Conference, London, England.

Shapiro, F. (1989a). Efficacy of the eye movement desensitization procedure in the treatment of traumatic memories. *Journal of Traumatic Stress, 2,* 199–223.

Shapiro, F. (1989b). Eye movement desensitization: A new treatment for post-traumatic stress disorder. *Journal of Behavior Therapy and Experimental Psychiatry, 20,* 211–217.

Shapiro, F. (1991). Eye movement desensitization and reprocessing procedure: From EMD to EMDR: A new treatment model for anxiety and related traumata. *Behavior Therapist, 14,* 133–135.

Shapiro, F. (1995). *Eye movement desensitization and reprocessing: Basic principles, protocols and procedures.* New York: Guilford Press.

Shapiro, F. (1999). Eye movement desensitization and reprocessing (EMDR) and the anxiety disorders: Clinical and research implications of an integrated psychotherapy treatment. *Journal of Anxiety Disorders, 13*(1–2, Excerpt), 35–67.

Shapiro, F. (2001). *Eye movement desensitization and reprocessing: Basic principles, protocols and procedures* (2nd ed.). New York: Guilford Press.

Shapiro, F. (2003). *EMDR facilitator listserv.*

Shapiro, F. (2004). *Adaptive information processing: EMDR clinical application and case conceptualization.* Plenary presented at EMDR International Conference, Montreal, Canada.

Shapiro, F. (2006). *EMDR: New notes on adaptive information processing with case formulation principles, forms, scripts and worksheets.* Watsonville, CA: EMDR Institute.

Shapiro, F. (2007). *EMDR: Part 1 training manual.* Watsonville, CA: EMDR Institute, Inc.

Short, S. E., & Short, M. W. (2005). Differences between high- and low-confident football players on imagery functions: A consideration of the athletes' perceptions. *Journal of Applied Sport Psychology, 17*(3), 197–208.

Silver, S. M., Rogers, S., Knipe, J., & Colelli, G. (2005). EMDR therapy following the 9/11 terrorist attacks: A community-based intervention project in New York City. *International Journal of Stress Management, 12,* 29–42.

Simons, J. (2000). Doing imagery in the field. In M. Andersen (Ed.), *Doing sport psychology* (pp. 77–92). Champaign, IL: Human Kinetics.

Simonton, O. C., & Creighton, J. (1982). *Getting well again.* New York: Bantam.

Soberman, G. B., Greenwald, R., & Rule, D. L. (2002). A controlled study of eye movement desensitization and reprocessing (EMDR) for boys with conduct problems. *Journal of Aggression, Maltreatment, and Trauma, 6,* 217–236.

Solomon, R. (2008). Critical incident interventions. *Journal of EMDR Practice and Research, 2*(2), 160–165.

Stewart, K., & Bramson, T. (2000). Incorporating EMDR in residential treatment. *Residential Treatment for Children and Youth, 17,* 83–90.

Strupp, H. H., & Binder, J. L. (1984). *Psychotherapy in a new key: A guide to time-limited dynamic psychotherapy.* New York: Basic Books.

Taylor, R. (2002). Family unification with reactive attachment disorder: A brief treatment. *Contemporary Family Therapy: An International Journal, 24,* 475–481.

Taylor, S. E., Kemeny, M. E., Reed, G. M, Bower, J. E., & Gruenwald, T. L. (2000). Psychological resources, positive illusions, and health. *American Psychologist, 55,* 99–109.

Tedeschi, R., & Calhoun, L. (1995). *Trauma and transformation: Growing in the aftermath of suffering.* Thousand Oaks, CA: Sage.

Tinker, R. H., & Wilson, S. A. (1999). *Through the eyes of a child: EMDR with children.* New York: W. W. Norton.

Unestahl, L. E. (1982). *Better sport by IMT-inner mental training.* Orebro, Sweden: Veje.

Watkins, J. G., & Watkins, H. H. (1997). *Ego states: Theory and therapy.* New York: Norton.

White, M., & Epston, D. (1990). *Narrative means to therapeutic ends.* New York: Norton.

Whiting, H. T. A., & den Brinker, B. P. L. M. (1982). Image of the act. In J. P. Das, R. F. Mulcahy, & A. E. Wall (Eds.), *Theory and research in learning disabilities* (pp. 217–235). New York: Plenum Press.

Wildwind, L. (1992, April 4). *Treating chronic depression.* Paper presented at the First Annual EMDR Conference, San Jose, CA.

Wilson, S., Tinker, R., Hofmann, A., Becker, L., & Marshall, S. (2000). *A field study of EMDR with Kosovar-Albanian refugee children using a group treatment protocol.* Paper presented at the annual meeting of the International Society for the Study of Traumatic Stress, San Antonio, TX.

Wolpe, J. (1969). *The practice of behavior therapy.* New York: Pergamon Press.

Yoeli, F., & Prattos, T. A. (2005, November 2). *The 'Double Hai' paradigm: Tiered trans-generational dissociation unveiled.* Paper presented at the International Society for the Study of Trauma and Dissociation, Toronto, Canada.

Young, J. E., Zangwill, W. M., & Behary, W. E. (2002). Combining EMDR and schema-focused therapy: The whole may be greater than the sum of the parts. In F. Shapiro (Ed.), *EMDR as an integrative psychotherapy approach: Experts of diverse orientations explore the paradigm prism* (pp. 181–192). Washington, DC: American Psychological Association.

Zaghrout-Hodali, M., Ferdoos, A., & Dodgson, P. (2008). Building resilience and dismantling fear: EMDR group protocol with children in an area of ongoing trauma. *Journal of EMDR Practice & Research, 2*(2), 106–113.

Further Readings and Presentations

Bender, S. S. (2006). *Wash your hands: Healthy and practical EMDR practices.* Paper presented at EMDR International Association annual meeting, Philadelphia, PA.

Bender, S. S., & Britt, V. (2000). *Present in the past: Genograms, family themes & EMDR.* Paper presented at the New Jersey Regional EMDR International Association Semi-annual meeting, Piscataway, NJ.

Bender, S. S., & Britt, V. (2003). *Real world EMDR: Integrating EMDR into everyday clinical practice.* Workshop presented Bender/Britt Seminars, Iselin, NJ.

Bender, S. S., Hollander, H. E., & Accaria, P. (2001). *EMDR and hypnosis.* Paper presented at the EMDR International Association Conference, Austin, TX.

Bender, S. S., & Sise, M. T. (2007). *The energy of belief: Psychology's power tools to focus intention and release blocking beliefs.* Fulton, CA: Energy Psychology Press.

Blore, D. C. (1993). Treating a miner with underground phobia. *British Journal of Nursing, 2*(20), 1017, 1020–1021.

Blore, D. C. (2000). EMDR for mining and related trauma: The underground trauma protocol. *The EMDR Practitioner—Articles Archived.* Retrieved February 23, 2007, from www.emdr-practitioner.net

Blore, D. C., & Holmshaw, E. M. (2006). *The railway experience: "Being in control" the non-disclosure of traumatic memory content and EMDR.* 4th Annual Conference of EMDR UK & Ireland, Royal Institute of British Architects, March 3, 2006, London, England.

Briere, J. A., & Scott, C. (2006). *Principles of trauma therapy: A guide to symptoms, evaluation, and treatment.* Thousand Oaks, CA: Sage Publications, Inc.

Brown, K. W., McGoldrick, T., & Buchanan, R. (1997). Body dysmorphic disorder: Seven cases treated with eye movement desensitization and reprocessing. *Behavioural and Cognitive Psychotherapy, 25,* 203–207.

Bryant, R. A., & Harvey, A. G. (2000). *Acute stress disorder: A handbook of theory, assessment, and treatment.* Washington, DC: American Psychological Association.

Carver, C. S., & Scheier, M. F. (1999). Stress, coping, and self-regulatory processes. In O. P. John & L. A. Pervin (Eds.), *Handbook of personality: Theory and research* (pp. 553–575). New York: Guilford Press.

Classen, C., Koopman, C., Hales, R., & Spiegel, D. (1998). Acute stress disorder as a predictor of posttraumatic stress symptoms. *American Journal of Psychiatry, 155,* 620–624.

Daly, E., & Wulff, J. (1987). Treatment of a post-traumatic headache. *British Journal of Medical Psychology, 60,* 85–88.

Eichelman, B. (1985). Hypnotic change in combat dreams of two veterans with posttraumatic stress disorder. *American Journal of Psychiatry, 143*(1), 112–114.

Etzel, C. (2000). Hypnosis in the treatment of trauma: A promising, but not fully supported, efficacious intervention. *International Journal of Clinical and Experimental Hypnosis, 48*(2), 225–238.

Felz, D. L., & Landers, D. M. (1983). The effects of mental practice on motor skill learning and performance: A meta-analysis. *Journal of Sport Psychology, 5,* 25–57.

Foa, E. B., Davidson, J. R. T., & Frances, A. (1999). The expert consensus guideline series: Treatment of PTSD. *Journal of Clinical Psychology, 60*(Suppl. 16), pp. 1–76.

Freiha, T. (1998). *Sakkadische Augenbewegungen und Lidschläge bei cortikalen Läsionen.* Reihe: Psychophysiologie in Labor und Feld Band 6. Dissertation Universität zu Köln. Peter Lang Verlag, Frankfurt. (*Saccadic eye movements and eyelid frequency by patients with cortical lesions.* Psychobiology in the Laboratory and Field, Volume 6. Dissertation at the University of Cologne, Frankfurt: Peter Lang Publishers.)

Freiha, T. (2005). Behandlung einer PTBS mit EMDR: Kasuistik II. In F. Resch & M. Schulte-Markwort (Hrsg.), *Kursbuch für Integrative Kinder- und Jugendpsychotherapie Schwerpunkt: Dissoziation und Trauma.* Weinheim, Germany: Beltz Verlag. (Using EMDR in the treatment of PTSD of a youth with PTSD diagnosis: Casuistics II: In F. Resch & M. Schulte-Markwort (Eds.), *Integrative child and adolescent psychotherapy with the focus on dissociation and trauma.* Weinheim, Germany: Beltz Verlag.)

Goldstein, A., & Feske, U. (1994). Eye movement desensitization and reprocessing for panic disorder: A case series. *Journal of Anxiety Disorders, 8,* 351–362.

Graham, L. (2004). Traumatic swimming events reprocessed with EMDR. *The Sport Journal, 7*(1), 1–5.

Hofmann, A., & Freiha, T. (2002). Neuere Forschungen zur Posttarumatischen Belastungsstörung und Therapieverläufe bei schwersttraumatisierten Kindern. In *Kinder auf der Flucht* (pp. 4–14). Köln, Germany: Caritas Therapiezentrum für Folteropfer. (*New research about treating patients with posttraumatic stress disorder and a case study about treating a girl with severe traumatic stress disorder.* In Children on the run, Special Issue, pp. 4–14. Caritas Therapy Center for Torture Victims: Cologne, Germany.)

Hollander, H. E., & Bender, S. S. (2001). ECEM (eye closure eye movements): Integrating aspects of EMDR with hypnosis for treatment of trauma. *American Journal of Clinical Hypnosis, 43,* 187–202.

Jiranek, D. (1993). Use of hypnosis in pain management in post-traumatic stress disorder. *Australian Journal of Clinical and Experimental Hypnosis, 21,*(1), 75–84.

Kiessling, R. (1998). *Implementing present & future templates (utilizing the 3 stages of EMDR protocol).* Paper presented at the EMDR International Association Conference, July 10–12, Baltimore, MD.

Kiessling, R. (2000). *Integrating the EMDR approach into your clinical practice.* Paper presented at the EMDR International Association Conference, September 8–10, Toronto, Canada.

Kiessling, R. (2000). *Using a conference room of resources to process, past, present, and future issues.* Paper presented at the EMDR International Association Conference, September 8–10, Toronto, Canada.

Kiessling, R. (2001). *A resource focused model of EMDR (getting beyond pathology).* Paper presented at the EMDR International Association Conference, June 22–24, Austin, TX.

Kiessling, R. (2003). *Using resources as cognitive interweaves.* Paper presented at the EMDR International Association Conference, September 18–21, Denver, CO.

Kiessling, R. (2005). *Extending safe place/resource development protocols to increase client stability.* Paper presented at the EMDR International Association Conference, September 15–18, Seattle, WA.

Kiessling, R. (2006). *From BLS to EMDR: Treating survivors of trauma, natural disaster, and combat along a time and stability continuum.* Paper presented at the EMDR International Association Conference, September 7–10, Philadelphia, PA.

Kiessling, R., & Kacsur, R. (2002). *Being brief with EMDR.* Paper presented at the EMDR International Association Conference, June 20–23, San Diego, CA.

Kingsbury, S. J. (1993). Brief hypnotic treatment of repetitive nightmares. *American Journal of Clinical Hypnosis, 35*(3), 161–169.

Kohl, R. M., & Fisicaro, S. A. (1995). Imaging goal-directed movement. *Research Quarterly for Exercise and Sport, 66,* 17–31.

Kutz, I. (2005). Psychological first aid, acute and long-term treatment following terrorist attacks: Mental health interventions in a general hospital following terrorist attacks: The Israeli experience. *Journal of Aggression, Maltreatment & Trauma, 10*(1/2), 425–437.

Laub, B. (2000). *The healing power of resource connection in the EMDR protocol.* Paper presented at the EMDR Europe Association Conference, June 5–7, London, England.

Laub, B. (2002). *The healing power of resource connection in the EMDR protocol.* Paper presented at the EMDR Association Canada Conference, November 29–30, Vancouver.

Laub, B. (2003). *Various uses of connections to resources within and without the standard EMDR protocol.* Paper presented at the EMDR International Association Conference, September 18–21, Denver, CO.

Laub, B. (2006). *Resource connection envelope (RCE).* Paper presented at the EMDR Europe Association Conference, June 9–11, Istanbul, Turkey.

Lee, T. D., Chamberlin, C. J., & Hodges, N. (2001). Practice. In R. Singer, H. Hausen Blas, & C. Janelle (Eds.), *Handbook of sport psychology* (pp. 115–143). New York: John Wiley & Sons.

Ogelsby, C. (1999, September). *Report of a study of EMDR with college athletes.* Symposium presented at the Annual Conference of the Association for the Advancement of Applied Sport Psychology, Banff, Canada.

Orlick, T. (1986). *Psyching for sport: Mental training for athletes.* Champaign, IL: Human Kinetics.

Quinn, G. (2005). *Eye movement desensitization and reprocessing with victims of traffic accidents, suicide bus bombings, and terrorist attacks in Israel.* Paper presented at the American Psychiatric Association Annual Conference, May 21–26, Atlanta, Georgia.

Quinn, G. (2007). *Emergency EMDR-treating victims from man made to natural disasters.* Paper presented at the EMDR England Ireland Conference, March 23, Glasgow, Scotland.

Quinn, G. (2007). *Emergency EMDR-treating victims from man made to natural disasters.* Paper presented at the World Psychiatric Association Meeting, April 18–21, Seoul, Korea.

Quinn, G. (2007). *Emergency EMDR-treating victims from man made to natural disasters.* Paper presented at the EMDR Europe Conference, June 15–17, Paris, France.

Quinn, G. (2008, June). *Emergency EMDR & emergency response procedure (ERP).* Paper presented at the EMDR European Conference, June 13–15, London, England.

Quinn, G. (2008, July). *Acute stress reaction: To treat or not to treat. . . .* Keynote address presented at the Singapore International Conference-Traumatic Incidents: Early Intervention, July 24–26, Singapore.

Quinn, G. (2008, September). *PTSD and EMDR.* Paper presented at Grand Rounds Ohio State University, Columbus, OH.

Rothbaum, B. O. (2001). Virtual reality exposure therapy for Vietnam veterans with posttraumatic stress disorder. *Journal of Clinical Psychiatry, 62*(8), 617–622.

Russell, M. C., & Silver, S. M. (2007). Training needs for the treatment of combat-related posttraumatic stress disorder. *Traumatology, 13,* 4–10.

Sartory, G., Rachman, S., & Grey, S. J. (1982). Return of ear: The role of rehearsal. *Behavior Research and Therapy, 20,* 123–133.

Shapiro, F. (Ed.). (2002). *EMDR as an integrative psychotherapy approach: Experts of diverse orientations explore the paradigm prism.* Washington, DC: American Psychological Association Books.

Shapiro, F. (2004). *Military and post-disaster field manual.* Hamden, CT: EMDR Humanitarian Assistance Program.

Shapiro, R. (2005). The two-hand interweave. In R. Shapiro (Ed.), *EMDR solutions: Pathways to healing.* New York: W. W. Norton.

Snyder, M. (1996). Intimate partners: A context for the intensification and healing of emotional pain. *Women and Therapy, 19,* 79–92.

Terr, L. C. (1983). Chowchilla revisited: The effects of psychic trauma four years after a school-bus kidnapping. *American Journal of Psychiatry, 140,* 1543–1550.

Terr, L. (1990). *Too scared to cry: Psychic trauma in childhood.* New York: Harper and Row.

Tinker, R. H., & Wilson, S. A. (2006). The phantom limb pain protocol. In R. Shapiro (Ed.), *EMDR solutions: Pathways to healing* (pp. 147–159). New York: W. W. Norton.

Van Etten, M. L., & Taylor, S. (1998). Comparative efficacy of treatments for post-traumatic stress disorder: A meta-analysis. *Clinical Psychology & Psychotherapy, 5*(3), 126–144.

Weiss, D. S., & Marmar, C. R. (1995). The impact of event scale-revised. In J. P. Wilson & T. M. Keane (Eds.), *Assessing psychological trauma and PTSD: A practitioner's handbook.* New York: Guilford Press.

Wernik, U. (1993). The role of the traumatic component in the etiology of sexual dysfunctions and its treatment with eye movement desensitization procedure. *Journal of Sex Education and Therapy, 19,* 212–222.